William J. Mattson, Jean Levieux, C. Bernard-Dagan
Editors

Mechanisms of Woody Plant Defenses Against Insects

Search for Pattern

With 106 Illustrations

Springer-Verlag
New York Berlin Heidelberg
London Paris Tokyo

William J. Mattson
U.S. Department of Agriculture
Forest Service
North Central Forest Experiment Station
East Lansing, Michigan 48823, USA

Jean Levieux
Institut National de la Recherche Agronomique
Station de Zoologie Forestière
Ardon, 45160 Olivet, France

C. Bernard-Dagan
Universite de Bordeaux I
Laboratoire de Physiologie Cellulaire Vegetale
Avenue des Facultes
33405 Talence Cedex, France

Library of Congress Cataloging-in-Publication Data
Mechanisms of woody plant defenses against insects.
Includes index.
1. Woody plants—Disease and pest resistance.
2. Insect pests. I. Mattson, William J.
II. Levieux, Jean. III Bernard-Dagan, C.
SB761.M46 1988 634.9'67 87-32102

Softcover reprint of the hardcover 1st edition 1988

Camera-ready copy provided by the editors.

9 8 7 6 5 4 3 2 1

ISBN-13:978-1-4612-8368-3 e-ISBN-13:978-1-4612-3828-7
DOI:10.1007/978-1-4612-3828-7

Preface

In 1984, a new research working party on mechanisms of woody plant resistance against insects and pathogens (IUFRO S2.05-06) was formed in the International Union of Forestry Research Organizations. The purpose of this working party is to stimulate and facilitate research progress in this area through enhanced communication among the many research scientists scattered among the various countries of the world. This volume is the result of the first international symposium of this working party, which took place in Orleans, France on August 26–29, 1986. Thanks are due to Institute National de la Recherche Agronomique, Station de Zoologie, Forestière, for their instrumental part in organizing this symposium, and to the University and the City of Orleans for generous financial support.

The intent of this proceedings is to (a) bring together a diverse array of research results on the mechanisms of woody plant resistance against different kinds of insects, and (b) to search for threads of commonality among these different plant/insect associations to further our fundamental understanding of how plants defend themselves against phytophagous organisms.

The research papers are organized into three main groups. The first group examines plant defenses from various basic physiological and ecological considerations. The remaining papers, which are mainly case studies of plant resistance against insects, are categorized on the basis of insect intimacy with host tissues: (a) highly mobile, free feeders such as moth larvae and sawflies, and (b) poorly mobile, "attached" or imbedded feeders such as aphids, scales, miners, and bark beetles. Each of these sections is further organized on the basis of kind of tissue attacked by the insects, either leaves or stem/shoot cortex and vascular tissues.

Contents

Contributors

Jean-Pierre Allais, Centre National de la Recherche Scientifique (CNRS), Institut de Chimie des Substances Naturelles (ICSN) 91190 GIF/YVETTE, France

Marianne Baisier, Laboratoire de Biologie Animale et Cellulaire, Université Libre de Bruxelles, 50, Av. Franklin Roosevelt, 1050 Bruxelles, Belgium

Michel Barbier, Centre National de la Recherche Scientifique (CNRS), Institut de Chimie des Substances Naturelles (ICSN), 91190 GIF/YVETTE, France

Colette Bernard-Dagan, Laboratoire de Physiologie Cellulaire Végétale, Université de Bordeaux I, Avenue des Facultés, 33405 Talence Cedex, France

Alan A. Berryman, Department of Entomology, Washington State University, Pullman, WA 99164, U.S.A.

Odile Bonnard, Laboratoire de Zoologie, Université de Dijon, Boulevard Gabriel, F-21100 Dijon, France

John P. Bryant, Institute of Arctic Biology, University of Alaska, Fairbanks, Alaska 99701, U.S.A.

Lionel Buratti, Centre National de la Recherche Scientifique (CNRS), Institut de Chimie des Substances Naturelles (ICSN), 91190 GIF/YVETTE, France

F. Stuart Chapin, III, Institute of Arctic Biology, University of Alaska, Fairbanks, Alaska 99701, U.S.A.

Constantin Chararas, Ministère de l'agriculture, Institut National Agronomique, Paris-Grignon, Laboratoire de Chimie Analytique

Pierre-Jean Charles, Deceased, I.N.R.A., Station de Zoologie Forestière, Ardon, 45160 Olivet, France

Catherine Cheniclet, Laboratoire de Physiologie Cellulaire Végétale, Université de Bordeaux I, Avenue des Facultés, 33405 Talence Cedex, France

Karen M. Clancy, U.S. Department of Agriculture, Forest Service, Rocky Mountain Forest and Range Experiment Station, Forestry Sciences Laboratory, 700 S. Knoles Dr., Flagstaff, AZ 86001, U.S.A.

Stephen P. Cook, Department of Entomology, Box 7626, North Carolina State University, Raleigh, NC 27695, U.S.A.

Robert N. Coulson, Department of Entomology, Texas A & M University, College Station, TX 77843, U.S.A.

Karin Delinte, Laboratoire de Zoologie, Université de Dijon, Boulevard Gabriel, F-21100 Dijon, France

Pau. Du Merle, I.N.R.A., Station de Zoologie Forestière, Avenue A. Vivaldi, F-84000 Avignon, France

Christian J. Ducauze, Ministère de l'agriculture, Institut National Agronomique, Paris-Grignon, Laboratoire de Chimie Analytique

Anders Ericsson, Department of Forest Genetics and Plant Physiology, Swedish University of Agricultural Sciences, S-90183 Umeå, Sweden

Claude Everaerts, Laboratoire de Zoologie, Université de Bourgogne, 6 Boulevard Gabriel, F-21100 Dijon, France

George T. Ferrell, Research Entomologist, U.S. Department of Agriculture, Forest Service, Pacific Southwest Forest and Range Experiment Station, Berkeley, California 94701, U.S.A.

Richard O. Flamm, Department of Entomology, Texas A & M University, College Station, TX 77843, U.S.A.

Jacques Garcia, I.N.R.A., Station de Zoologie Forestière, Ardon, 45160 Olivet, France

Imogen M. Gate, Forestry Commission Research Station, Alice Holt Lodge, Wrecclesham, Farnham, Surrey, GU10 4LH, UK

Claude Geri, I.N.R.A. Station de Zoologie Forestière, Ardon, 45160 Olivet, France

Jean-Claude Grégoire, Laboratoire de Biologie Animale et Cellulaire, CP 160, Université Libre de Bruxelles, 50 Av. F.D. Roosevelt, B-1050 Bruxelles, Belgium

Rolf Gref, Department of Forest Genetics and Plant Physiology, Swedish University of Agricultural Sciences, S-90183 Umeå, Sweden

Robert A. Haack, U.S. Department of Agriculture, Forest Service, North Central Forest Experiment Station, 1407 S. Harrison, East Lansing, MI 48823, U.S.A.

Fred P. Hain, Department of Entomology, Box 7626, North Carolina State University, Raleigh, NC 27695, U.S.A.

Claes Hellqvist, Department of Plant and Forest Protection, Swedish University of Agricultural Sciences, S-77073 Garpenberg, Sweden

Daniel A. Herms, Department of Entomology, Michigan State University, East Lansing, MI, 48824, U.S.A.

Robert K. Lawrence, Department of Entomology, Michigan State University, East Lansing, MI, 48824, U.S.A.

Bo Långström, Department of Plant and Forest Protection, Swedish University of Agricultural Sciences, S-77073 Garpenberg, Sweden

Jean Levieux, I.N.R.A., Station de Zoologie Forestière, Ardon, 45160 Olivet, France

François Lieutier, I.N.R.A, Station de Zoologie Forestière, Ardon, 45160 Olivet, France

David Lonsdale, Forestry Commission Research Station, Alice Holt Lodge, Wrecclesham, Farnham, Surrey, GU10 4LH, UK

Peter L. Lorio, Jr., Research Forester, Forest Insect Research, U.S. Department of Agriculture, Forest Service, Southern Forest Experiment Station, 2500 Shreveport Highway, Pineville, Louisiana 71360, U.S.A.

Jörg Lunderstädt, Institut für Forstzoologie der Universität Göttingen, Büsgenweg 3, D-3400 Göttigen

William J. Mattson, U.S. Department of Agriculture, Forest Service, North Central Forest Experiment Station, 1407 S. Harrison, East Lansing, MI 48823, U.S.A.

Joël Merlin, Laboratoire de Biologie Animale et Cellulaire, CP 160, Université Libre de Bruxelles, 50 Av. F.D. Roosevelt, B-1050 Bruxelles, Belgium

Ludovic Nef, Centre pour la Lutte Intégrée contre les Insectes Forestiers, AGRO/EFOR, Université Catholique de Louvain, Place Croix du Sud, 2 1348 Louvain-la-Neuve, Belgium

Pekka Niemelä, Department of Biology, University of Turku, SF-20500 Turku, Finland

Sean R. Palmer, Department of Entomology, Hodson Hall, University of Minnesota, St. Paul, MN, 55108, U.S.A.

Ginette Pauly, Laboratoire de Physiologie Cellulaire Végétale, Université de Bordeaux I, Avenue des Facultés, 33405 Talence Cedex, France

Blandine Poupinel, I.N.R.A., Station de Zoologie Forestière, Ardon, 45160 Olivet, France

Kenneth F. Raffa, Department of Entomology, University of Wisconsin, Madison, WI 53706, U.S.A.

Odette Rohfritsch, Laboratoire de Cécidologie, U.A. C.N.R.S. 04 1182, Institut de Botanique, 28 rue Goethe, 67083 Strasbourg, France

Douglas N. Rutledge, Ministère de l'agriculture, Institut National Agronomique, Paris-Grignon, Laboratoire de Chimie Analytique

Daniel Schvester, I.N.R.A., Station de Zoologie Forestière, Avenue Vivaldi, 84000 Avignon, France

Seija Sirén, Department of Biology, University of Turku, SF-20500 Turku, Finland

Richard W. Tinus, U.S. Department of Agriculture, Forest Service, Rocky Mountain Forest and Range Experiment Station, Forestry Sciences Laboratory, 700 S. Knoles Dr., Flagstaff, AZ 86001, U.S.A.

Juha Tuomi, Department of Theoretical Ecology, University of Lund, Ecology Building, S-223 62 Lund, Sweden

David Wainhouse, Forestry Commission Research Station, Alice Holt Lodge, Wrecclesham, Farnham, Surrey, GU10 4LH, UK

Michael R. Wagner, Northern Arizona University, School of Forestry, Flagstaff, AZ 86011, U.S.A.

Annie Yart, I.N.R.A., Station de Zoologie Forestière, Ardon, 45160 Olivet, France

I. Basic Physiological and Ecological Considerations

1

Defensive Strategies of Woody Plants Against Different Insect-Feeding Guilds in Relation to Plant Ecological Strategies and Intimacy of Association with Insects

William J. Mattson, Robert K. Lawrence, Robert A. Haack, Daniel A. Herms, and Pierre-Jean Charles

A major question confronting scientists who want to exploit plant resistance in the management of a particular insect or pathogen pest is whether the plant in question has any exploitable resistance, and if so, what are the likely resistance mechanisms (Harris 1980, 1982). This question is not trivial because its answer affects the entire research approach--how to search for resistance. To this end, we offer here, a framework for classifying defensive strategies by certain classes of plants against various feeding guilds of herbivores.

PLANT DEFENSIVE STRATEGIES FOR REGULATION OF INJURY LEVEL PER PLANT

The defensive strategies utilized by individual plants against herbivores may be broadly classified according to the plant's capacity to influence its short- and long-term herbivore damage (Table 1). For example, at one extreme is the wholly susceptible plant which by definition has no capacity to regulate or influence the amount of consumer damage. Instead, injury level is entirely under the control of the consumer population and, of course, the abiotic and biotic factors affecting the consumer. Such a plant/consumer relationship is not likely to be long-lived owing to the high probability of the plant dying. However, if the abiotic and biotic factors affecting the consumer are frequently severe enough to drastically lower its population densities, then some plants may survive and thereby allow the continued coexistence of both. Next, consider the completely tolerant plant which can fully compensate for any and all injury. Hence, it is not debilitated in any way by the consumer, and therefore there is no selection pressure upon its population to evolve attributes to reduce herbivory. Such a perfect compensatory capacity is a viable defensive strategy, although on the surface it may not appear to be so. Next, consider the partially tolerant plant which has some but not complete tolerance capacity for herbivory. Herein lie the vast majority of plant/herbivore relationships. These plant populations may respond to herbivore selection pressure (which will be proportional to their lack of tolerance capacity for a particular kind of consumer damage) by evolving attributes that confer additional defensive capacity (e.g., additional tolerance or injury reduction capacity). We consider tolerance to be the first line of plant "defense" against any debilitating agent, both biotic or abiotic. If repair and compensatory reactions are not sufficient to prevent significant loss of fitness for a particular kind of injury, then there will be selection pressure on the plant population for the evolution of mechanisms that limit or lower injury levels by that class of injuring agent (Bryant et al. 1985). If a plant population has a relatively large tolerance capacity for a particular class of herbivore injury, selection will favor (if defenses are costly) a minimal back-up defensive system--one perhaps that engages only after rather high and/or sustained levels of injury. We propose that for this kind of injury, plants will evolve an escape or a lagging, inducible defense mechanism. Escape can occur in space or time (Harris 1980) and involves alternating episodes of available and unavailable plant tissues such as years of high and low fruit/seed abundance or unpredictable (from the consumer's

Table 1. Classification of plant defensive strategies according to their ability to influence the amount of short- and long-term herbivore damage/plant.

Defensive strategy	Effect of defense on insect damage level per plant
Tolerance (=Accommodation)	No influence
Partial tolerance and escape	Regulation to high/variable levels
Partial tolerance and lagging inducible defenses	Regulation to high/variable levels
Partial tolerance and immediate inducible defenses	Regulation to low/constant levels
Immunity	Regulation to zero damage

perspective) phenology (Du Merle in this volume). Lagging inducible defenses, on the other hand, are cumulative build-ups in the levels of toxic or deterrent plant properties, be they structural or chemical in nature, or bioassociations (Harris 1980). Both escape and lagging inducible defense systems are rather imprecise regulatory mechanisms.

On the other hand, if a plant population can evolve only a very limited tolerance capacity for a particular class of consumer injury (owing to some physiological or other constraints), then selection will likely favor a more potent defensive system. This system must be highly sensitive to small levels of consumer damage and must be fast acting. We call it the immediate inducible defense system. It will allow only low levels of injury per plant.

Finally, if a plant population cannot evolve any significant tolerance capacity for a particular type of consumer's injury, then the only viable defensive strategy may be complete or near-complete immunity. This system will be employed against those consumers whose damage is normally so rapidly debilitating that most plants either quickly die or soon lose most of their reproductive potential. It will consist of a blend of high constitutive defenses as well as potent, immediate inducible defenses. We recognize that no defense system is inviolable and therefore even "immune" plants may become susceptible during periods of severe stress or when under mass attack (Mattson and Haack 1987).

CLASSIFYING PHYTOPHAGOUS INSECTS ACCORDING TO THEIR PLANT INJURY POTENTIAL

We have implied so far that plant defense systems evolve incrementally and that at each step, selection pressure for more and new defenses will be proportional to the kind and amount of injury inflicted by herbivores. Here we attempt to rank the type of herbivore feeding (feeding-guild classes) according to their likely severity of injury to plants (McNaughton 1983). We hypothesize that the least severe injuries will result from organisms that remove tissues, organs, or fluids at rates lower than which the plants can simply and quickly compensate. In other words, severity of physiological injury to a plant is inversely correlated with the plant's ability to compensate for the injury.

Attributes of Herbivores That Affect Plant Compensatory Ability

There are several attributes of herbivores that relate to the plant's compensatory ability (Fig 1). One is the type of tissue on which an herbivore feeds. If the tissue is relatively inactive, such

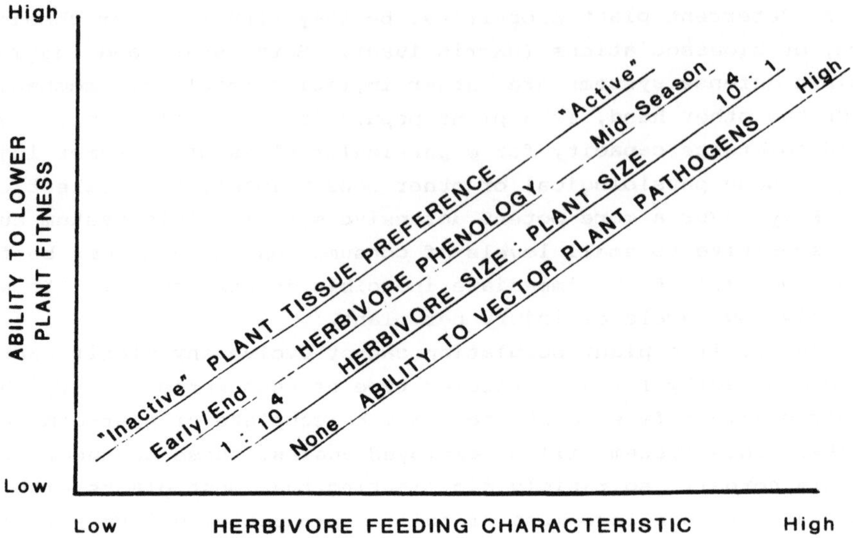

Figure 1. Ability to lower plant fitness is dependent on the feeding characteristics of various herbivores. Each line in the graph represents a single characteristic, and suggests that as the character goes from low to high, there is a concomitant increase in the herbivore's potential to reduce plant fitness.

as nearly senescent leaves or the pith or heartwood of woody stems, then there is nominal impact on plant growth/reproduction processes (Bauer 1986, Pemberton 1986). On the other hand, if an herbivore feeds on meristematic tissues (e.g., apical or cambial meristems), it has much more impact because it reduces the plant's generative ability. Likewise, if an organism's feeding seriously interrupts the transport of water, and nutrients to meristematic or storage tissues, such as do phloem/xylem feeders, the impact can be severe (Haack and Slansky 1987).

Secondly, timing of the attack is crucial. For example, folivores that remove foliage very early in the growing season are usually less debilitating than those in the middle to late season. This is generally true because early season defoliation allows plants to regenerate their canopies and to restore essential nutrient and energy reserves before the dormant season. Normally this is not so for middle- to late-season defoliation. For example, severe middle- to late-season defoliation results in less abundant canopy regrowth and less accumulation of energy reserves for the leafless period. This results in lower cold hardiness, and insufficient energy for dormant-season respiration, and for the production of new growth in the subsequent growing season (Gregory and Wargo 1986, Gregory _et al_. 1987). Lower energy reserves may also diminish the fuel for biosynthesis of rapid inducible defenses that may be dominant during the plant's active growth stages (Braga _et al_. 1986). It may also lower constitutive defenses which in fact are typically produced during mid-late season when plant growth has ceased and differentiation processes normally dominate (Lorio 1986, Lorio in this volume). Hence herbivores that interrupt differentiation processes and thereby interfere with the accumulation of adequate energy reserves are highly injurious.

Thirdly, the size of the individual herbivore, or the typical herbivore social-feeding unit relative to that of the plant genet is important to its impact (McNaughton 1985, Rhoades 1985). For example, an herbivore that tends to be large relative to its host plants or attacks _en masse_ has the potential to have a more serious impact on a host than an herbivore which is small relative to host size or normally feeds singly. Cutworms that encounter tree seedlings can debilitate them in a single feeding bout. On the other hand, the impact of an equivalently sized noctuid on high shrubs and sapling-sized trees is not nearly so potentially injurious. Similarly, bark beetles which attack _en masse_ and consume much of the cambium/phloem represent a more serious threat to trees than do small, cambium-feeding agromyzid flies (e.g., _Phytobia setosa_) that feed singly. The former may habitually attack in a group in order to overwhelm the plant's defenses, whereas the latter may attack singly in order to avoid eliciting defenses (Rhoades 1985).

Finally, if the herbivore facilitates the entry of debilitating plant pathogens or the success of other more damaging insects/ invertebrates into the plant, then its injury potential is really far greater than its tissue or fluid removal alone would indicate. Some examples are the introduction of viruses, bacteria, and mycoplasma into plants by planthoppers and leafhoppers (Conti 1985, Purcell 1985) as well as the transmission of vascular wilt pathogens by bark beetles and nematodes by cerambycid beetles. Similarly, serious defoliation of trees often predisposes them to attack by lethal cambium/phloem/ sapwood borers (Dewey et al. 1974, Schultz and Allen 1977, Mosher 1982, Haack 1985, Langor and Raske 1987).

Ranking Phytophagous Insects

Based on the preceding logic, we have ranked different feeding guilds of phytophagous insects based on their likely severity of injury to woody plants (Table 2).

The least severe injury ranking goes to gall insects of leaves and twigs. These insects may cause reductions in growth and reproduction (Price et al. 1987), but rarely interfere substantially with overall plant growth. Close to gall insects in ranking are folivores that feed on nearly senescent, current-year leaves, or folivores that exclusively consume old foliage of evergreens. Old foliage is usually not photosynthetically very active because of low levels of the carboxylating enzyme (Rubisco), and for other reasons such as poor ability/position to receive and capture light. It may serve as a storage depot for energy reserves (Bryant and Chapin 1982) but so do twigs, stem, and roots (Bernard-Dagan in this volume). Under most circumstances, trees which lose old foliage do not die and show smaller reductions in height, diameter, and shoot growth than for other kinds of defoliation (Kulman 1971).

Next higher in severity ranking are those insects that feed only on early season/current-year leaves. Even in the most severe cases, when such leaves are completely removed, deciduous trees can usually refoliate within a few weeks and continue to grow, although at reduced rates (Kulman 1971). Usually, however, low levels of defoliation bring about nearly full compensatory growth by the remaining leaves owing to improved levels of water, nutrients, light, and growth promoting hormones (Kulman 1971, Mattson and Addy 1975, McNaughton 1983, Bassman and Dickmann 1985, although see Belsky 1986). If more than 40 to 50 percent of the leaves have been destroyed, growth will decline in proportion to damage.

Table 2. Ranking insect feeding guilds (with select examples) according to their potential impact on host plant fitness.

Herbivore guild	Potential impact on host growth and reproduction
Gall formers: leaves Cynipidae, Cecidomyidae, Psyllidae	Least ↓
Gall formers: twigs/stems Adelgidae, Cynipidae	
Folivores: end of season or prior-year's leaves Diprionidae	
Folivores: beginning of season/current-year leaves Geometridae, Lasiocampidae, Lymantriidae, Tortricidae	
Sap feeders: leaves/twigs/branches Aphididae, Coccidae, Diaspididae	
Phloem/sapwood/pith borers: twigs/branches/shoots Buprestidae, Cerambycidae, Curculionidae, Olethreutidae	
Root sap feeders Cicadidae	
Root free feeders Curculionidae, Scarabaeidae	
Folivores: middle-late season Arctiidae, Lymantriidae, Notodontidae, Saturniidae	
Folivores: both current and prior year's leaves Diprionidae, Lymantriidae	
Sap feeders: stem phloem/xylem Aphididae, Coccidae, Diaspididae	
Phloem/cambium/sapwood borers: root and root crown Buprestidae, Curculionidae, Scolytidae	
Phloem/cambium/sapwood borers: main stem Buprestidae, Cerambycidae, Sesiidae, Scolytidae	Most

Next in severity of injury are insects affecting vitality of twigs and branches, such as twig/branch sap feeders and borers. These insects may kill whole branches, especially terminal shoots. These injuries, like the former, are usually not fatal, but could severely depress the plant's competitive ability, especially in environments where competition is keen. Where competition is not keen, the damage inflicted by such insects may not be any more serious than simple leaf removal (Whitham and Mopper 1985).

Next in potential severity of plant injury are those insects affecting the vitality of plant roots. Although little substantive evidence exists to confirm their ranking, we believe that they are potentially serious because their feeding can (1) reduce the available mechanical support system (Simberloff et al. 1978), (2) reduce the amount of nutrient uptake and nutrient transport to the aerial portions (Karban 1980), and (3) open potential infection courts for soil fungi.

Next higher in potential severity of injury are the current-year, mid-season, leaf-feeding insects. Their damage, as mentioned above, can cause the trees to refoliate as does early season defoliation, but in this case foliage may fail to become cold hardy before late-season frosts and consequently dies before leaf nutrients can be translocated to storage sites. The net result appears to be greater subsequent bud and tree mortality owing to shortages of stored energy and nutrients (Kulman 1971, Gregory and Wargo 1986, Gregory et al. 1987).

Next higher in severity are those insects that consume both new and older foliage of evergreen tree species. Removing both classes of foliage is highly debilitating and very often results in tree mortality or at least serious growth reductions (Kulman 1971).

The most severe category of insects are those normally feeding on or in the main stem or trunk. These could be aggregations of sap feeders or borers in the phloem/cambium/sapwood regions. Such insects are especially damaging because they can destroy the plant's essential conductive tissue at a rate exceeding the plant's capacity to replace it (Haack and Slansky 1987). Hence, tree death may be nearly inevitable once infestations start.

PLANT DEFENSES IN RELATION TO ECOLOGICAL STRATEGIES

So far, our discussion has focused primarily on the innate physiological capacity of individual plants to compensate for a particular kind of insect damage. Obviously, more than this is involved because a plant must not only recover physiologically, it must do so while competing with other plants. In other words, an ecological recovery must also take place, or the affected plant may be displaced by others of the same or a different species.

We argue here that plants which typically form extensive, species-poor communities will tend to have different defensive strategies than those in species-rich plant communities. Our basis for this argument is that in the former case, individual plants compete primarily with conspecifics whereas in the latter they compete mostly with other species. Hence, the indirect effects of herbivory (enhancing the growth of competitors) can be vastly different under these two circumstances.

Defenses and Competition in Species-Poor Communities.

Loss of relative competitive status will be negligible if the affected plant has immediate and perfect compensatory ability. However, perfect compensatory ability has yet to be demonstrated for any plant (Belsky 1986, however, see McNaughton and Chapin 1985). Loss in relative competitive status will likewise be negligible if all other individuals in the community suffer nearly equivalent levels of herbivory. In fact, equivalent levels of herbivory among conspecifics seems to be the rule in many tropical and temperate tree species that form oligo-species communities (Harris 1982, 1983; Coley 1983a, 1983b; and personal observations). We propose that plants in such communities can employ simple tolerance as their primary line of defense against herbivore damage for which the plant can easily compensate (Fig. 2). Increased tolerance is probably the first evolutionary response by plant populations to most kinds of damage. However, if a few individuals were to lack tolerance and employed some other injury-lowering strategy such as near-immunity (immediate inducible defense), these phenotypes might be selected against during any subsequent outbreaks because they would very likely still be overcome by the vast numbers of starving herbivores that redistribute themselves after having stripped the more abundant tolerant phenotypes. For example, in many temperate- and boreal-zone insect folivore outbreaks, the larvae eventually encounter and strip even nonhost plant species which are often substantially different from their primary host(s) (Langor and Raske 1987). Hence, if the near-immune phenotypes had little or no tolerance capacity whatsoever, they could be eliminated during outbreaks. On the other hand, even if they went unscathed during outbreaks, it is questionable whether their net long-term fitness would be higher than the tolerant types because of the long term "cost" of their defense system.

This argument again raises the question about the relationship between a plant's tolerance capacity for various kinds of injury and its level of constitutive and inducible defenses against the injury-causing agents. Evidence addressing this hypothesis is circumstantial, and compares levels of constitutive defenses between inherently slow- and fast-growing plant species (Coley et al. 1985, Bryant et al. 1985, Bazzaz et al. 1987). The emerging pattern suggests that strong constitutive defenses are coupled to low growth, which in turn implies lower tolerance or recovery capacity following herbivore injury. For example, Knapp (1986), reported that a very toxic spring ephemeral of grasslands had poorly developed intrinsic mechanisms for compensating for herbivory. Likewise, the concept of growth-differentiation balance (Lorio in this volume) suggests that plants may be either

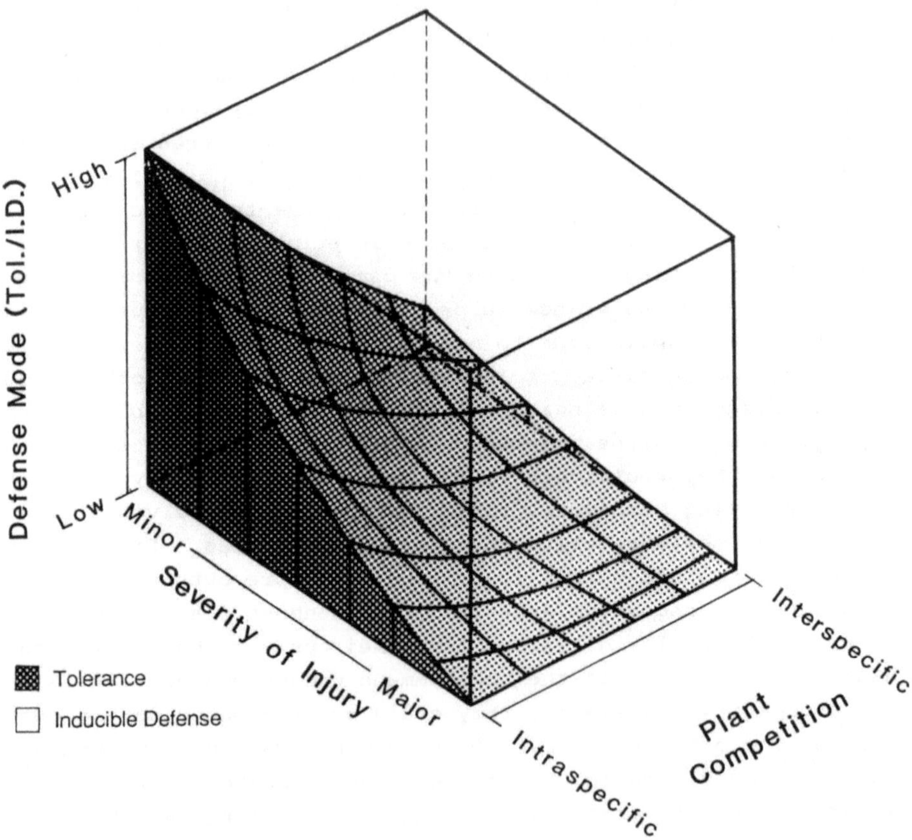

Figure 2. Plant defense modes (tolerance: inducible defense ratios) which may have evolved under various conditions of selection pressure from herbivores (minor to major injury potentials) and from plant-plant competition (intra- to inter-specific).

growth- or differentiation-dominated, having been evolved for more rapid growth, or for more powerful defense, respectively. Within a species there appears to be some flexibility in energy allocation between growth and defense. However Bazzaz et al. (1987) maintain that most intraspecific variation in carbon/nutrient allocation to defense is due to environment (spatial and temporal variability in resources) rather than genetics. If this is true, it implies that within a species there can be little or no selection pressure from herbivores for more or less defense because it's relatively invariant. We feel that there are insufficient data to make such a generalization. Until more is known about the relative shape of the cost and benefit curves (to plant fitness) of differential allocation to plant defense, it will be impossible to resolve this issue.

We propose that tolerance alone and tolerance coupled to lagging defenses (those that develop and subside slowly) are the most likely evolutionary strategies for coping with many less serious kinds of herbivores in species-poor communities. However, if the herbivore's feeding damage is of the type for which there can be only little compensatory capacity (cambial meristem destruction, phloem/xylem disruption), then plants may universally employ immunity or near-immunity as the main line of defense. If all individuals employ the same iron-clad defense, then there is no cost to the plant's fitness. However, there is still a physiological cost.

Defenses and Competition in Species-rich Communities

In contrast to monospecific communities, simple tolerance is less likely to evolve as a plant species' main line of defense in species-rich plant communities because the inevitable losses in growth and reproduction that result from simple tolerance (it's usually always imperfect) will not be similar across all members in the community. For example, identical growth losses on plant species A when occurring both as the minor member of a species-rich community, and the predominant member in a species-poor community, will have different ecological effects. In the first case, other plant species will usurp the space and abiotic flux (moisture, heat, nutrients, light) which were unused by species A. In the second case, this competitive displacement is likely to be much slower, if not negligible, because of the more complete domination of the site by the affected plant species. Moreover, even the less common plant species of a species-poor community are often themselves overwhelmed by the major herbivore affecting plant species A during outbreaks.

Figure 3 shows the effects of an herbivore (which prefers plant species A) in a plant community consisting of three species (A, B, and C) and in which every member of species A competes directly with at least one member of species B and C. Here, herbivory directly reduces the growth of A and indirectly increases growth of B and C. Hence, the effects of herbivory on A consists of two components: the direct effects which are negative and the indirect effects through species B and C which are also negative. In a mono-species community consisting of three genotypes A, B, and C, equivalent herbivory has a direct negative effect and an indirect positive effect on all three owing to reduced competition with the other genotypes. The net result is no significant change in the competitive balance among all three genotypes. Hence, there is less selection pressure to evolve active defenses against herbivory when all members of the plant community suffer equally from herbivory.

If all major herbivores are polyphages or if each plant species has its own community of specialist monophages so that all plants in a species-rich community sustain nearly equivalent levels of herbivory, this would favor the evolution of simple tolerance. However, polyphages will not bring about equal levels of herbivory among all plant species because even they have clear host species preferences until their options become limited. The gypsy moth, Lymantria dispar, is a classic example of polyphagy in North American mixed deciduous forests. It preferentially feeds on Quercus, although it can feed on nearly 300 other species. As a result, Quercus typically suffers much higher growth losses and mortality than other hosts (Campbell and Sloan 1977).

Because each species of plant in a species-rich community will likely have some unique herbivores as well as share some polyphagous ones, the opportunity exists for substantially different herbivore impact on the growth and survival among the various plants. To minimize the negative impact of herbivory, all such plant species may evolve defenses which tend to regulate herbivore injury to low and rather consistent levels--as in the near-immune defenses. We argue that the cost to plants which adopt such a strategy will on the average be less than the cost to plants which employ only simple tolerance as their main line of defense. The advantage of a near-immune defense occurs because the cost is more consistently "charged" against the plants, unlike partial tolerance in which cost fluctuates with herbivore pressure. Near-immunity decreases the plant's chance of suffering periodic, severe losses to herbivores which can cause irreparable setbacks in the plant's competitive status.

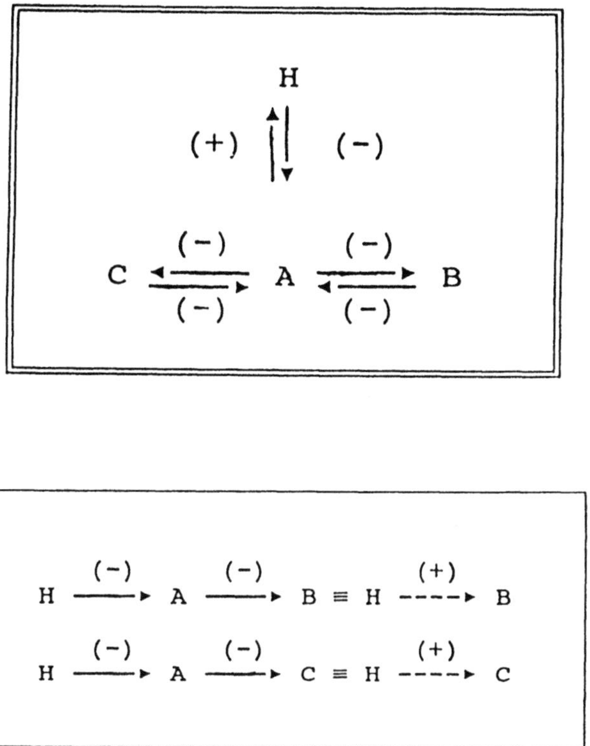

H → B = Direct Effect (0) + Indirect Effect (+) ≡ +
H → C = Direct Effect (0) + Indirect Effect (+) ≡ +
H → A = Direct Effect (-) + Indirect Effect (-) ≡ -

Figure 3. Herbivory (H) can significantly change the intensity of competitive interaction among plants (A, B, C are either different species or types of conspecifics) if it preferentially attacks and lowers the vigor of some types (e.g., type A). In so doing, it indirectly enhances (dashed lines) the success of the less preferred types (B, C). Herbivory has then two significant effects on the attacked species (A); a direct negative effect (-) through tissue/nutrient removal, and an indirect negative effect (-) through the enhancement of unattacked competitor plants.

Defenses in Relation to Resource Availability

Besides the question of how intra- and interspecific competition may affect the evolution of plant defenses, there is also the question of how the shortage or abundance of resources can influence this process. For example, in nutrient-impoverished environments high tolerance is unlikely to evolve as the plant's main line of defense against herbivory because of its inability to recover from and compensate for high levels of injury (Bryant et al. 1985, Coley et al. 1985). Nutrient sequestration is slow, consequently most plants adapted to chronic nutrient limitation are inherently slow growing (Chapin et al. 1987, Coley et al. 1985). If feeding damage to such plants typically exceeds the plant's rate of recovery from the damage, then selection pressure will favor the evolution of back-up defenses to supplement their limited tolerance. We argue as have others (Bryant et al. 1985, Coley et al. 1985) that high stress will select for near immunity (immediate inducible defense systems) or immunity (high levels of constitutive defenses and immediate inducible defenses).

Plants occurring in high stress environments will tend to be differentiation- rather than growth-dominated because differentiation processes are less limited by nutrient and water stresses than growth processes (Sharpe et al. 1986, Lorio 1986, Lorio in this volume). Hence, a stressful physical environment predisposes plants to evolve strong constitutive defenses for lowering herbivore damage. However, high levels of constitutive defenses may diminish the probability of the evolution of inducible defenses for certain kinds of herbivores (mobile free feeders such as folivores) because inducible defenses are unlikely to increase plant defense efficacy. Why? Because high, and consistent levels of constitutive defenses select for specialized herbivores having substantial behavioral/physiological/biochemical mechanisms (Tallamy 1985, Ahmad 1986) for coping with defenses, much as have pesticides (Taylor 1986). This predisposes them to be cross "resistant" to the evolution of (a) novel toxins or generalized increments in the existing package of constitutive defenses, and (b) new inducible defenses. To increase the efficacy of their defense systems such plants may be required during induction to so overload the attacked tissues with toxins that tissue death results (as in the case of bark beetles/fungi in stem phloem/sapwood). This is a self-defeating inducible defense against free-feeders because they can simply move to another, as yet unaffected site on the same plant. On the other hand, it's a workable solution against small numbers of imbedded, relatively immobile feeders such as gall insects and bark beetles.

We speculate that the apparent lack of evidence for efficacious inducible defenses in the foliage of stress-adapted plants (Tuomi et al. in this volume, Wagner in this volume) may be due to the actual absence of such defenses but more likely to the extraordinary capacity of the specialized folivores of such plants to cope with them.

On the other hand, in a nutrient-rich environment, plants will tend to be growth- rather than differentiation-dominated because the ready availability of nutrients will result in keen competition for space, water, and light. Thus, plants in nutrient-rich environments may be able to keep up with herbivore damage strictly through a well-developed tolerance capacity or perhaps tolerance coupled to lagging, inducible defenses or escape (Bryant et al. 1985). Whether tolerance alone is enough or some active back-up defense is necessary depends on the magnitude of the difference between the plant's capacity for recovery and the herbivore's average capacity for biomass or fluid removal.

A similar argument about energy limitation may apply in the case of shaded or very cold environments (Bryant et al. 1985, Coley et al. 1985, Bazzaz et al. 1987). Both nutrient and energy stress will select for the evolution of potent defenses because of the plant's very limited capacity for recovery from herbivory.

If resource availability and degree of intra- or interspecific competition both affect evolutionary responses, we suggest that a tolerance-dominated defense is a viable option only where resource availability is consistently relatively high and competition is mainly intraspecific or lacking altogether (Fig. 4). Moving toward low resource availability or largely interspecific competition creates selection pressure for rapid inducible, and high constitutive defense systems.

DEFENSES IN RELATIONSHIP TO INTIMACY OF CONTACT BETWEEN PLANT AND CONSUMER

Theoretical Considerations

Besides the plant's physiological and ecological capacities to recover from herbivory, another significant factor affecting the plant's repertoire of evolutionary responses to injury is intimacy of association between host and insect (Price 1980, Harris and Frederiksen 1984). We propose that the intimacy of surface contact

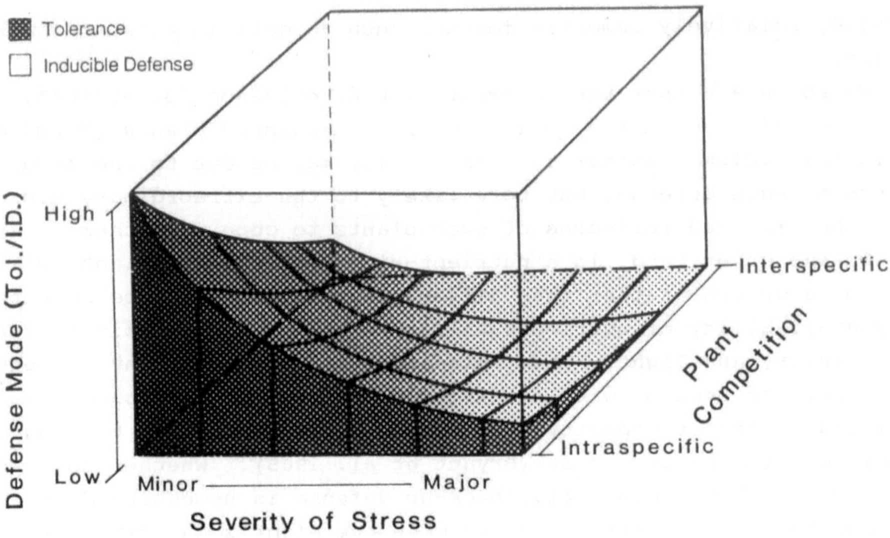

Figure 4. Plant defense modes (tolerance: inducible defense ratios) which may have evolved under various conditions of selection pressure from stress (high to low resources) and from plant-plant competition (intra- to inter-specific).

between plant and consumer has a marked effect on the plant's evolutionary options to deal with that consumer because the more physically intimate the relationship, the more likely it is that the plant population can evolve a wide variety of powerful, inducible defenses that can confer near-immunity or immunity. The converse is also true--the more limited the degree of plant-to-insect surface contact, the less likely that the plant population can evolve toward a near-immune defense system, all other things being equal.

Ranking Host Intimacy. The most intimate association occurs where all life stages of an insect (eggs, immatures, adults) are enclosed within living plant tissue, such as might be the case for some gall makers and some wood borers like bark beetles (Table 3). Less intimate associations would be those in which an insect has only one or some of its life stages enclosed within living plant tissue, such as the egg stage or perhaps both egg and immature feeding stages. Typical examples of the former might be species of sawflies that insert their eggs into leaf tissue, but later free feed externally. Examples of the latter might be species of leaf miners that live both as eggs and larvae in the leaf but pupate in the soil; or agromyzid cambium borers which live only as larvae enclosed in plant cambial tissue.

Table 3. Ranking selected insects according to their host intimacy (0.0 = min., 1.0 = max.).

Insect examples	Host intimacy rank[a]
	0 .25 .50 .75 1.00
Stem-twig borers	
Scolytidae, Platypodidae	***********************************
Cerambycidae, Siricidae	****************************
Buprestidae, Curculionidae	****************************
Gall-formers	
Adelgidae, Cynipidae	****************************
Leaf-miners	
Agromyzidae, Tenthredinidae	************************
Leaf/stem sap feeders	
Aphididae, Psyllidae	********
Coccoidea	********
Cicadellidae, Membracidae	****
Folivores-free feeders	
Tortricidae, Diprionidae	**
Lasiocampidae, Lymantriidae	*
Notodontidae, Saturniidae	*

[a]Intimacy rank = proportion of life cycle spent in intimate contact with living host tissue x proportion of body surface area exposed directly to host tissue.

The least intimate associations are those where none of the life stages are actually enclosed in living plant tissue. The primary plant/insect contact occurs when the insect's mouth parts periodically, but only briefly, pierce the plant tissue and when part of that tissue is swallowed, bringing it into contact with the surface of the digestive tract. Significantly more intimate are sucking insects, such as aphids, scales, and other Homopterans, that insert long, rather elaborate mouth parts into plant tissue, often for long periods. Some aphids take 40 minutes or more to merely insert their stylets (Dixon 1985). Many of these insects rely on salivary secretions to assist in placement and perhaps protection of their mouth parts while in the plant.

Plant/Pathogen Defense Model. We hypothesize that the longer the exposure and the larger the relative surface area of the consumer exposed to intimate contact with living plant tissue, the more likely the plant can deploy diverse and highly specific defensive systems against a consumer. For example, in the case of pathogenic microorganisms, mere wounding of the plant cells causes a general but limited production of phytoalexins owing to endoelicitors (sensu Berryman in this volume) which are products of the plant, e.g., cell wall fragments, etc. (Bell 1981, Ebel 1986, Keen 1986). However, when pathogen cells and certain specific molecules elaborated by the pathogen (e.g., pathogen cell wall components including carbohydrates, fatty acids, and glycoproteins as well as toxins) contact plant cells they may elicit further generalized as well as more specific and more abundant phytoalexin production by the plant (Bell 1981, Yoshikawa 1983, Ebel 1986, Keen 1986). In fact, plant inducible resistance to pathogens is believed to be triggered by the "recognition" process which occurs between certain pathogen-elaborated molecules and plant receptors (Bailey 1983, Yoshikawa 1983, Ayres et al. 1985).

If recognition of the pathogen fails to occur, the pathogen can then invade more plant tissue and further proliferate. Browning et al. (1982) argued that yet another set of more complex plant factors gov-ern the pathogen's rate of spread within a plant. These factors ap-parently are usually controlled by complex units of multiple genes in contrast to the recognition process whose basic parts are often mono-genically controlled (Bailey 1983, Browning et al. 1982, Ayres et al. 1985).

Plant/Insect Defense Model. We propose that this general model is also appropriate for most plant/insect interactions, allowing, of course, for the additional behavioral responses of insects to plant properties (Table 4).

Considering first the physiological-level interactions, we suggest that mere wounding of plant tissue by insects triggers the immediate, initial generalized plant reactions, i.e., the release of nonspecifice endoelicitors. Some of these (cell wall carbohydrates, proteins) will elicit a highly localized reaction, whereas others may elicit a systemic reaction (Ebel 1986, Meyer et al. 1987, Ryan et al. 1986). This is followed by more specific, immediate biochemical "re-cognition" processes which occur between plant cell receptors and insect-elaborated molecules (as when an insect tissue is inserted into plant tissue). Some insect-elaborated molecules may serve as general, and others as highly specific exogenous elicitors (exolicitors--sensu

Table 4. Categorizing inducible defenses (chemical and structural changes) by their induction time, their proximate eliciting agents, and their localization within plants.

Type of Defense	Triggering Mechanisms[a]	Localization
Immediate:		
a.) Low specificity	Endoelicitors--cell wall proteins, carbohydrates, ethylene, ethane, etc.	Local to systemic
b.) Low specificity	Exoelicitors (abiotic)--salts, UV light, herbicides	Local to systemic
c.) Low specificity (recognition--I)	Exoelicitors (biotic)--common carbohydrates, proteins, toxins of insects	Local
d.) High specificity (recognition--II)	Exoelicitors (biotic)--biotype specific proteins, carbohydrates, toxins of insects	Local
Lagging:		
a.) Low specificity	Nutrient imbalances (endogenous)--defoliation	Local to systemic
b.) Low specificity	Nutrient imbalances (exogenous)--nutrients, alleochemicals, chitin in frass	Systemic
c.) Low specificity	Turgor imbalances--defoliation	Local to systemic

[a]Derived from Bell 1981, Haukioja et al. 1985, Keen 1986, Broadway et al. 1986, Ebel 1986, Sharpe et al. 1986, Spiegel et al. 1986, and Tuomi et al. in this volume.

Berryman in this volume) of phytoalexin production in the plant (Nielson and Don 1974, Kennedy and Kishiba 1977), but only at a local level because cell/tissue death may accompany the process (Cheniclet et al. in this volume).

If the plant fails to "recognize" the invading insect tissue, then yet another set of general, less immediate (lagging), stress-related defensive mechanisms may be engaged, module by module, up to the whole plant level, to limit the rate of development and spread of the insect (Table 4). We speculate that these defenses are primarily a fortification of constitutive level defenses which occurs via an enhancement of differentiation processes. This may result from at first localized and then wide-spread carbon-nutrient, and turgor imbalances which tend to favor production of secondary products or differentiation processes in general (Lorio in this volume, Sharpe et al. 1986). Haukioja et al. (1985) have demonstrated that some components of insect frass may also contribute to build-ups in long-term plant defenses. They reasoned that the nutrients in the frass were probably the triggering agent but speculated that it might also be plant allelochemicals that were metabolized by the insect. Such allelochemicals may volatize or more likely have an effect in the plant's rhizosphere--perhaps interfering with the usual balance in nutrient uptake. Chitin in the frass derived from the insects' exoskeleton during the feeding process and/or from molting may also contribute in some way to this exogenous enhancement of plant defenses (Spiegel et al. 1986). It is likely that only the pre- and post-recognition parts of this defense model apply to free-feeding insects such as grasshoppers and Macrolepidoptera, because the more specific recognition process is probably never triggered or permitted to complete its usual chain reactions.

We propose, therefore, that the most diverse and most specific defensive systems will be employed against insects that are enclosed within plant tissue for one or more of their life stages. Very small insects which live intimately on the surface of plants (within the boundary layer) and those that have mouth parts that must be inserted into living plant tissues for long periods are probably also included in this category. Conversely, we propose that the least diverse and yet most general defensive systems will be employed against insects that are largely free-feeders. These defenses could theoretically be employed against any phytophagous insect because they will be either general behavioral deterrents or physiological deterrents that affect the external sensory and the gut systems.

At the behavioral level, how might intimacy of host association affect the evolution of plant defenses? Because "intimates" are either imbedded in or on plants, plants may have greater potential to biochemically and/or physically disrupt the insect's behavioral linkages to the plant. For example, a plant may alter the levels and balance of compounds that serve as feeding stimulants (e.g., sugars, amino acids, salts, and secondary compounds) and deterrents in the vicinity of an intimate associate to become behaviorally unacceptable. Being confined to a tissue, the insect may cease feeding and die. A plant may also alter the physical/ecological environment of an insect-infested tissue by changing its size, color, posture, texture, and rates of volatile emissions. For example, changing colors or rates of volatile emissions may attract natural enemies (although see Price et al. 1987) to the damaged tissue where the insects are "held captive." Also "dropping" a damaged leaf or fruit before the insect can complete its development may be a viable defense (Potter 1985).

Such defensive reactions by plants to free-feeders may not bring about substantial reductions in their population levels. Therefore, we argue that plants have a different repertoire of evolutionary options for intimate than for free-feeding insect associates. We argue that intimate interactions may select for more specific and more complex defenses because of the greater and more varied opportunities that the host plant has for regulating the lives of the intimate associates.

Evidence for Different Defenses in Relation to Intimacy of Host Association

Host Specificity. We believe that there is substantial circumstantial evidence to support the preceding hypotheses. First of all, if the host plant relations of intimates are more specific and more complex than the host plant relations of free-feeders, then this should be reflected in their average levels of host specificity. This seems to be the case because aphids, psyllids, scolytids, scales, and thrips appear to be much more host specific than the Macrolepidoptera (Table 5). However, armored scales (Diaspididae: Homoptera) which are largely polyphagous (McClure 1987) do not seem to fit this pattern. Nevertheless, because scales (Coccoidea) are so poorly understood, it's possible that they may be much more oligophagous than current evidence suggests--especially if they are predisposed to biotype development on novel host plants (Alstad and Edmunds 1983). Secondly, most gall-forming insects are highly host specific--being monophagous in the strictest sense of the word (Table 6)--largely confined to a single species. Thirdly, subdividing the Scolytidae on the basis of tissue specialization (Table 7), demonstrates that those species which feed in living tissues of trees (phloem) or on herbs are far more host specific than those feeding on mostly dead tissue (xylem) or on ambrosia fungi (Atkinson and Equihua 1986). Tree infesting buprestids, cerambycids, and sessiids demonstrate a similar pattern (Haack and Slansky 1987).

Table 5. Percentage of insect species within different taxonomic/ trophic groups that specialize on a single genus, more than one genus in a single plant family, or more than one family of plants.[a]

Insect group	Percentage of species per family feeding on			
	Only one genus	>1 Genus in one family	>One family	Number of insect species considered
Psyllidae	94	3	0	78
Aphidinae	91	7	2	445
Scolytidae	59	38	3	NA
Diaspididae	58	8	34	64
Thysanoptera	56	15	29	88
Nymphalidae	56	11	33	88
Lycaenidae	55	14	31	89
Pieridae	33	53	14	43
Papilionidae	25	21	54	89
Macrolepidoptera	17	23	60	430

[a]Data from Eastop 1973, Slansky 1976, Holloway and Hebert 1979, Stark 1982, Ananthakrishnan 1984, and McClure 1987.

Variations in Susceptibility. Finally, data about variations in native or indigenous insect population levels per individual plant in natural and man-made forests reveal that many of the "intimates" (e.g., scales/aphids) show distinctly different patterns than the best known free feeders (Macrolepidoptera). As a rule, the intimates tend to exhibit much greater tree-to-tree differences in population and injury levels than do free feeders, ranging along a spectrum from immune/near-immune tree phenotypes to low, medium, and highly susceptible phenotypes. In the latter, however, the evidence is mainly for nearly equal high levels of susceptibility among all individual trees and no immune or near-immune phenotypes.

In the case of scales (Coccoidea), Edmunds and Alstad (1981) reported that outbreaks of black pineleaf scale, *Nuculapsis californica*, are characterized by extreme tree-to-tree variations in density because of differences among trees in their resistance to leaf scale. Likewise, Mendel (1984) reported that the Israeli pine bast scale, *Matsucoccus josephi*, exhibits significant differences in population levels among different seed sources of *Pinus halapensis* (Table 8). The less susceptible seed sources have a higher percentage of

Table 6. Percentage of gall-forming insect species within different taxonomic groups that specialize on a single genus, more than one genus in a single plant family, or more than one family of plants.

Insect group	Percentage of species per family feeding on[a]			
	Only one genus	> 1 genus in one family	> one family	Number of insect species considered
Aphidoidea				
Adelgidae	100	0	0	18
Eriostomatidae	100	0	0	32
Phylloxerinae	100	0	0	80
Coccoidea				
Asterolecanidae	100	0	0	10
Diaspididae	100	0	0	16
Eriococcidae	100	0	0	93
Kermesidae	100	0	0	3
Lecanodiaspididae	100	0	0	3
Margarodidae	100	0	0	2
Pseudococcidae	100	0	0	7
Others				
Cynipidae	Typical	rare	0	719
Psylloidea	Typical	rare	rare	NA
Tephritidae	100	0	0	29

[a]Data from Askew 1984, Beardsley 1984, Freidberg 1984, Hodkinson 1984, Wool 1984.

unaffected trees, lower rates of injury, and lower scale densities. Also see Wainhouse et al. (in this volume) and Schvester (in this volume).

Similarly, in the case of aphids (Aphidoidea), there are many reports of substantial inter-tree differences in susceptibility (Wilson and Moore 1986). Meijnartowicz and Szmidt (1978) reported that infestations of the Douglas fir wooly aphid, Gilletteela cooleyi, differed significantly (0 to 94 percent) among 59 seed sources of Pseudotsuga menziesii. DeHayes (1981) and Mattson et al. (1987) made the same conclusion about the balsam twig aphid, Mindarus abietinus, on various North American seed sources of Abies balsamea.

Furthermore, we have found (unpublished data) that there are large differences in susceptibility to M. abietinus among A. balsamea

Table 7. Percentage of Scolytidae/Platypodidae in different feeding groups that specialize on a single genus, more than one genus in a single plant family, or more than one family of plants.

Feeding group	Percentage of insect species feeding on[a]			
	1 genus	> 1 genus	> 1 family	Number of insect species considered
Phloem	79	12	9	43
Herbs	60	40	0	5
Xylem	38	0	62	8
Pith	15	0	85	13
Ambrosia fungi	0	4	96	13

[a]Adapted from Atkinson and Equihua 1986 and Atkinson and Equihua-Martinez 1986.

half siblings. For example, from one mother: five progeny had negligible, 14 had light, 10 had medium, and one had heavy infestations of aphids. Brown (1953) reported variations in susceptibility of Picea glauca to the spruce gall aphid, Adelges lariciatus, as did Rohfritsch (1981) for Picea excelsa to Adelges abietis and Tjia and Houston (1975) for Picea abies to A. abietis. Carpenter et al. (1979) discussed numerous instances of resistant sources of Carya illinoensis to several species of aphids.

Other evidence of substantial inherent variations in tree resistance exists for pine gall and resin midges (Duffield 1985, Hong et al. 1985), various pine shoot borers (Hodson et al. 1982, Charles et al. 1982, Fogal et al. 1982), a pitch twig moth (Hodson et al. 1982), and various pine coneworms (Askew et al. 1985) and a leaf miner (Mazanec 1985) (Table 8).

In contrast is the apparent lack of substantial evidence for significant genetic variation among trees in resistance to most free-feeding leaf folivores, (but see Wright et al. 1967 and McDonald 1985). For example, Connor et al. (1982) reported no significant differences in the susceptibility of 25 seed sources of Picea glauca to the yellow-headed spruce sawfly, Pikonema alaskensis. Likewise, our own research (Lawrence et al. unpublished) suggests that neither P. glauca nor A. balsamea shows any consistent significant genetic variation in its high susceptibility to the spruce budworm, Choristoneura fumiferana (Fig. 5). On the other hand, these two tree

Table 8. Indigenous insect/host tree associations for which there is evidence of genetic variation desusceptibility/resistance by the tree to the insect.

Insect Species		Host Species
Pine scale[a]	_Matsucoccus feytaudi_	_Pinus pinaster_
Pine bast scale[b]	_Matsucoccus josephi_	_Pinus ponderosa_
Black pine leaf scale[c]	_Nuculapsis californica_	_Pinus halepensis_
Spruce gall aphid[d]	_Adelges abietis_	_Picea excelsa_
Spruce gall aphid[e]	_Adelges abietis_	_Picea abies_
Spruce gall aphid[f]	_Adelges lariciatus_	_Picea glauca_
Larch wooly aphid[g]	_Adelges laricis_	_Larix decidua_
Douglas-fir wooly aphid[h]	_Gilletteela cooley_	_Pseudotsuga menziesi_
Balsam twig aphid[i]	_Mindarus abietinus_	_Abies balsamea_
Aphids/Phylloxerans[j]	_Monellia_/_Monelliopsis_/ _Phylloxera_	_Carya illinoensis_
Pine gall midge[k]	_Thecodiplosis japonensis_	_Pinus thunbergii_
Pine resin midge[l]	_Cecidomyia piniinopsis_	_Pinus ponderosa_
Pine shoot borer[m]	_Eucosma gloriola_	_Pinus banksiana_
European pine shoot moth[n]	_Rhyacionia buoliana_	_Pinus nigra_
White pine weevil[o]	_Pissodes strobi_	_Pinus banksiana_
Pitch twig moth[m]	_Petrova albicapitana_	_Pinus banksiana_
Jarra leaf miner[p]	_Perthidia glyphora_	_Eucalyptus marginata_
Pine coneworms[q]	_Dioryctria spp_.	_Pinus taeda_

[a]Schvester and Ughetto 1986
[b]Edmunds and Alstad 1981
[c]Mendel 1984
[d]Rohfritsch 1981
[e]Tjia and Houston 1975
[f]Brown 1953
[g]Blada 1982
[h]Meijnartowicz and Szmidt 1978
[i]DeHayes 1981
[j]Carpenter _et al_. 1979
[k]Hong _et al_. 1985
[l]Duffield 1985
[m]Hodson _et al_. 1982
[n]Charles _et al_. 1982
[o]King 1971
[p]Mazanec 1985
[q]Askew _et al_. 1985

species do exhibit significant genetic variation in susceptibility to attack by various aphids (DeHayes 1981, Brown 1953).

Similarly, Harris (1982) reported that during an extensive outbreak of the walnut caterpillar, Datana integerrima, in Texas, every pecan, Carya illinoensis, was defoliated unless protected with insecticides. Yet, there is significant variation among pecan trees in their resistance to many sap feeders (Harris 1982, Carpenter et al. 1979).

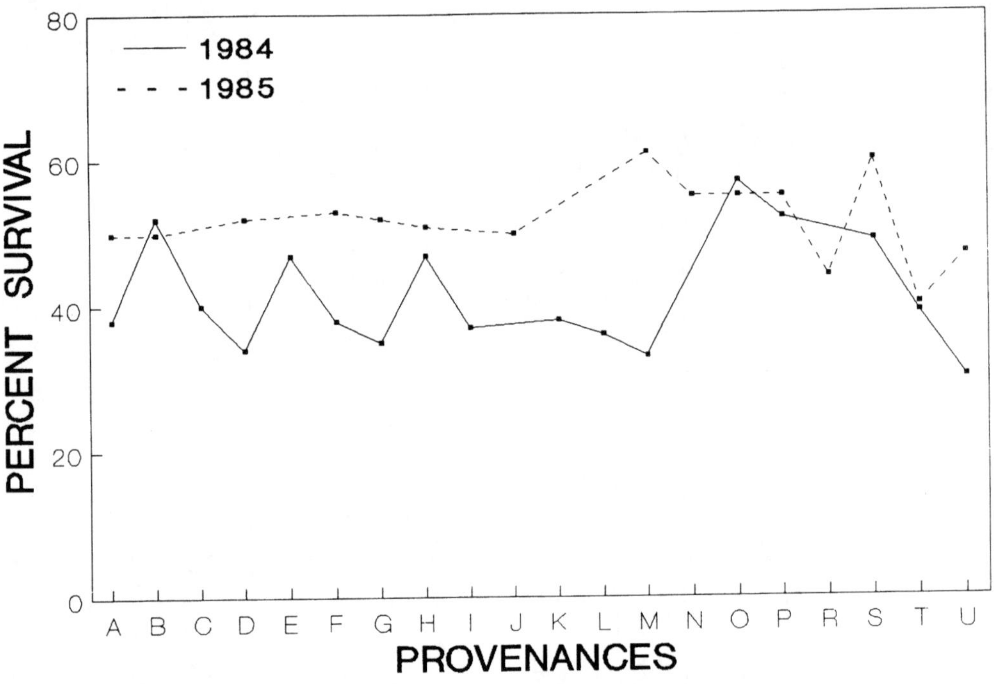

Figure 5. Survival (percent) of spruce budworm reared in Michigan (USA) on 20 different rangewide provenances (A = Alaska, U = Labrador) of white spruce during 1984 and 1985.

Field studies of many other temperate zone, free-feeding folivores have failed to discover any genetically immune or near-immune individuals in spite of the fact that millions of trees were being screened by insect epidemics. For example, our own extensive but casual observations on the forest tent caterpillar, Malacosoma disstria, outbreaks in Northern Minnesota and Michigan suggest that virtually every individual Populus tremuloides tree in an epicenter is attacked and stripped. The same appears true for outbreaks of the eastern tent caterpillar, M. americanum, on Prunus spp., the larch sawfly, Pristiphora erichsonii on Larix laricina, and the jackpine budworm, Choristoneura pinus, on Pinus banksiana.

We believe that most existing evidence for variations in susceptibility can be explained on the basis of variations in tree phenology (Du Merle in this volume), and environment-related variations in foliar nutrients and allelochemicals (Clancy et al. in this volume). Real genetic differences in susceptibility probably exist but are not sufficient to confer immunity/near immunity (Ayres et al. 1987).

CONCLUSIONS

We conclude that the modes of plant resistance against different feeding guilds of insects are different. At the basis of this are two key factors: (1) the ability or capacity of the plant to evolve tolerance for the insects' injuries, and (2) the repertoire of physiological mechanisms that a plant population can call upon in the evolution of defenses to back up its limited tolerance capacity (Fig. 6).

Studies by Maddox and Root (1987) on resistance of goldenrod, Solidago altissima, to 16 diverse herbivorous insects provide some limited support for these hypotheses. For example, they found that heritable differences among clones for resistance to galling insects were consistently larger than for other kinds of insects. This might be expected on the basis of the large number of intricate linkages needed for galling insects to successfully colonize plants. On the other hand, they concluded that an insect's apparent destructiveness (ability to lower plant fitness) did not necessarily correlate with the presence of heritable variations in plant resistance. Maddox and Root (1987) offered several explanations (based on historical events experienced by the plant populations) for this apparent contradiction.

We hypothesize that as the repertoire of available physiological mechanisms increases (as from free-feeders to gall makers), the variety of evolutionary "solutions" adopted by plant populations increases (Fig. 6). Hence, different populations of a plant species may exhibit different defenses against the same insect. Likewise as the capacity to recover from an insect's injuries increases so also do evolutionary options increase. We hypothesize that when tolerance capacity is high, any defense mode is possible (e.g., immunity, immediate-defenses, lagging-defense, or tolerance alone), but

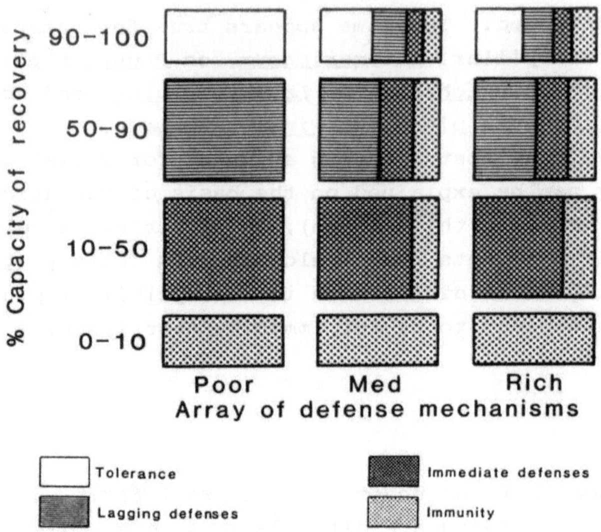

Figure 6. Likely plant defense modes in relation to the plant's physiological capacity to recover from insect injury, and the richness of the array of physiological mechanisms that the plant may employ against insects (e.g., free feeders to gall formers).

tolerance is the most likely mode because its "cost" is, on the average, less. If both the repertoire of mechanisms is rich and tolerance capacity is high, then we propose that there will be the most varied mixture of evolutionary solutions by various populations of a plant species to its interaction with a given insect (Fig. 6).

Ecological conditions can exert a powerful influence on the kind of evolutionary pathways that are taken in the plant/insect coevolutionary scenario (Fig. 7, Table 9). In Fig. 7, we have suggested that as competition proceeds from largely intra-specific to largely inter-specific, the array of evolutionary solutions or defense modes declines. Likewise, as stress proceeds from low to high, the array of evolutionary defense modes decline. And, under conditions of both high stress and largely inter-specific competition, the array of plant defense modes will be most restricted.

The ideas presented in this paper are obviously only skeletal hypotheses. Nevertheless, we feel that they have sufficient merit to

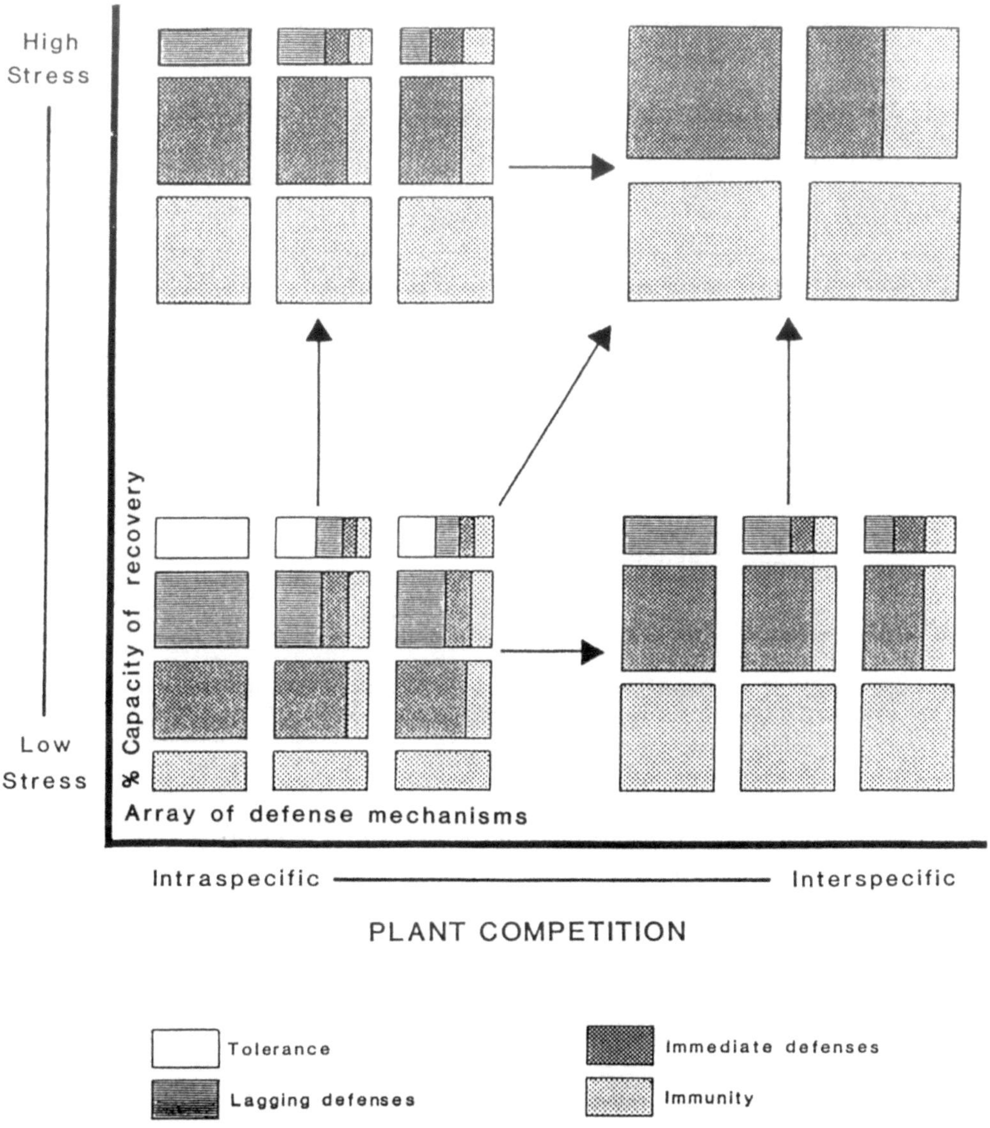

Figure 7. The effect of environment (type of competition and stress levels) on the evolution of various defensive modes for herbivores.

Table 9. Array of evolved plant defensive strategies[a] against different insect feeding guilds in different quality environments and community types.

Environment quality	Feeding guild type	Community Type	
		Mono-species	Poly-species
Resource rich	Phloem-cambium borers	1,2	1,2
	Early season folivores	3,4	3,2,1
	Gall formers	4,3,2,1	3,2,1,4
Resource Poor	Phloem-cambium borers	1,2	1,2
	Early season folivores	3,2,1	2,1
	Gall formers	3,2,1,4	3,2,1

[a] 1 = immunity, 2 = immediate inducible defense/tolerance, 3 = tolerance/lagging inducible defense, 4 = tolerance/escape.

be presented to the scientific community for wider consideration and critique. Others may be better able to quickly substantiate or refute what we believe are key girders in the conceptual framework of plant/insect interactions.

ACKNOWLEDGEMENTS

We gratefully acknowledge the challenging and stimulating discussions with Dr. Pekka Niemelä and Dr. Erkki Haukioja and the critical reviews by Matt Ayres, Dr. James Miller, and Dr. J. Mark Scriber.

REFERENCES

Ahmad, S. 1986. Enzymatic adaptations of herbivorous insects and mites to phytochemicals. J. Chem. Ecol. 12: 533-560.

Alstad D. N. and G. F. Edmunds. 1983. Adaptation, host specificity, and gene flow in the black pine leaf scale. In: Variable plants and herbivores in natural and managed systems (R. F. Denno and M. S. McClure, Eds.). New York: Academic Press; 413-426.

Ananthakrishnan, T. N. 1984. Bioecology of thrips. Oak Park, MI: Indira Publishing House, 233 p.

Askew, R. R. 1984. The biology of gall wasps. In: The biology of gall insects (T. N. Ananthakrishnan, Ed.). London: Edward Arnold; 223-271.
Askew, R. R., R. L. Hedden, and G. L. Debarr. 1985. Clonal variation in susceptibility to coneworms (Dioryctria spp.) in young loblolly pine seed orchards. For. Sci. 31: 794-798.
Atkinson, T. H. and A. Equihua. 1986. Biology of the Scolytidae and Platypodidae (Coleoptera) in a tropical deciduous forest at Chamela, Talisco, Mexico. Fla. Entomol. 69: 303-310.
Atkinson, T. H. and A. Equihua-Martinez. 1986. Biology of bark and ambrosia beetles (Coleoptera: Scolytidae and Blatypodidae) of a tropical rain forest in Southeastern Mexico with an annotated check-list of species. Ann. Entomol. Soc. Am. 79: 414-423.
Ayers, A. R., J. J. Goodell, and P. L. DeAngelis. 1985. Plant detection of pathogens. Recent Adv. Phytochem. 19: 1-20.
Ayres, M. P., J. Suomela, and S. F. Mclean. 1987. Growth performance of Epirrita autumnata (Lepidoptera: Geometridae) on mountain birch: trees, broods, and tree x brood interactions. Oecologia: Submitted.
Bailey, J. A. 1983. Biological perspectives of host-pathogen interactions. In: The dynamics of host defense (J. A. Bailey and B. J. Deverall, Eds.). New York: Academic Press; 1-32.
Bassman, J. H. and D. I. Dickmann. 1985. Effects of defoliation in the developing leaf zone on young Populus x euramericana plants. II. Distribution of ^{14}C-photosynthate after defoliation. For. Sci. 31: 358-366.
Bauer, G. 1986. Life-history strategy of Rhagoletis alternata (Diptera: Trypetidae), a fruit fly operating in a non-interactive system. J. Anim. Ecol. 55: 785-794.
Bazzaz, F. A., N. R. Chiariello, P. D. Coley, and L. F. Pitelka. 1987. Allocating resources to reproduction and defense. BioScience 37: 58-67.
Beardsley, T. W. 1984. Gall-forming Coccoidea. In: The biology of gall insects (T. N. Ananthakrishnan, Ed.). London: Edward Arnold; 79-106.
Bell, A. A. 1981. Biochemical mechanisms of disease resistance. Annu. Rev. Plant Physiol. 32: 21-81.
Belsky, A. T. 1986. Does herbivory benefit plants? A review of the evidence. Am. Nat. 127: 870-982.
Blada, I. 1982. Testing larch clones for Adelges laricis resistance. In: Resistance to diseases and pests in forest trees (H. M. Heybroek, B. R. Stephan, and K. von Weissenberg, Eds.). Wageningen, Netherlands: Pudoc; 466-471.
Braga, M. R., M. C. M. Young, J. V. A. Ponte, S. M. C. Dietrich, V. De P. Emernciano, and O. R. Gottlieb. 1986. Phytoalexin production in plants of tropical environment. Biochem. Syst. and Ecol. 14: 507-514.
Broadway, R. M., S. S. Duffey, G. Pearce, and C. A. Ryan. 1986. Plant proteinase inhibitors: a defense against herbivorous insects? Entomol. Exp. Appl. 41: 33-38.

Brown, R. C. 1953. Genetic variation in resistance of trees to insect attack. In: Proceedings, North Eastern Forest Tree Improvement. Conference; 1: 30-32.
Browning, J. A., J. Manistersk, A. Segal, G. Fischbeck, and I. Wahl. 1982. Extrapolation of genetic and epidemiologic concepts from indigenous ecosystems to agro-ecosystems. In: Resistance to diseases and pests in forest trees (H. M. Heybroek, B. R. Stephan, and K. von Weissenberg, Eds.). Wageningen, Netherlands: Pudoc; 371-380.

Bryant, J. P., F. S. Chapin III. 1982. Carbon/nutrient balance of boreal plants in relation to snowshoe are (Lepus americanus) browsing. In: Carbon uptake and allocation in subalpine ecosystems as a key to management (R. H. Waring, Ed). Forestry Res. Lab., Oregon State Univ.; 45-51.
Bryant, J. P., F. S. Chapin III, P. Reichardt, and T. Clausen. 1985. Adaptation to resource availability as a determinant of chemical defense strategies in woody plants. Recent Adv. Phytochem. 19: 219-237.
Campbell, R. W. and R. J. Sloan. 1977. Forest stand responses to defoliation by the gypsy moth. For. Sci. Monogr. 19.
Carpenter, T. L., W. W. Neel, and P. A. Hedin. 1979. A review of host plant resistance of pecan, Carya illinoensis, to Insecta and Acarina. Bull. Entomol. Soc. Amer. 25; 251-257.
Chapin, F. S., III, A. J. Bloom, C. B. Field, and R. H. Waring. 1987. Plant responses to multiple environmental factors. BioScience 37: 49-57.
Charles, P. J., A. Delphanque, A. Marpeau, C. Bernard-Dagan, and M. Arbez. 1982. Susceptibility of European black pine (Pinus nigra) to the European pine shoot moth (Rhyacionia buoliana): variations of susceptibility at the provenance and individual level of pine and the effect of terpene composition. In: Resistance to diseases and pests in forest trees (H. M. Heybroek, B. R. Stephan, and K. von Weissenberg, Eds.). Wageningen, Netherlands: Pudoc; 206-212.
Coley, P. D. 1983a. Intraspecific variation in herbivory on two tropical tree species. Ecology 64: 426-433.
Coley, P. D. 1983b. Herbivory and defensive characteristics of tree species in a lowland tropical forest. Ecol. Monogr. 53: 209-233.
Coley, P. D., J. P. Bryant, and F. S. Chapin. 1985. Resource availability and plant antiherbivore defense. Science 230: 895-899.
Connor, M. D., M. W. Houseweart, and H. M. Kulman. 1982. Susceptibility of white spruce seed sources to yellowheaded spruce sawfly, Pikonema alaskensis, (Hymenoptera: Tenthredinidae). Great Lakes Entomol. 15: 207-211.
Conti, M. 1985. Transmission of plant viruses by leafhoppers and planthoppers. In: The leafhoppers and planthoppers. New York: John Wiley and Sons; 298-307.
DeHayes, D. H. 1981. Genetic variation in susceptibility of Abies balsamea to Mindarus abietinus. Can. J. For. Res. 11: 30-35.
Dewey, J. E., W. M. Ciesla, and H. E. Meyer. 1974. Insect defoliation as a predisposing agent to a bark beetle outbreak in eastern Montana. Environ. Entomol. 3: 722.
Dixon, A. F. G. 1985. Aphid ecology. London: Blackie; 157 p.
Duffield, J. W. 1985. Inheritance of shoot coatings and their relation to resin midge attack on ponderosa pine. For. Sci. 31: 427-429.
Eastop, V. F. 1973. Deductions from the present day host plants of aphids and related insects. In: Insect/plant relationships (H. F. vanEmden, Ed.). New York: John Wiley and Sons; 157-178.
Ebel, J. 1986. Phytoalexin synthesis: the biochemical analysis of the induction process. Annu. Rev. Phytopathol. 24: 235-264.
Edmunds, G. F. and D. N. Alstad. 1981. Responses of black pineleaf scales to host plant variability. In: Insect life history patterns: habitat and geographic variation (Denno, R. F. and H. Dingle, Eds.). New York: Springer-Verlag; 29-38.
Fogal, W. H., E. K. Morgenstern, P. Viidik, and C. W. Yeatman. 1982. Variation in susceptibility of native and introduced coniferous trees to some insects of eastern Canada. In: Resistance to diseases and pests in forest trees (H. M. Heybroek, B. R. Stephan, and K. von Weissenberg, Eds.). Wageningen, Netherlands: Pudoc; 472-477.

Freidberg, A. 1984. Gall tephritidae. In: The biology of gall insects (T. N. Ananthakrishnan, Ed.). London: Edward Arnold; 129-167.
Gregory, R. A. and P. M. Wargo. 1986. Timing of defoliation and its effect on bud development, starch reserves, and sap sugar concentrations in sugar maple. Can. J. For. Res. 16: 10-17.
Gregory, R. A., M. W. Williams, B. L. Wong, and G. T. Hawley. 1987. (In press). Proposed scenario for dieback and decline of Acer saccharum in the Northeastern U.S.A. and Southeastern Canada. IAWA Bull.
Haack, R. A. 1985. Management prescriptions for the twolined chestnut borer. In: Challenges in oak management and utilization (J. Johnson, Ed.). Madison, WI: Coop. Exten. Serv., Univ. Wisconsin-Extension; 43-54.
Haack, R. A. and F. Slansky Jr. 1987. Nutritional ecology of wood-feeding Coleoptera, Lepidoptera, and Hymenoptera. In: The nutritional ecology of insects, mites, spiders, and related invertebrates (G. Slansky Jr. and J. G. Rodriquez, Eds.). New York: John Wiley and Sons; 449-489.
Harris, M. K. 1980. Arthropod-plant interactions related to agriculture, emphasing host plant resistance. In: Biology and breeding for resistance to arthropods and pathogens in agricultural plants (M. K. Harris, Ed.). College Station, TX: Texas Agric. Exp. Sta.; 23-51.
Harris, M. K. 1982. Genes for resistance to insects in agriculture with a discussion of host-parasite interactions in Carya. In: Resistance to diseases and pests in forest trees (H. M. Heybroek, B. R. Stephan, and K. von Weissenberg, Eds.). Wageningen, Netherlands: Pudoc; 72-83.
Harris, M. K. 1983. Outbreak biology of walnut caterpillar in Texas. Southwest. Entomol. 8: 231-240.
Harris, M. K. and R. A. Frederiksen. 1984. Concepts and methods regarding host plant resistance to arthropods and pathogens. Ann. Rev. Phytopathol. 22: 247-272.
Haukioja, E., J. Suomela, and S. Neuvonen. 1985. Long-term inducible resistance in birch foliage: triggering cues and efficacy on a defoliater. Oecologia 65: 363-369.
Hodkinson, I. D. 1984. The biology and ecology of the gall-forming Psylloidea (Homoptera). In: The biology of gall insects (T. N. Ananthakrishnan, Ed.). London: Edward Arnold; 59-106.
Hodson, A. C., D. W. French, R. A. Jensen, and R. J. Bartelt. 1982. The susceptibility of jack pine from Lake States seed sources to insects and diseases. St. Paul, MN: North Central Forest Experimental Station. Res. Pap. NC-235.
Holloway, J. D. and P. D. N. Hebert. 1979. Ecological and taxonomic trends in macrolepidopteran host plant selection. Biol. J. Linn. Soc. 11: 229-251.
Hong, S. H., G. S. Thun, S. I. Sohn, K. S. Kim, and H. S. Park. 1985. Research on breeding pines resistant to the pine gall midge in Korea. In: Proceedings, Joint Conference of IUFRO Working Parties on forest gall midges and rusts of pines (J. H. Ko and Y. J. La, Eds.). Korean Forestry Society. Suweon 170, Korea: College of Agriculture, Seoul National. Univ.; 87-99.
Karban, R. 1980. Periodical cicada nymphs impose periodical oak tree wood accumulation. Nature 287: 326-327.
Keen, N. T. 1986. Phytoalexins and their involvement in plant disease resistance. Iowa State J. of Res. 60: 477-499.
Kennedy, G. G. and A. N. Kishiba. 1977. Response of alate melon aphids to resistant and susceptible melon lines. J. Econ. Entomol. 70: 407-410.
King, J. P. 1971. Pest susceptibility variation in Lake States jack pine seed sources. St. Paul, MN: North Central Forest Experimental Station. Res. Pap. NC-53.

Knapp, A. K. 1986. Ecophysiology of Zigadenus nuttalli, a toxic spring ephemeral in a warm season grassland: effect of defoliation and fire. Oecologia 71: 69-74.
Kulman, H. M. 1971. Effects of insect defoliation on growth and mortality of trees. Annu. Rev. Entomol. 16: 289-324.
Langor, D. W. and A. G. Raske. 1987. (In press). Life history of the eastern larch beetle, Dendroctonus simples LeConte (Coleoptera: Scolytidae), in Newfoundland. Can. Entomol.
Lorio, P. L. 1986. Growth-differentiation balance: a basis for understanding southern pine beetle-tree interactions. For. Ecol. Manage. 14: 1-15.
Maddox, G. D. and R. B. Root. 1987. Resistance to 16 diverse species of herbivorous insects wtihin a popualtion of goldenrod, Solidage altissima: genetic variaiton and heritability. Oecologia 72: 8-14.
Mattson, W. J. and N. D. Addy. 1975. Phytophagous insects as regulators of forest primary production. Science 190: 515-522.
Mattson, W. J. and R. A. Haack. 1987. The role of drought in outbreaks of plant-eating insects. BioScience 37: 100-118.
Mattson, W. J., R. A. Haack, and R. K. Lawrence. 1987. (In press). Do balsam twig aphids lower tree susceptibility to spruce budworm? Can. Entomol.
Mazanec, Z. 1985. Resistance of Eucalyptus marginata to Perthidia glyphopa (Lepidoptera: Incurvariidae). J. Aust. Entomol. Soc. 24: 209-221.
McClure, M. S. 1987. (In press). Patterns of host specificity in armored scales: monophagy, oligophagy and polyphagy. Armored scales: their biology, natural enemies, and control (D. Rosen, Ed.). Amsterdam: Elsevier.
McDonald, G. I. 1985. Heritability of resistance in Douglas-fir to western spruce budworm. In: The role of the host plant in the population dynamics of forest insects (L. Safranyik, Ed.); Proceedings, IUFRO Conference; 1983 September 4-7; Banff, Alberta. Victoria, BC: Canadian Forestry Service and USDA, Forest Service; 96-107.
McNaughton, S. J. 1983. Physiological and ecological implications of herbivory. In: Physiological plant ecology III. Responses to the chemical and biological environment. (O. L. Lange, P. S. Nobel, C. B. Osmond, and H. Ziegler, Eds.). New York: Springer Verlag; 657-677.
McNaughton, S. J. 1985. Grazing lawns: animals in herds, plant form, and coevolution. Am. Nat. 124: 863-886.
McNaughton, S. J. and F. S. Chapin. 1985. Effects of phosphorus and defoliation on C_4 graminoids from the Serengeti plains. Ecology 66: 1617-1629.
Meijnartowicz, L. E. and A. Szmidt. 1978. Investigations into the resistance of Douglas-fir (Pseudotsuga menziesii) populations to the Douglas-fir wooly aphid (Gilletteela cooleyi Gill). Silvae Genet. 27: 59-62.
Mendel, Z. 1984. Provenance as a factor in susceptibility of Pinus halepensis to Matsucoccus josephi (Homoptera: Margarodidae). For. Ecol. Manage. 9: 259-266.
Meyer, A., P. Müller, and G. Sembolner. 1987. Air pollution and plant hormones. Biochem. Physiol. Pflanzen 182: 1-21.
Mosher, D. G. 1982. Determining shade tree values: adjusting for insect pest damage. In: Urban and suburban trees: pest problems, needs, prospects, and solutions (B. O. Parks, F. A. Fear, M. T. Lambur, and G. A. Simmons, Eds.). Department of Resource Development, Michigan State Univ. 235-237.
Nielson, M. W. and H. Don. 1974. Probing behavior of biotypes of the spotted alfalfa aphid on resistant and susceptible alfalfa clones. Entomol. Exp. Appl. 17: 477-486.

Pemberton, R. W. 1986. The impact of a stem-boring insect on the tissues, physiology, and reproduction of Russian Thistle. Entomol. Exp. App. 42: 169-177.

Potter, D. A. 1985. Population regulation of the native holly leafminer, Phytomyza ilicicola Loew (Diptera: Agromyzidae), on American holly. Oecologia 66: 499-505.

Price, P. W. 1980. Evolutionary biology of parasites. Princeton, NJ: Princeton Univ. Press, 237 p.

Price, P. W., G. Wilson Fernandes, and G. L. Waring. 1987. Adaptive nature of insect galls. Environ. Entomol. 16-24.

Purcell, A. H. 1985. The ecology of bacterial and mycoplasma plant diseases spread by leafhoppers and planthoppers. In: The leafhoppers and planthoppers (L. R. Nault and T. G. Rodriguez, Eds.). New York: John Wiley and Sons; 351-380.

Rhoades, D. F. 1985. Offensive-defensive interactions between herbivores and plants: their relavance in herbivore population dynamics and ecological theory. Am. Nat. 125: 205-238.

Rohfritsch, O. 1981. A "defense" mechanism of Picea excelsa L. against the gall former Chermes abietis L. (Homoptera: Adelgidae). Z. Angew. Entomol. 92: 18-26.

Ryan, C. A., P. D. Bishop, J. S. Graham, R. M. Broadway, S. S. Duffey. 1986. Plant and fungal cell wall fragments activate expression of proteinase inhibitor genes for plant defense. J. Chem. Ecol. 12: 1025-1036.

Schultz, D. E. and D. C. Allen. 1977. Characteristics of sites with high black cherry mortality due to bark beetles following defoliation by Hydria prunivorata. Environ. Entomol. 6: 77-81.

Schvester, D. and F. Ughetto. 1986. Differénces de sensibilité à Matsucoccus feytaudi Duc. (Homoptera: Margarodidae) selon des provenances de Pin maritime (Pinus pinaster Ait.). Ann. Sci. For. 43: 459-474.

Sharpe, P. J. H., R. J. Newton, and R. D. Spence. 1986. Forest pests: the role of phloem osmotic adjustment in the defensive response of conifers to bark beetle attack. In: Stress physiology and forest productivity (T. C. Hennessary, P. M. Dougherty, S. V. Kossuth, and J. D. Johnson, Eds.). Boston: Martinus Nijhoff Publishers; 113-131.

Simberloff, D., B. J. Brown, and S. Lowrie. 1978. Isopod and insect root borers may benefit Florida mangroves. Science 201: 630-632.

Slansky, F. 1976. Phagism relationships among butterflies. J. N. Y. Entomol. Soc. 84: 91-105.

Spiegel, Y., E. Cohn, and I. Chet. 1986. Use of chitin for controlling plant parasitic nematodes. I. Direct effects on nematode reporuction and plant performance. Plant and Soil 95: 97-95.

Stark, R. W. 1982. Generalized ecology and life cycle of bark beetles. In: Bark beetles in North American conifers (J. B. Mitton and K. B. Sturgeon, Eds.). Austin, TX: Univ. Texas Press; 21-45.

Tallamy, D. W. 1985. Squash beetle feeding behavior: an adaptation against induced curcurbit defenses. Ecology 66: 1574-1579.

Taylor, C. E. 1986. Genetics and evolution of resistance to insecticides. Biol. J. Linn. Soc. 27: 103-112.

Tjia, B. and D. B. Houston. 1975. Phenolic constituents of Norway spruce resistant or susceptible to the eastern spruce gall aphid. For. Sci. 21: 180-184.

Whitham, T. G. and S. Mopper. 1985. Chronic herbivory: impacts on architecture and sex expression in pinyon pine. Science 228: 1089-1091.

Wilson, L. F. and L. M. Moore. 1986. Preference for some nursery-grown hybrid Populus trees by the spotted poplar aphid and its suppression by insecticidal soaps (Homoptera: Aphididae). Great Lakes Entomol. 19: 21-26.

Wool, D. 1984. Gall forming aphids. In: The biology of gall insects (T. N. Ananthakrishnan, Ed.). London: Edward Arnold; 11-58.
Wright, J. W., L. F. Wilson, and W. K. Randall. 1967. Differences among Scotch pine varieties in susceptibility to European pine sawfly. For. Sci. 13: 175-181.
Yoshikawa, M. 1983. Macromolecules, recognition, and triggering of resistance. In: Biochemical plant pathology (J. A. Callow, Ed.). New York: John Wiley and Sons; 267-298.

2

Towards a Unified Theory of Plant Defense

Alan A. Berryman

Current theories of plant defense have arisen from several different viewpoints. Plant pathologists, being mainly interested in organisms that invade plant tissues and in problems involving exotic (unadapted) plant/pathogen interactions, have concentrated on the dynamic aspects of cellular defense (e.g., hypersensitive reactions and phytoalexins) and the genetic basis of plant resistance (e.g., the gene-for-gene hypothesis) (see Bailey and Deverall 1983). On the other hand, entomologists have been strongly influenced by the concepts of static (preformed or constitutive) plant resistance (Painter 1951). A few, however, borrowed from the pathology literature to develop concepts of dynamic (induced) defense against insect herbivores. Not surprisingly, these early workers studied insects that penetrate plant tissues and/or vector plant pathogens, e.g., aphids, (Homoptera: Aphididae) (Balch et al. 1964, Mullick 1977, Rohfritsch in this volume); siricid woodwasps, (Hymenoptera: Siricidae) (Coutts and Dolezal 1966); and scolytid bark beetles, (Coleoptera: Scolytidae) (Reid et al. 1967; Berryman 1969, 1972; Shrimpton 1978; Cook and Hain in this volume; Lieutier and Berryman in this volume). These studies provided an important bridge between pathology and entomology and drew attention to environmental influences on plant defensive capacity (i.e., predisposition). Theories emerging from these studies, however, have been functional rather than evolutionary.

Research on plant defenses against foliage-feeding herbivores has evolved more slowly, perhaps because the defenses are much more subtle. Nevertheless, researchers working with defoliators have recently been active in developing an evolutionary theory of plant defense (Feeny 1976; Rhoades 1979, 1985; Coley et al. 1985). These theories draw attention to the adaptive strategies of plants and herbivores, particularly in relation to plant apparency (the likelihood of being found by herbivores), herbivore specialization, availability of resources, and the diversity of the plant's defensive arsenal. A major weakness, however, is their lack of attention to literature on organisms that penetrate plant tissues. As such, they are mainly theories of plant defense against free-feeding herbivores. The present paper attempts to consolidate some of these ideas as a step towards a unified theory of plant defense.

ADAPTIVE PATHWAYS IN DEFENSE AND OFFENSE

The first living organisms, by their very existence, supplied resources on which other, as yet nonexistent, organisms could feed. It was inevitable, therefore, that herbivores evolved to feed on plants (Fig. 1a) and they in turn supplied resources for the evolution of carnivores (Fig. 1b). In this way, the trophic structure of present day communities has evolved as an inevitable consequence of organisms adapting to exploit supplies of available nutrients and energy. It was just as inevitable that the second round would involve the evolution of defensive traits in the organisms under attack, both plants and herbivores (Fig. 1c), and that this in turn would give rise to offensive counter-adaptations in the consumers (Fig. 1d). We should also note that although the evolution of trophic levels has a finite limit because resources (energy sources) become progressively more scarce as one ascends the trophic pyramid, the defense/offense feedback loop can give rise to a potentially infinite series of adaptations and counter-adaptations. Notice also that besides the direct adaptive pathways (solid arrows in Fig. 1), where adaptions directly affect the fitness of the evolving organism, we may also find indirect pathways where adaptations affect the fitness of one organism through serial effects on other organisms (broken arrows). Hence, plants can indirectly defend themselves by increasing the offensive capabilities of carnivores (Fig. 1e) or by compromising the defenses of herbivores against carnivores (Fig. 1f). Alternatively, herbivores can adapt to utilize plant allelochemicals to defend themselves or to find host plants.

In order to develop an evolutionary theory of plant defense, I have adopted the "optimal defense theory" platform suggested by Rhoades (1979). This theory, which is the reciprocal of "optimal foraging theory," rests on the following assumptions: (1) Defensive adaptions evolve to maximize the inclusive fitness of the individual organism, and (2) All defensive traits have a cost in terms of individual fitness because energy and/or nutrients are diverted from

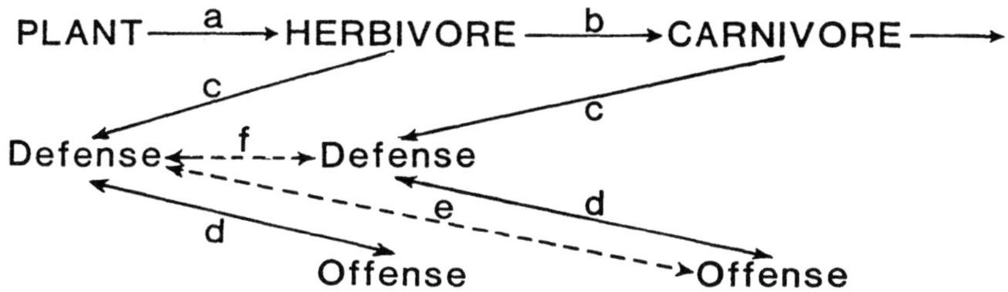

Figure 1. Adaptive pathways in the evolution of trophic interactions and defensive-offensive tactics: Direct adaptive pathways (solid arrows)--Plants provide the opportunity for the evolution of herbivores (a) and herbivores for the evolution of carnivores (b). The presence of herbivores selects for the evolution of plant defensive adaptations and (c) this selects for counter-offensive adaptations in the herbivore (d). Indirect adaptive pathways (broken arrows)--Plant defenses can act by increasing the effectiveness of carnivore offensive tactics (e) or by compromising the defensive tactics of the herbivore (f). Also, herbivores can exploit plant defensive traits to defend themselves against carnivores (f) or to attack plants (d).

other essential functions such as growth and reproduction. From these assumptions, it is evident that a particular trait will evolve only if the benefit to fitness exceeds its cost. It is also apparent that the benefit of a particular trait depends upon the impact of a particular herbivore on plant fitness. I will use these fundamental concepts of optimal defense theory to develop the following arguments.

MECHANISMS OF PLANT DEFENSE

There are three basic ways to deal with the attack of an enemy: (1) do nothing and tolerate the attack, (2) avoid or escape the attack, and (3) employ defensive tactics.

Tolerance

Tolerance is basically a passive, nonadaptive strategy in which the selection pressure for any and all adaptations is zero or less. In other words, the impact of herbivory is so small (or is beneficial), or the adaptive traits are so costly or ineffective, that none will be selected for. For these reasons, tolerance is usually observed when herbivores feed on nonessential tissues or on plant parts just prior to their natural death; for example, leaves just before abscission, branches just prior to natural death from shading, and post-reproductive, overmature plants. Tolerance could also appear as a secondary adaptation if the herbivore shifts its feeding to nonessential tissues. Galls may be an example of this kind of secondary adaptive pathway. In this scenario, the plant initially produced callus/parenchyma tissue as a defense against the insect; the insect then adapted to feed on this defensive tissue rather than on functioning plant parts; the plant then reduced its investment in defense and, through a series of adaptations and counter-adaptations, a stable (tolerant) condition emerged with the herbivore confined to nonfunctional plant tissues. This interpretation seems reasonable because both callus and parenchymous tissues are normally associated with active defense and wound healing (Berryman 1972, Rohfritsch in this volume).

Avoidance

Avoidance (or escape) occurs when an organism escapes attack some of the time and thereby reduces the likelihood of damage or death. Avoidance is possible if the plant can become permanently or temporarily "invisible" or nonapparent to the enemy (Feeny 1976), i.e., by hiding, camouflage, flight, or varying the time at which the attacked structures are present. Large, long-lived plants presumably find it difficult to escape herbivores by hiding or disguise. However, because plants are such incredible chemical factories, it would not be surprising to find examples of "chemical camouflage" or "chemical confusion."

Flight, or escape in space, is possible during seed dispersal, particularly in short-lived plants. Annual plants, for example, can disappear form one locality, where herbivores may be abundant, to reappear where they are scarce. In this way, they can reduce the likelihood of damage, particularly by specific herbivores (Feeny 1976). Specific herbivores may even have acted as selective pressures in the evolution of the annual life cycle.

Even long-lived plants have the potential to escape intense herbivory by varying the time of appearance of structures on which the herbivore feeds (e.g., buds, foliage, reproductive structures). Certainly, the extreme variability and synchrony of fruit production by many trees significantly reduces the impact of herbivores feeding on these structures (Mattson 1980, Roques 1987); e.g., compared to the situation in orchards or plantations where continuous fruiting is maintained by fertilization. Variability in the time of bud flushing may also confuse the timing strategies of bud- and leaf-feeding insects (Isaev et al. 1987, Du Merle in this volume).

The strategy of avoidance is never completely effective, however, because numerous counter-adaptations are available to the herbivores, particularly the more mobile ones. Thus, insects have evolved complex behavioral mechanisms (olfaction, dispersal, prolonged diapause) to exploit spatial and temporal variations in their food supplies. On the other hand, avoidance is a fairly cheap adaptation for long-lived plants and, on this basis, we might expect it to evolve when a certain degree of herbivory can be tolerated; i.e., in the case of seed-eating herbivores because a proportion of the seeds can often be sacrificed by long-lived plants without much loss of fitness. Under these conditions, the development of a cheap, low-efficiency defensive trait is a reasonable strategy.

Defense

Defense is a common strategy in plants which, being immobile, have difficulty in avoiding their enemies. However, it is also found in mobile animals when attacked by "nonapparent" enemies such as those too small to see. There are two basic approaches to defense: passive or constitutive defense, which is analogous to fortification, and dynamic or induced defense, which is more similar to counter-attack (Cowling and Horsfall 1980).

Constitutive Defense. Plants have evolved a multitude of structures and chemicals that are incorporated into their tissues for the purpose of defense. These constitutive defenses can deter, repel, intoxicate, or interfere with the development or reproduction of herbivores. Some examples are leaf spines and hairs (Carter and Nichols 1985); fiberous or resin-covered foliage (Baltensweiler et al. 1977); thick, corky bark (Wainhouse et al. in this volume); resin-filled cavities and ducts (Hanover 1975); lignified or phenol-impregnated cell walls (Nef in this volume, Wainhouse et al. in this volume); and cells containing phenolics or hormone analogues (Mullick 1977, Rhoades and Cates 1976). In addition, healthy plants may tie up nitrogen in forms unavailable to herbivores (White 1978).

Plants contain an extremely rich and diverse array of chemicals. Many of these chemicals were originally thought to be secondary by-products of cellular metabolism, hence their common name "secondary plant metabolites." Current thinking, however, considers many of these as primary defensive compounds, particularly the terpenoids, alkaloids, phenolics, and their many derivatives.

Biosynthesis of defensive chemicals is a metabolically expensive process so that the cost to fitness may be quite high. For example, isopentenyl pyrophosphate, the basic condensing unit in terpene synthesis, consumes three molecules of acetyl-CoA, two of NADPH, and three of ATP (Croteau and Johnson 1985). This is equivalent to a total cost of 18 ATP's, or 2 molecules of glucose, for every monoterpene molecule produced (Miller and Berryman 1985). If we consider the cost in terms of lost tissue, growth, or reproductive output, it becomes much greater; i.e., 90 ATP's, or 10 glucose molecules (Wright *et al*. 1979, however see Tuomi *et al*. in this volume).

The advantage of some constitutive defenses is that they can be laid down during periods of energy or nutrient surplus and may then serve over an extended period of time; for example, during periods of stress when energy is limited. The problem is that their genetically determined cost, in terms of reduced growth and reproductive output, is fixed. We should, therefore, expect constitutive defenses to evolve in long-lived, shade-tolerant, late successional plants which do not require fast juvenile growth or massive reproductive efforts to persist in the environment but which must survive over long periods in the face of unpredictable resources. This expectation is borne out by the long-lived climax tree species which seem particularly rich in constitutive chemical defenses; e.g., the genera *Taxus*, *Cedrus*, *Thuja*, *Sequoia*, *Libocedrus*, *Cupressus*, *Chamaecyparis* (Alfaro *et al*. 1981, Croteau and Johnson 1985).

Although passive constitutive defenses may be effective against an array of generalist herbivores, they encourage the evolution of specialists because they exert strong selective pressure continuously on the herbivore population--much like the continual use of chemical pesticides encourages the evolution of resistant pests. Thus, even the best defended species are attacked by a few specialist herbivores.

Induced Defense. Induced or dynamic defense involves the production of chemicals or physical structures, or the removal of nutrients essential to the herbivore, *in response* to attack. Induced defenses may take several forms of increasing cost: (1) *Nutrient removal*, which involves the tie-up of nutrients (such as nitrogen) that are essential for herbivore growth in a form that is unavailable to the herbivore (White 1978). (2) *Cell lignification* in which tougher (heavily lignified), less digestible food is produced after attack (Baltensweiler *et al*. 1977). (3) *Controlled chemical biosynthesis* in which relatively small quantities of defensive chemicals are produced by living cells close to or even distant (systemic effect) from the point of injury, or the transport of water-soluble chemicals from their point of origin to other plant parts (e.g., Kuc 1983). Controlled biosynthesis does not result in cell death or necrosis because the toxic chemicals are contained within membrane limited structures (e.g., vacuoles) or intercellular spaces (e.g., resin ducts), are impregnated into cell walls, or are secreted at nontoxic doses. (4) Uncontrolled chemical biosynthesis in which very large quantities of defensive chemicals are produced by living cells close to the site of injury, sometimes called a local or hypersensitive reaction. During this response, sugars and starches are rapidly converted into indigestible or toxic compounds (terpenes, phenols, etc.) as a result of apparently uncontrolled chemical reactions; i.e., cell membranes of the secretory cells rupture and release their contents into intercellular spaces and the lumens of conducting tissues (Reid et al. 1967, Berryman 1969, Shrimpton 1978, Cheniclet et al. in this volume, Bernard-Dagan in this volume). These secretions plug the transport systems (sieve cells and tracheids) and form a necrotic lesion of dead plant cells impregnated with defensive chemicals that may act as a physical, nutritional, and/or chemical barrier to the herbivore (Wong and Berryman 1977). Local reactions also involve the formation of wound periderm and, when the cambium is damaged, callus tissue at the perimeter of the necrosis. Wound periderm, which isolates the necrosis from living tissue, contains a water-proof layer (NIT) and often phenolic compounds (Mullick 1977).

Chemicals seem to be the main components of both constitutive and induced plant defenses against herbivores, and their biosynthesis appears to be a major function of parenchyma and, probably, other living cells (Reid et al. 1967, Berryman 1969, Lieutier and Berryman in this volume, Cheniclet et al. in this volume, Bernard-Dagan in this volume). The speed and intensity of biosynthesis may depend on the distance from the site of injury, the amount of damage done, and/or the kinds of elicitors involved (Fig. 2)

The evidence suggests that parenchyma cells react to all kinds of injuries, including those caused by viruses, bacteria, fungi, nematodes and insects, in a fundamentally similar way (see reviews by Berryman 1972, Grandison 1977, VanLoon 1983, Klement and Goodman 1967, Kuc 1983). This view is supported by recent research on chemicals that induce, or elicit, defensive reactions. One type of elicitor is a plant cell-wall fragment released when cells are damaged. These are

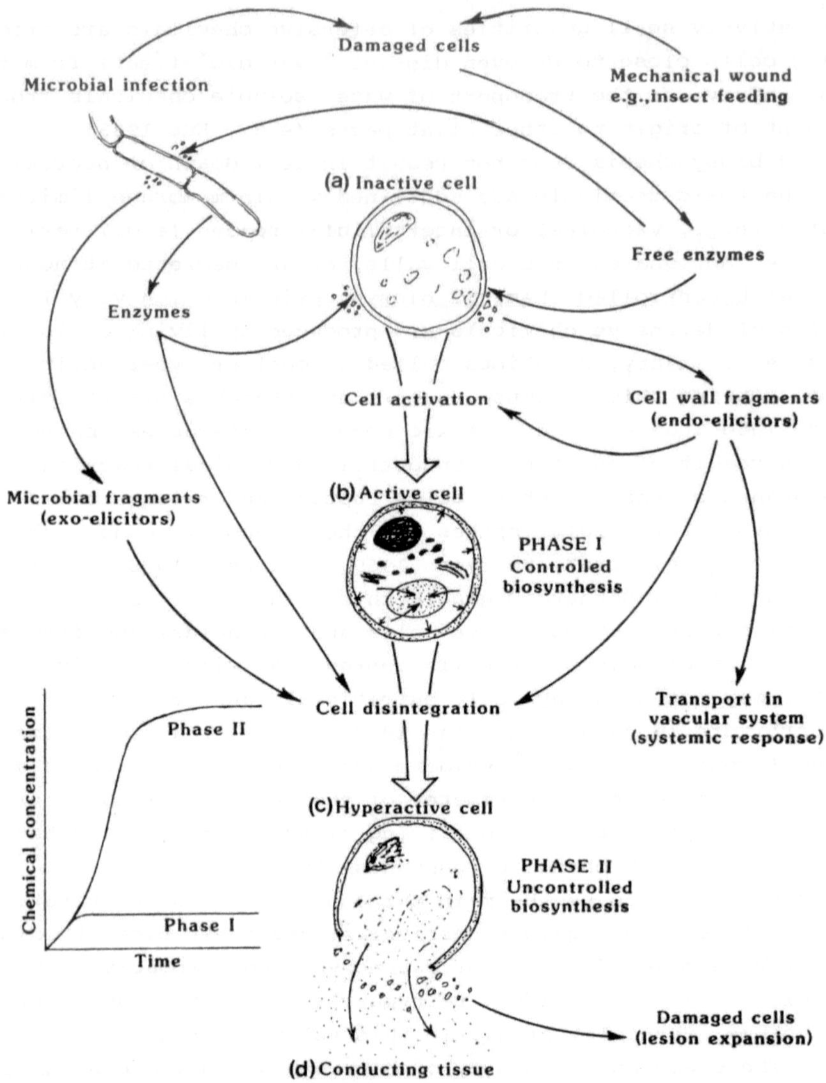

Figure 2. Hypothetical scheme for the activation of defensive metabolism in *Pinus* and, possibly, other plants (developed, in part, from Cheniclet *et al*. in this volume, and Lieutier and Berryman in this volume). Parenchyma cells shown in (a) the inactive state (or involved in activities other than defense), (b) the active state of controlled defensive metabolism (Phase I) initiated by endoelicitors, and (c) the hyperactive state of uncontrolled defensive metabolism (Phase II) activated by exoelicitors, possibly synergized by endoelicitors. (d) Dynamics of defensive chemical accumulation per unit of plant tissue in each phase.

endogenous or endoelicitors because they are products of the plant itself. These polysaccharide fragments may be released by herbivore feeding, any other mechanical damage, or by the action of enzymes secreted by either plant or herbivore (Ryan 1974, Darvill and Albersheim 1984). I hypothesize that these endoelicitors activate parenchyma cells to synthesize defensive chemicals in a controlled manner (Phase I in Fig. 2), controlled in the sense that toxic chemicals are contained within membrane bounded structures (vacuoles) or within nonliving tissues (cell walls or intercellular spaces). Endoelicitors may also be transported via the conducting tissue to activate cells remote from the point of injury, thus explaining the systemic reaction observed in some plants (see Kuc 1983, Sequeira 1983, Edwards and Wratten 1983 for reviews).

The second type of elicitor is released by the invading organism and is therefore called an exogenous or exoelicitor (Fig. 2). These elicitors may be enzymes or toxins secreted by the invader or fragments of their external skin released by the action of plant enzymes (see Ryan 1984, Darvill and Albersheim 1984, Miller et al. 1986). I hypothesize that these materials, either alone or synergized by endoelicitors (see Fig. 9 in Darvill and Albersheim 1984), cause parenchyma cells to become hyperactive (Phase II in Fig. 2). During this phase, large quantities of defensive materials are synthesized in an apparently uncontrolled chemical reaction, cell contents lose their structural integrity, and cell membranes and walls rupture (Cheniclet et al. in this volume, Bernard-Dagan in this volume). Defensive substances or their precursors and cell fragments are released into the conducting tissue, blocking the penetration of the pathogen and extending the reaction zone; i.e., newly formed cell fragments initiate phase I reactions in adjacent parenchyma cells. In this way, controlled defensive metabolism is initiated in cells ahead of the invasion front, while hyperactive, degenerative metabolism continues just in advance of the invader. With this eliciting mechanism, hyperactivity will cease as soon as the invasion is contained, but controlled phase I reactions may continue for some time and may even affect herbivores that attack at a much later date (e.g., Haukioja 1980, Bryant 1981).

The induced defensive system of plants forms a flexible mechanism for dealing with injury and infection; the intensity of the reaction may be a graded response proportional to the persistence of the attack. However, because the synthesis of defensive chemicals is an energy-expensive process, the success of an induced defense is dependent on the current availability of energy. Constitutive defenses, by contrast, can be built up during periods of energy surplus and thus provide flexibility in when energy is utilized. Induced defenses permit more flexibility in how energy is allocated because they are used only for defense when absolutely necessary.

Because of their dependency on current energy reserves, plants relying on induced defenses become susceptible to herbivory during periods of energy shortage or when the pathways of biosynthesis or energy translocation are disrupted; e.g., when plants come under severe stress from competition, drought, nutrient deficiency (see Lorio in this volume). This problem may be less severe for pioneer species which are less likely to encounter stress from competition or nutrient deficiency before reproductive maturity. In addition, inherent variability in the induced response of plant populations will act to retard the evolution of counter-adaptations in the herbivore. Variability exists because susceptible (undefended) plants will always be available, and herbivores attacking those individuals will not experience selective pressure to evolve counter-offensive traits against the induced defenses. As long as disturbances and the natural processes of growth and aging provide a continuous supply of nondefended plants, herbivores that are unadapted to the induced response will enter the gene pool and retard or halt the evolution of counter-offensive traits. Induced defenses, therefore, tend to create a more stable evolutionary strategy than constitutive defenses (Thompson 1986).

PLANT DEFENSIVE STRATEGIES

As others have pointed out, it is meaningless to discuss the defensive strategies of plants without considering their overall life history strategies (Feeny 1976, Rhoades 1979, Coley et al. 1985, Raffa and Berryman 1987). From fundamental evolutionary considerations, we expect selective forces to maximize a fitness function that includes genes controlling the timing of bud-burst and fruit production (avoidance possibilities) as well as constitutive physical and chemical defenses. In addition, selection should also act on genes that govern the allocation of available resources, especially energy, to various physiological functions; i.e., basal metabolism, growth, reproduction, and defense. Plants have to deal with many conflicting demands for their energy resources, but the optimal allocation scheme should be the one that provides the individual with the greatest chance of maximizing its fitness function.

Let us consider the two extreme life-cycle strategies of forest trees--that of the opportunistic (pioneer or r-selected) and that of the conservative (climax or K-selected). The opportunist strategy is to occupy disturbed sites quickly and to hold them temporarily through the "advantage of numbers" (Berryman 1981). To do this, opportunists have to grow rapidly and to produce seed at the correct time and place; e.g., they often have good seed dispersal mechanisms or their seeds are released by disturbances that prepare the site for germination (e.g., fire and serotinous cones). Because of these requirements, opportunistic species usually have high, but not necessarily efficient, photosynthetic rates, low tolerance to shade, relatively short life spans, and high demands for light and nutrients.

Conservative species, on the other hand, play a waiting game, becoming established in the understory and gradually replacing the pioneer species. These species, therefore, must be longer lived, must be shade tolerant, and must have more modest resource requirements.

Because of their different life history strategies, opportunist and conservative species would be expected to have different priorities for investing in defense. Rapid growth is so important for opportunists that we would expect them to utilize energy-cheap defenses or defenses that have flexibility in how energy is allocated; e.g., to use avoidance whenever possible and induced defenses otherwise, because energy for defenses is only used as needed. We would also expect them to defend their growing points (buds) and, in some cases, their reproductive structures. Defense of seeds or seed-containing structures is particularly important for trees which store seed in preparation for release on disturbed sites (e.g., serotinous cones). In these cases we might expect seeds or seed-bearing structures to be protected by constitutive physical or chemical mechanisms. On the other hand, conservative species would not be expected to invest heavily in defense against bud and seed feeders because rapid growth is not so critical and seed can be produced over long periods of time. Because long-term survival is so important, however, conservative species would be expected to invest heavily in defenses against herbivores that threaten life such as stem and root penetrators and browsers on mature leaves and roots. Evergreen species should also defend mature leaves because their survival depends on it. In fact, climax tree species are attacked by few, if any, life-threatening insects (e.g., aggressive bark beetles), and most defoliators feed on new rather than old foliage. Pioneer species, however, are often attacked by one or more aggressive bark beetles, particularly after reproductive maturity has been reached. Peterman (1978) has even argued that the fitness of lodgepole pine (a pioneer) is maximized if bark beetles destroy the stand at 60 to 80 years of age. This is because fires during this period, which are encouraged by dead beetle-killed trees, are most likely to result in the perpetuation of the populations.

Because the immediate utilization of energy for growth and reproduction is not so critical for conservative plants, and because longevity is so important, we would expect them to channel a higher proportion of their energy into constitutive defenses. This generally seems true of climax species whose tissues often have a complex chemical composition and are highly resistant to insects and pathogens. However, because longevity is so critical to the life history strategy of these species, they should also have effective induced defenses against specific, life-threatening herbivores.

The preceding discussion has been largely concerned with long-lived forest trees and with defense rather than avoidance. Short-lived plants (e.g., annuals) have a greater opportunity to adopt the cheaper strategy of avoidance against specific herbivores. This ephemeral tactic prevents herbivore populations from reaching high densities on local plant populations and also provides newly established plants with greater freedom from herbivores. Because rapid growth and early reproduction are essential for this strategy, expensive induced chemical defense would not be expected. Cheap constitutive defenses against generalist herbivores may, however, be a cost-effective tactic (Feeny 1976, Rhoades and Cates 1976).

Perennials of intermediate longevity face somewhat different problems. Escape from specific herbivores in time and space is a less effective strategy because time is available for herbivores to locate their food supplies. In addition, avoidance of seed predation through varying production, which is a viable, low-cost strategy for long-lived species, can become much more costly because reproduction is time-limited. These species would be expected to invest more heavily in defense of seeds and seed-containing structures. Similarly, those that can reproduce by sprouting would be expected to invest heavily in defending their young growth (e.g., see Bryant 1981).

Although I have attempted to develop some generalizations about plant defenses, a word of caution should be added. The opportunist/conservative dichotomy represents the extremes of a continuum. Intermediate strategies evolving rapid growth and long life can be found, particularly among deciduous species. Thus, the defensive strategy of particular species will be tuned to their particular life-history strategies, investments in defense being balanced against lost growth, reproduction, etc. Defensive investments will also be related to the impact of the particular herbivore on the critical plant life-history parameters (i.e., its fitness). This impact will be a function of the life-history strategy of the specific herbivore (e.g., see Thompson 1982). Thus, if the impact of herbivory on plant fitness is a function of the life-history strategy of the herbivore, and if the cost of defense in terms of lost fitness is dependent on the life history strategy of the plant, then selection for a particular trait against a particular herbivore is only likely to occur when

$$E_{i,j} > g(P_i)/f(H_j) \quad (1)$$

Where $E_{i,j}$ is the effectiveness of the ith defensive trait in preventing damage by the jth herbivore, $g(P_i)$ is the cost of the ith trait in terms of lost fitness, which is a complex function of the plant life-history strategy, and $f(H_j)$ is the impact of the jth herbivore on plant fitness, which is a function of its life-history strategy. In other words, the evolution of more efficient (and costly) defensive adaptations will be favored as long as the herbivore life-history strategy causes impacts in excess of the costs incurred under the particular plant life-history strategy.

COMPARISON OF PLANT DEFENSE THEORIES

Two theories have been put forth in an attempt to explain the evolution of plant defenses. First, Feeny (1976) proposed that defensive adaptations were selected on the basis of the probability of being found by herbivores and the host specificity of the herbivore, i.e., whether it feeds on a few or many plant species. He suggested that apparent plants, because they are easily found by most herbivores, should invest heavily in highly effective and general quantitative defenses, whereas unapparent plants, which rely on avoidance to escape specialist herbivores, need only invest in low-cost qualitative defenses against generalists.

The second theory, as advanced by Coley *et al.* (1985), proposes that the availability of resources creates the selection pressure for different defensive strategies. In their view, the level of investment in defense will increase as plant growth rates or resource availability decreases. Thus, slow-growing plants on nutrient impoverished sites will invest more in costly quantitative defenses, while fast-growing species on nutrient rich sites will tend to use cheaper qualitative defenses.

The present thesis, based on the assumptions of optimal defense theory, proposes that defensive traits are selected to optimize plant fitness in the face of different herbivore attack patterns and life-history strategies (see also Raffa and Berryman 1987). In this view, initial selection for traits in things such as photosynthetic rates and energy allocation schemes tends to lock the organism into a particular life-style exemplified, at the extremes, by the opportunist/conservative strategies. The evolution of defensive traits is heavily influenced by the direction taken, for this determines the priorities for energy allocation. Plants locked into the opportunistic life-style must place a high priority on rapid growth and reproduction, for their fitness depends on it. Under these pressures, selection should favor avoidance (e.g., the annual life cycle or highly time-variable fruiting or bud-bursting), or defenses which only utilize energy when needed (e.g., induced defenses). Thus, nonapparency becomes a tactic which can be used by opportunistic species to escape specialized herbivores. Once locked into this strategy, however, plants may require defenses against generalist herbivores, and we should expect these to be low-cost constitutive defensives. Not all opportunists, however, are nonapparent, and those that are not should invest more heavily in induced defenses which are effective against specialists and generalists.

Conservative species, on the other hand, must often invest more heavily in defense because they have to out-wait their competitors. At the same time, early growth and reproduction are not so essential, and so energy drains on defense do not incur high fitness costs. Thus, low growth rates, resource scarcity, and heavy investments in defense are all consequences of the "chosen" conservative life-style.

ACKNOWLEDGEMENTS

I am grateful to Colette Bernard-Dagan, Ken Raffa, John Thompson, and Lee Hadwiger for their helpful comments on an earlier draft and to Bill Mattson for his careful editing.

REFERENCES

Alfaro, R. I., H. D. Pierce, J. H. Borden, and A. C. Oehlschlager. 1981. Insect feeding and oviposition deterrents from western red cedar foliage. J. Chem. Ecol. 7: 39-48.

Bailey, J. A. and B. J. Deverall. 1983. The dynamics of host defense. New York: Academic Press.

Balch, R. E., J. Clark, and J. M. Bonga. 1964. Hormonal action in production of tumors and compression wood by an aphid. Nature 202: 721-722.

Baltensweiler, W., G. Benz, P. Bovey, and V. Delucchi. 1977. Dynamics of larch bud moth populations. Annu. Rev. Entomol. 22: 79-100.

Berryman, A. A. 1969. Responses of Abies grandis to attack by Scolytus ventralis (Coleoptera: Scolytidae). Can. Entomol. 101: 1033-1042.

Berryman, A. A. 1972. Resistance of conifers to invasion by bark beetle-fungus associations. BioScience 22: 598-602.

Berryman, A. A. 1981. Population systems: a general introduction. New York: Plenum Press.

Bryant, J. P. 1981. Phytochemical deterrence of snowshoe hare browsing by adventitious shoots of four Alaskan trees. Science 213: 889-890.

Carter, C. I. and J. F. A. Nichols. 1985. Host plant susceptibility and choice by conifer aphids. In: Site characteristics and population dynamics of lepidopteran and hymenopteran forest pests (D. Bevan and J. T. Stoakley, Eds.). Edinburgh: For. Comm. Res. Dev. Pap. 135; 94-99.

Coley, P. D., J. P. Bryant, and F. S. Chapin, III. 1985. Resource availability and plant antiherbivore defense. Science 230: 895-899.

Coutts, M. P. and J. E. Dolezal. 1966. Polyphenols and resin in the resistance mechanism of Pinus radiata attacked by the wood wasp, Sirex noctilio and its associated fungus. Comm. Australia, For. Timb. Bur. Leaflet 101, 19 p.

Cowling, E. B. and J. G. Horsfall. 1980. Chapter 1. In: Plant disease: An advanced treatise (J. G. Horsfall and E. B. Cowling, Eds.). New York: Academic Press.

Croteau, R. and M.A. Johnson. 1985. Chapter 15. Biosynthesis of terpenoid wood extractives. In: Biosynthesis and degradation of wood components (P. Higuchi, Ed.). New York: Academic Press.

Darvill, A. G. and P. Albersheim. 1984. Phytoalexins and their elicitors--a defense against microbial infection in plants. Annu. Rev. Plant Physiol. 35: 243-275.

Edwards, P. J. and S. D. Wratten. 1983. Wound induced defenses in plants and their consequences for patterns of insect grazing. Oecologia (Berlin) 59: 88-93.

Feeny, P. 1976. Plant apparency and chemical defense. Rec. Adv. Phytochem. 10: 1-40.

Grandison, G. W. 1977. Relationship of plant-parasitic nematodes and their hosts. N. Z. Entomol. 6: 262-267.

Hanover, J. W. 1975. Physiology of tree resistance to insects. Annu. Rev. Entomol. 20: 75-95.

Haukioja, E. 1980. On the role of plant defenses in the fluctuation of herbivore populations. Oikos 35: 202-213.

Isaev, A. S., Y. N. Baranchikov, and V. S. Malutina. 1987. (In press). Chapter 2. The larch gall midge in seed orchards of South Siberia. In: Dynamics of forest insect populations: patterns, causes, implications (A. A. Berryman, Ed.). New York: Plenum Press.

Klement, Z. and R. N. Goodman. 1967. The hypersensitive reaction to infection by bacterial plant pathogens. Ann. Rev. Phytopath. 5: 17-44.

Kuc, J. 1983. Chapter 5. Induced systemic resistance in plants to diseases caused by fungi and bacteria. In: The dynamics of plant defense (J. A. Bailey and B. J. Deverall, Eds.). New York: Academic Press.

Mattson, W. J. 1980. Cone resources and the ecology of the red pine cone beetle, Conophthorus resinosae (Coleoptera: Scolytidae). Ann. Entomol. Soc. Amer. 73: 390-396.

Miller, R. A., and A. A. Berryman. 1985. Energetics of conifer defense against bark beetles and associated fungi. In: The role of the host in the population dynamics of forest insects (L. Safranyik, Ed.); Proceedings, IUFRO Conference; 1983 September 4-7; Banff, Alberta. Victoria, BC: Canadian Forestry Service and USDA, Forest Service; 13-23.

Miller, R. A., A. A. Berryman, and C. A. Ryan. 1986. Biotic elicitors of defense reactions in lodgepole pine. Phytochem. 25: 611-612.

Mullick, B. D. 1977. The non-specific nature of defense in bark and wood during wounding, insect and pathogen attack. Recent Adv. Phytochem. 11: 395-441.

Painter, R. H. 1951. Insect resistance in crop plants. New York: Macmillan.

Peterman, R. M. 1978. The ecological role of the mountain pine beetle in lodgepole pine forests. In: Theory and practice of mountain pine beetle management in lodgepole pine forests (A. A. Berryman, G. D. Amman, R. W. Stark, and D. L. Kibbee, Eds.). Moscow, ID: College of Forest Resources, Univ. Idaho; 16-26.

Raffa, K. F. and A. A. Berryman. 1987. Interacting selective pressures in conifer-bark beetle systems: a basis for reciprocal adaptations? Amer. Nat. 129: 234-262.

Reid, R. W., H. S. Whitney, and J. A. Watson. 1967. Reactions of lodgepole pine to attack by Dendroctonus ponderosae Hopkins and blue stain fungi. Can. J. Bot. 45: 1115-1116.

Rhoades, D. F. 1979. Chapter 1. Evolution of plant chemical defense against herbivores. In: Herbivores: their interaction with secondary plant metabolites (G. A. Rosenthal, Ed.). New York: Academic Press.

Rhoades, D. F. 1985. Offensive-defensive interactions between herbivores and plants: Their relevance in herbivore population dynamics and ecological theory. Am. Nat. 125: 205-238.

Rhoades, D. F. and R. G. Cates. 1976. Towards a general theory of plant antiherbivore chemistry. Recent. Adv. Phytochem. 10: 168-213.

Roques, A. 1987. (In press). Chapter 1. The larch cone fly in the French Alps. In: Dynamics of forest insect populations: patterns, causes, implications (A. A. Berryman, Ed.). New York: Plenum Press.

Ryan, C. A. 1974. Assay and biochemical properties of the proteinase inhibitor-inducing factor, a wound hormone. Plant Physiol. 54: 328-332.

Ryan, C. A. 1984. Defense responses of plants. In: Advances in plant gene research (O. S. P. Verma and T. Hohns, Eds.). Berlin: Springer-Verlag; 321-332.

Sequeira, L. 1983. Mechanisms of induced resistance in plants. Annu. Rev. Microbiol. 37: 51-79.

Shrimpton, D. M. 1978. Resistance of lodgepole pine to mountain pine beetle infestation. In: Theory and practice of mountain pine beetle management in lodgepole pine forests (A. A. Berryman, G. D. Amman, R. W. Stark, and D. L. Kibbee, Eds.). Moscow, ID: College of Forest Resources, Univ. Idaho; 64-76.

Thompson, J. N. 1982. Interaction and coevolution. New York: John Wiley and Sons, 179 p.

Thompson, J. N. 1986. Constraints on arms races in coevolution. Trends Ecol. Evol. 1: 105-107.

VanLoon, L. C. 1983. Chapter 4. Mechanisms of resistance in virus-infected plants. In: The dynamics of host defense (J. A. Bailey and B. J. Deverall, Eds.). New York: Academic Press.

White, T. C. R. 1978. The importance of relative food shortage in animal ecology. Oecologia (Berlin) 33: 71-86.

Wong, B. L. and A. A. Berryman. 1977. Host resistance to the fir engraver beetle. 3. Lesion development and containment of infection by resistance _Abies grandis_ inoculated with _Trichosporium symbioticum_. Can. J. Bot. 55: 2358-2365.

Wright, L. C., A. A. Berryman, and S. Gurusiddaiah. 1979. Host resistance to the fir engraver beetle, _Scolytus ventralis_ (Coleoptera: Scolytidae). 4. Effect of defoliation on wound monoterpenes and inner bark carbohydrate concentrations. Can. Entomol. 111: 1255-1261.

3

Defensive Responses of Trees in Relation to Their Carbon/Nutrient Balance

Juha Tuomi, Pekka Niemelä, F. Stuart Chapin, III, John P. Bryant, and Seija Sirén

Haukioja and Hakala (1975), Rhoades (1979), and Haukioja (1980) outlined the hypothesis that herbivore cycles are associated with changes in the inducible defense level of individual plants. For example, the herbivore population's increase begins when host-plant resistance decreases to a low level. On the other hand, the herbivore population's decrease is precipitated by an increasing plant resistance. The minimum length of the latent phase depends on the rate of relaxation of resistance as the plant recovers from defoliation (May 1975, Haukioja 1980). Although the detailed mechanisms of these changes in plant resistance are still unclear, defoliation has been shown to induce changes in trees that have adverse effects on the growth, reproduction, and survival of lepidopteran defoliators (Haukioja and Niemelä 1977, Wallner and Walton 1979, Werner 1979, Haukioja 1980) and which can have relaxation times of several years (Benz 1974, Haukioja 1982). However, in other cases, defoliation caused no observable increase in plant resistance (Myers 1981), and defoliation may even reduce resistance of the host plant (Niemelä et al. 1984). Furthermore, no evidence for defensive responses to clipping was found in dormant twigs of juvenile woody plants when twig age and diameter were controlled (Chapin et al. 1985).

Despite this variety of empirical findings, no general theory has emerged to predict the type of plants that can be induced to develop high resistance with long relaxation times and those that do not respond defensively to defoliation (Haukioja et al. 1983a). The optimal defense theory fails in this because it provides no explanation for the absence of induced responses, although their presence is considered to be an evolutionary adaptation to herbivory (Rhoades 1979, Haukioja and Neuvonen 1985). Further, bioassays measuring the performance of herbivores study mainly the defensive efficiency of induced responses on herbivores without specifying the underlying mechanisms and their effective components. These adverse effects on herbivores may depend upon several components of leaf quality so that the theory should initially explain each component separately rather than their combined effects on herbivores. For this purpose, we formulate a model for explaining phenotypic variation in carbon-based allelochemicals because their function as a defense against folivorous insects has been a key element in theories of plant/herbivore interactions (Feeny 1970, 1976; Whittaker and Feeny 1971; Rhoades and Cates 1976; Rhoades 1979).

The carbon-based allelochemicals implicated in the resistance of plants to herbivores include lignin, tannins, and other phenolic compounds (Feeny 1968, Lincoln et al. 1982, Swain 1979), as well as terpenes and resins (Ikeda et al. 1977, Bryant and Kuropat 1980, Bryant 1981). All are widely distributed in trees (Hegnauer 1966, Ricklefs and Matthew 1982, Janzen and Waterman 1984). We refer collectively to these compounds as carbon-based defenses or resistance because they contain no nitrogen or phosphorus. We suggest that the availability of plant carbon relative to available mineral nutrients or the plant carbon/nutrient balance (Chapin 1980, Mattson 1980, Bryant et al. 1983) determines basic constraints for the accumulation of carbon-based secondary compounds. These constraints influence the constitutive levels of carbon-based allelochemicals and can cause these levels to increase or decrease in a predictable fashion in response to defoliation. Therefore, we attempt to specify (1) how resource availability can alter the constitutive levels of carbon-based allelochemicals, (2) how the removal of foliar resources influences the accumulation of carbon-based secondary compounds in trees, and (3) how specific evolutionary responses of plants to herbivores can be expected to differ from these phenotypic responses to the plant carbon/nutrient balance.

PLANT CARBON/NUTRIENT BALANCE AS AN INTERNAL CONSTRAINT OF SECONDARY METABOLISM

Every plant has an optimal balance between internal reserves of carbon and mineral nutrients that promotes maximal growth (Chapin 1980, Ingestad 1982, Bloom et al. 1985, Larsson et al. 1986). Variations in environment can cause this reserve balance to shift such that either carbon or nutrients become suboptimal for plant growth. These changes in plant carbon/nutrient balance can, in turn, influence the accumulation of carbon-based secondary compounds. In the present formulation, we consider total net carbon gain per plant to be distributed between two functional pools, carbon used in resistance and storage (e.g., phenolics, lignin, terpenes, and starch) and carbon used in growth (e.g., cellulose and metabolic machinery). We assume that (1) both total carbon gain and growth are functions of plant nutrient reserves, (2) carbon is allocated to growth whenever there are sufficient mineral nutrients to construct new cells, and (3) the carbon surplus accumulated above the levels required for growth is allocated among different carbon-based allelochemicals and/or carbohydrate storage. This model of plant carbon/nutrient balance differs from the optimal defense theory of Rhoades (1979) in that it implies no reduction in growth to support carbon-based resistance; instead allocation to secondary metabolite production occurs only when growth demands for carbon have been met.

The accumulation of carbon surplus is consistent with known responses of plants to variation in plant carbon/nutrient balance. As nutrient availability declines below optimum, there are inadequate nutrients to support maximum growth (Ingestad 1982). However, growth generally declines more sharply with nutrient limitation than does photosynthesis (Warren-Wilson 1966, Chapin 1980), so that at moderately low nutrient availability carbon-based substances accumulate above levels that can be used for growth (White 1973, Brady 1973, Fig. 1a). At very low nutrient availability, photosynthesis declines precipitously because most nutrients are utilized in cellular maintenance and metabolism rather than in photosynthetic machinery (Field and Mooney 1985). Therefore, carbon-based substances again decline when plants are extremely nutrient-stressed (Fig. 1a). As a result, carbon-based compounds (including carbon-based secondary compounds, Fig. 1b) are expected to increase under conditions that cause an accumulation of plant carbon above levels required for growth.

Accumulation of starch and other carbon stores is well documented under conditions where mineral nutrients or water limit growth more than photosynthesis (Brady 1973, White 1973). Also carbon-based secondary compounds, especially phenolics, tend to accumulate in conditions where nutrient deficiency limits primary metabolism and growth (Lee and Aronoff 1967, Wender 1970, Del Moral 1972, Chew and Rodman 1979, Mattson 1980). For example, mineral deficiency, as well as other conditions suppressing protein synthesis (e.g., moderate drought and senescence of tissues), leads to the accumulation of polyphenols, while abundant nitrogen fertilization or administration of nitrogen to tissues promotes protein metabolism at the cost of phenylpropanoid accumulation (Margna 1977, Phillips and Henshaw 1977). Similarly, plants respond to nutrient limitation with increased concentrations of

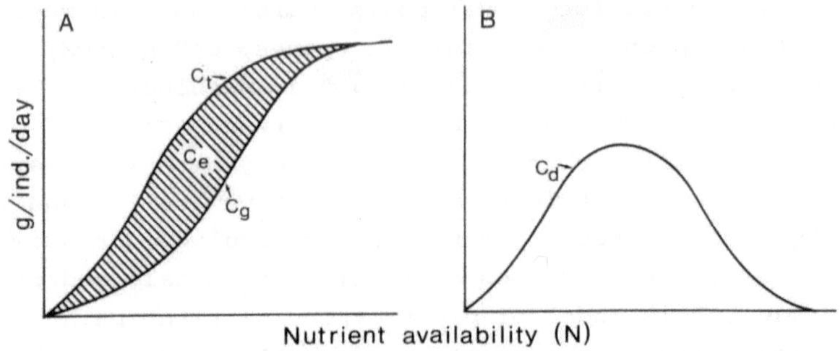

Figure 1. A model of plant carbon/nutrient balance in which secondary metabolite production is supported by carbon surplus. 1a. The amount of excess carbon (C_e) is determined by the total amount of available carbon (C_t) and the amount of carbon diverted to growth (C_g) that vary as functions of total nutrient reserves (N) of the plant. 1b. The total level of carbon-based allelochemicals (C_d) varies from low to high nutrient availability as function of carbon surplus (C_e, Fig. 1a).

tannins (Mattson et al. 1983), lignin (Waring et al. 1985), phenolics (Del Moral 1972, Mattson et al. 1983, Haukioja et al. 1985, Larsson et al. 1986), and even specific carbon-based secondary metabolites that deter feeding by herbivores (Bryant et al. 1985). These observations are consistent with the hypothesis that the production of carbon-based secondary compounds is supported by resource surplus accumulated above and beyond the requirements of plant primary metabolism. Under such conditions, secondary metabolites may also function as internal growth regulators that slow down plant metabolism and subsequently have acquired allelochemical functions against pathogens, competitors, and herbivores (Del Moral 1972, Gershenzon 1984).

The constitutive level of carbon-based defenses also tends to be high in species that typically occur on low-nutrient soils (Janzen 1974, Bryant et al. 1983, McKey et al. 1978, Gartlan et al. 1980, Coley et al. 1985). The present treatment allows at least two explanations. The species growing on nutrient-deficient soils are selected for a higher proportional allocation of available resources to carbon-based resistance against herbivores. Alternatively, these species grow under conditions which cause chronic carbon surplus supporting the accumulation of carbon-based allelochemicals. In the latter case, the carbon-based defense is a phenotypically plastic trait which varies as a function of resource availability and other factors influencing plant carbon/nutrient balance.

INDUCED RESPONSES TO THE REMOVAL OF FOLIAR RESOURCES

Defoliation reduces the capacity of a plant to gain carbon by removing the photosynthetic leaf area and removing any carbohydrate and nutrient pools that are stored in leaves (Harper 1977). Thus the removal of foliar resources can influence plant carbon/nutrient balance which, in turn, can modify the accumulation of carbon-based secondary compounds. Such effects of defoliation on the accumulation of carbon-based secondary allelochemicals should depend on whether leaf removal reduces more strongly the carbon or nutrient reserves of trees (Fig. 2).

Allelochemicals can accumulate as a response to the removal of foliar resources under conditions where defoliation reduces more strongly nutrient reserves than carbon reserves (nutrient stress, Fig. 2). Such responses should not take place under conditions where defoliation leads to nutrient surplus relative to carbon (carbon stress, Fig. 2) or reduced levels of both carbon and nutrient. Moreover, induced responses should be absent or relatively weak in conditions where defoliation has no major impact on plant carbon and nutrient reserves. Thus the capacity for induced carbon-based defenses should largely vary depending on whether carbon is primarily stored in leaves or stems and roots and whether trees are growing on nutrient-poor or nutrient-rich soils (Table 1).

Defoliation of Evergreen Trees

Defoliation can be expected to reduce carbon reserves more strongly than nutrient reserves in those species with small carbohydrate reserves in stems and roots. This includes many evergreen species which typically store carbon in leaves rather than roots (Bryant *et al*. 1983, Chapin *et al*. 1986). For example, defoliation or pruning of Scots pine (*Pinus sylvestris*) reduces its carbon reserves and increases foliar nitrogen (Ericsson *et al*. 1980, 1985). In Scots pine, browsing by moose increases the probability of further browsing on the same browsed trees (Löyttyniemi and Piisilä 1983) suggesting lack of induced long-term resistance and/or increased foliar mineral nutrients. Similarly, the larvae of the sawfly *Neodiprion sertifer*, a defoliator of Scots pine, grow better on trees that have been defoliated in the previous summer, suggesting that defoliation causes an improvement in the quality of mature foliage after defoliation (Niemelä et al. 1984). The end result of this positive feedback loop would be the destruction of the plant, if other factors (e.g., predators or parasites) do not stop herbivore damage. Consequently, evergreen trees may have a limited capacity to respond defensively to defoliation in terms of carbon-based secondary metabolites. On nutrient-deficient growing sites, defoliation likely depletes both the carbon and nutrient reserves of evergreen trees. However, at higher nutrient availability, defoliation may lead to a relative surplus of mineral nutrients and, therefore, foliar nutrient levels can increase as a response to defoliation (Table 1).

Defoliation of Deciduous Trees

Defoliation is less likely to cause carbon limitation in deciduous trees with large carbon reserves in stems or below the

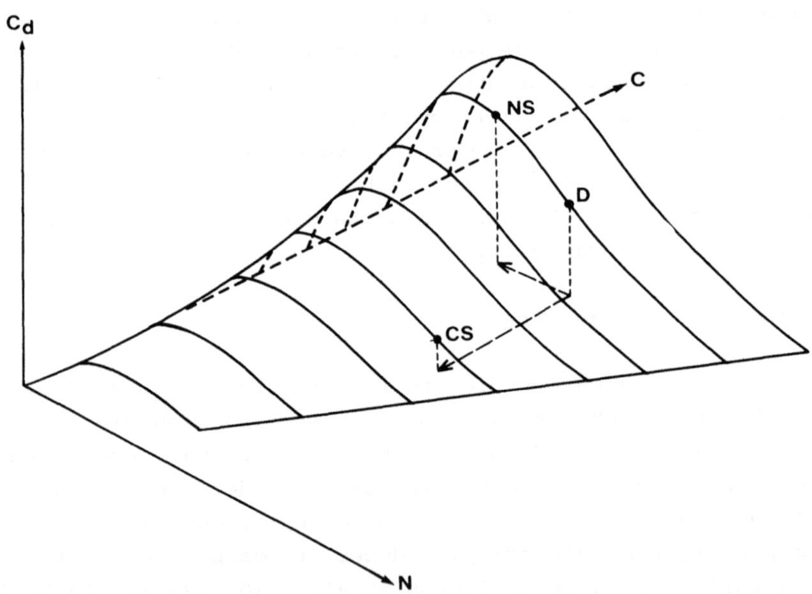

Figure 2. Accumulation of carbon-based secondary compounds (C_d) as a function of plant carbon (C) and nutrient (N) reserves. The removal of foliar resources can cause carbon stress (CS) or nutrient stress (NS). CS is expected to decrease and NS to increase C_d as compared with undefoliated control trees. (D).

Table 1. The expected effects of defoliation on plant carbon/nutrient balance (CNB) and induced responses of evergreen and deciduous trees to the removal of foliar resources (increase +, decline -, no significant response 0).

Species and conditions	Effects on CNB	Induced responses
Evergreen trees		
1. low nutrient availability	carbon and nutrient stress	carbon-based defense - foliar nutrients -
2. high nutrient availability	carbon stress, relative nutrient surplus	carbon-based defense -0 foliar nutrients +
Deciduous trees		
1. low nutrient availability	nutrient stress, relative carbon surplus	carbon-based defenses ++ foliar nutrients -- long relaxation times
2. high nutrient availability	a. nutrient stress, relative carbon surplus	carbon-based defense + foliar nutrients - short relaxation times
	b. neither carbon nor nutrient stress	carbon-based defense 0 foliar nutrients 0

ground. Below-ground carbohydrate reserves are particularly well developed in deciduous trees growing on nutrient-poor sites (Grime 1977, 1979). In such species, defoliation removes substantial nutrient capital, but large carbohydrate reserves remain in the roots. Consequently, defoliation should lead to a carbon surplus relative to nutrients (nutrient stress, Fig. 2) and thus the amount of carbon available for secondary metabolite production may increase after defoliation (Table 1). For example, larch (*Larix decidua*) and mountain birch (*Betula pubescens ssp. tortuosa*) grow in a tree-line environment, and it is just these species in which defoliation induces an increased resistance to herbivores (Benz 1974, Baltensweiler *et al*. 1977, Haukioja 1982). Defoliation also increases leaf phenolic content of red oak (Schultz and Baldwin 1982), and in mountain birch it both decreases leaf nitrogen content and increases leaf phenolic content (Tuomi *et al*. 1984). By these means, defoliation can efficiently reduce the quality of foliage as a resource for defoliators that are forced to cope with both low leaf nutrient content and high levels of carbon-based allelochemicals in the year(s) following defoliation. Leaf nitrogen content of mountain birch returns back to its original level within 3 years while the relaxation time of leaf phenolic content can be 4 years (Tuomi et al. 1984). These changes induced by defoliation are in agreement with the inverse relation of phenolic compounds to plant nutrients (Del Moral 1972, Margna 1977, Phillips and Henshaw 1977, Gershenzon 1984).

Sensitivity and Relaxation of Induced Responses

Because the capacity for induced responses in deciduous trees is assumed to depend on their stem and below-ground carbon reserves, this capacity should be minimal under conditions where the major part of their carbon reserves has been diverted to growth. Similarly, the relaxation times of such induced responses should be maximal under conditions where the foliar nutrients removed by defoliators are most difficult to replace. Thus defoliation may produce relatively weak or no long-lasting induction of carbon-based defenses in trees that grow on sites of high nutrient availability or that have symbiotic nitrogen fixers. Such species should have a relatively low capacity for induced responses due to their smaller carbohydrate reserves, and their relaxation times of carbon-based allelochemicals should be shorter due to high nutrient availability, as compared with species growing on nutrient-deficient sites. This may explain why mountain birch shows stronger induced responses to defoliation in more nutrient-deficient conditions (Haukioja and Niemelä 1976, Haukioja et al. 1983b). This reasoning is also in agreement with the results of Myers (1981) who showed no increase in the resistance of roses growing in extremely nutrient-rich conditions. Jeker (1981) has shown that grey alder (Alnus incana), a tree with symbiotic nitrogen fixers, can be induced to develop a resistance, but the relaxation time of these induced responses is relatively short, about a year (Cf. Benz 1974, Haukioja 1982). Induced resistance in red alder (A. rubra) likely represents responses to the altered carbon/nutrient because an increase in the resistance of red alder is found only after successive defoliations during 2 to 3 years (Myers and Williams 1984, Williams and Myers 1984).

In summary, the induced responses of carbon-based allelochemicals to the removal of foliar resources are expected to vary between evergreen and deciduous trees and between low and high nutrient availability (Table 1). Many of the observed patterns of induced responses to defoliation are consistent with the idea that defoliation causes a change in plant carbon/nutrient balance which, in turn, alters the pool of carbon available for secondary metabolite production. The available carbon surplus determines the potential capacity for induced responses of carbon-based allelochemicals, which among other components of leaf quality contribute to plant resistance to herbivores.

EVOLUTIONARY RESPONSES OF PLANTS TO HERBIVORES

Because the increase in carbon-based allelochemicals can be a phenotypic response of the plant to internal carbon/nutrient balance, the variation in carbon-based resistance need not always be the result of a detailed evolutionary optimization where costs and profits determine the basic patterns of carbon allocation. In fact, plant/herbivore interactions may have only a secondary role in the evolution of carbon-based resistance. Below we outline a hypothesis, summarized in Table 2, that the total level of carbon-based secondary compounds primarily varies as a function of plant carbon/nutrient balance, while the proportional distribution of available carbon between various carbon-based substances may depend on the selective importance of specific herbivores over the evolutionary history of the plant population.

Table 2. A hypothesis for a division of carbon-based resistance into a nonspecific component that is assumed to depend on plant carbon/nutrient balance (CNB) and specific evolutionary responses (SER) of plants to herbivores.

	Carbon-Based Resistance	
	Constitutive defense	Induced defense
CNB	Total level of carbon-based secondary compounds varies as a function of resources that cannot be used for primary metabolism.	Removal of foliar carbon and nutrient reserves causes nonspecific changes in the total level of carbon-based secondary substances.
SER	The proportional allocation of available carbon between specific secondary substances depends on their metabolic costs and defensive effectiveness.	Factors that indicate the presence of herbivores induce the production of specific, defensively effective secondary compounds.

Constitutive Carbon-Based Defense

The plant carbon/nutrient balance modifies the amount of carbon available for storage and defense. However, it does not explain how this available carbon is distributed between different carbon-based substances. Therefore, the evolutionary response of plants to herbivores may be primarily to influence the proportion of available carbon allocated to the production of given carbon-based substances. This leads to two alternative hypotheses of constitutive carbon-based resistance in plants: (1) If no herbivore pressure has influenced the patterns of carbon allocation, the available carbon should be allocated among various carbon-based substances independent of their defensive effectiveness (null hypothesis). (2) Selection pressures fostered by plant/herbivore interactions should change the composition of the total pool of carbon-based substances depending on the metabolic costs and defensive effectiveness of specific compounds (defense hypothesis).

Thus, selection may cause elimination or reduction in chemical pathways leading to substances that do not prevent herbivore attacks or that may even increase the probability of defoliation (e.g., sugar storage). Similarly, there may be selection for pathways that lead to substances that efficiently reduce the susceptibility of the plant to specific herbivores (Rhoades 1979). In environments where herbivory is less intense, there may be selection for pathways by which energy is efficiently stored and retrieved, and consequently, a smaller proportional allocation to defensively effective compounds. Selection can also have a crucial role in determining how specific secondary metabolites are allocated among different parts and tissues of the plant (McKey 1979).

Specific Induced Responses to Herbivory

Similarly, the defoliation-induced perturbations in plant carbon/nutrient balance should primarily cause changes in the total level of carbon-based secondary substances. Thus, the removal of foliar carbon and nutrient reserves is expected to cause nonspecific induced responses where both defensively effective and noneffective substances are equally affected by carbon or nutrient stress. In contrast, specific induced responses to herbivory may involve increased production of effective allelochemicals and a corresponding decrease in stores and other defensively inefficient carbon-based compounds.

If such specific induced responses really occur, they would require triggering mechanisms that stimulate specific chemical pathways leading to defensively effective allelochemicals. Specific triggering mechanisms are likely to be present in the case of rapid induced responses that occur before herbivores have a major impact on carbon/nutrient balance, as, for example, in (1) the rapid induction of resistance immediately following leaf damage (Ryan and Green 1974, Karban and Carey 1984) and (2) the induction of resistance as a result of damage to neighboring trees (see Baldwin and Schultz 1983; Rhoades 1983, 1985; Fowler and Lawton 1985). Even in long-term induced resistance, there is evidence for specific triggering of defense responses of trees to herbivores. For example, feeding by larvae of Epirrita autumnata causes more effective induction of resistance in mountain birch than does removal of the same amount of leaf material by leaf tearing (Haukioja and Neuvonen 1985). In such cases, induced responses are triggered by the presence of herbivores rather than the removal of foliar resources as such. However, in other cases artificial and natural leaf damage produce similar induced effects (Ryan and Green 1974, Raupp and Denno 1984), implying that leaf damage as such may trigger induced responses.

Although the mechanisms of specific induced responses are unclear, the following prediction can be presented: (1) specific induced responses should occur only in plant species and populations that have experienced intensive feeding by herbivores, while (2) induced responses to the altered carbon/nutrient balance will occur even in plants that have not experienced successive outbreaks of herbivores during their past evolutionary history.

CONCLUSIONS

Theories of plant/herbivore interactions generally assume that plant secondary metabolites function primarily as a defense against herbivores and that secondary substances are synthesized at the cost of other demands of resource investment. Alternatively, we suggest that secondary compounds are not costly and that their accumulation varies as a function of plant carbon/nutrient balance.

Carbon stress should cause a decline in carbon-based substances, whereas nutrient stress can lead to their accumulation. When a carbon surplus accumulates above levels required for growth, it supports the production of carbon-based allelochemicals which, in turn, supports plant resistance to herbivores. The effects of defoliation on plant carbon/nutrient balance depends on whether carbon is mainly stored in leaves rather than in stems and roots. Evergreen trees (stores in leaves) are expected to have a limited capacity for responding defensively to defoliation that depletes foliar carbon reserves. On the other hand, deciduous trees (large below-ground carbon stores) can respond defensively to defoliation which causes a relative carbon surplus in nutrient-deficient growing sites. Such induced responses to defoliation should weaken in nutrient-rich conditions where defoliation leads to weaker nutrient stress and nutrient losses are more rapidly replaced.

These phenotypic responses of carbon-based allelochemicals are separated from specific evolutionary responses of plants to herbivores. Selection is considered to shift carbon allocation between specific carbon-based compounds depending on their defensive effectiveness, while the plant carbon/nutrient balance should primarily lead to nonspecific changes in the total pool of carbon-based substances (including carbon-based allelochemicals).

ACKNOWLEDGEMENTS

The ideas presented here evolve from joint research through the Finland-U. S. Cooperative Science Agreement funded by the Academy of Finland and the U. S. National Science Foundation. We are especially grateful to Erkki Haukioja and Seppo Neuvonen for critical comments and to Hämeenportti for working facilities.

REFERENCES

Baldwin, I. T and J. C. Schultz. 1983. Rapid changes in tree leaf chemistry induced by damage: evidence for communication between plants. Science 221: 277-279.

Baltensweiler, W., G. Benz, P. Bovey, and V. Delucchi. 1977. Dynamics of larch bud moth populations. Ann. Rev. Entomol. 22: 79-100.

Benz, G. 1974. Negative Rückkoppelung durch Raum- und Nahrungskonkurrenz sowie zyklische Veränderung der Nahrungsgrundlage als Regelprinzip in der Populationsdynamik des Grauen Lärchenwicklers, Zeiraphera diniana (Guenee) (Lep., Tortricidae). Z. Angew. Entomol. 76: 196-228.

Bloom, A. J., F. S. Chapin, III, and H. A. Mooney. 1985. Resource limitation in plants--an economic analogy. Ann. Rev. Ecol. Syst. 16: 363-392.

Brady, C. J. 1973. Changes accompanying growth and senescence and effect of physiological stress. In: Chemistry and biochemistry of herbage (G. W. Butter and R. W. Bailey, Eds.). London: Academic Press; 317-351.

Bryant, J. P. 1981. Phytochemical deterrence of snowshoe hare browsing by adventitious shoots of four Alaskan trees. Science 213: 889-890.

Bryant, J. P., F. S. Chaplin, III, and D. R. Klein. 1983. Carbon/nutrient balance of boreal plants in relation to vertebrate herbivory. Oikos 40: 357-368.

Bryant, J. P., F. S. Chapin, III, P. B. Reichardt and T. P. Clausen. 1985. Adaptation to resource availability as a determinant of chemical defense strategies in woody plants. In: Chemically mediated interactions between plants and other organisms (G. A. Cooper-Driver, T. Swain, and E. E. Conn, Eds.). New York: Plenum Publishing Corporation; 219-237.
Bryant, J. P. and P. J. Kuropat. 1980. Selection of winter forage by subarctic browsing vertebrates: the role of plant chemisty. Ann. Rev. Ecol. Syst. 11: 261-285.
Chapin, F. S., III. 1980. The mineral nutrition of wild plants. Ann. Rev. Ecol. Syst. 11: 233-260.
Chapin, F. S., III, J. P. Bryant, and J. F. Fox. 1985. Lack of induced chemical defense in juvenile Alaskan woody plants in response to simulated browsing. Oecologia (Berlin). 67: 457-459.
Chapin, F. S. III, J. D. McKendrick, and D. A. Johnson. 1986. Seasonal changes in carbon fractions in Alaskan tundra plants of differing growth form: implications for herbivory. J. Ecol. 74: 707-731.
Chew, F. S. and J. E. Rodman. 1979. Plant resources for chemical defense. In: Herbivores: their interaction with secondary plant metabolites (G. A. Rosenthal and D. H. Janzen, Eds.). New York: Academic press; 271-307.
Coley, P. D., J. P. Bryant, and F. S. Chapin, III. 1985. Resource availability and plant anti-herbivore defense. Science 230: 895-899.
Del Moral, R. 1972. On the variability of chlorogenic acid concentration. Oecologia (Berlin). 9: 289-300.
Ericsson, A., J. Hellkvist, K. Hillerdal-Hagströmer, S. Larrson, E. E. Mattson-Djos, and O. Tenow. 1980. Consumption and pine growth--hypotheses on effects on growth processes by needle-eating insects. In: Structure and function of northern coniferous forests--an ecosystem study" (T. Persson, Ed.). Ecol. Bull. (Stockholm). 32: 537-545.
Ericsson, A., C. Hellqvist, B. Långström, S. Larsson, and O. Tenow. 1985. Effects on growth of simulated and induced shoot pruning by _Tomicus pinipedra_ as related to carbohydrate and nitrogen dynamics of Scots pine. J. Appl. Ecol. 22: 105-124.
Feeny, P. P. 1968. Effects of oak leaf tannins on larval growth of the winter moth _Operophtera brumata_. J. Insect Physiol. 14: 805-817.
Feeny, P. P. 1970. Seasonal changes in oak leaf tannins and nutrients as a cause of spring feeding by winter moth caterpillars. Ecology 51: 565-581.
Feeny, P. P. 1976. Plant apparency and chemical defense. In: Biochemical interactions between plants and insects (J. W. Wallace and R. L. Mansell, Eds.). Recent Adv. Phytochem. 10: 1-40.
Field, C. and H. A. Mooney. 1985. The photosynthesis--nitrogen relationship of wild plants. In: On the economy of plant form and function (T. J. Gwnish, Ed.). Cambridge: Cambridge Univ. Press.
Fowler, S. V. and J. H. Lawton. 1985. Rapidly induced defenses and talking trees: the devil's advocate position. Am. Nat. 126: 181-195.
Gartlan, J. A., D. B. McKey, P. G. Waterman, C. N. Mbi and T. T. Struhsaker. 1980. A comparative study of the phytochemistry of two African rain forests. Biochem. Syst. Ecol. 8: 401-422.
Gershenzon, J. 1984. Changes in the levels of plant secondary metabolites under water and nutrient stress. Recent Adv. Phytochem. 18: 273-320.
Grime, J. P. 1977. Evidence for the existence of three primary strategies in plants and its relevance to ecological and evolutionary theory. Am. Nat. 111: 1169-1194.
Grime, J. P. 1979. Plant strategies and vegetative processes. Chichester, England: John Wiley and Sons, 222 p.

Harper, J. L. 1977. Population biology of plants. London: Academic Press.
Haukioja, E. 1980. On the role of plant defences in the fluctuation of herbivore populations. Oikos 35: 202-213.
Haukioja, E. 1982. Inducible defences of white birch to a geometrid defoliator, Epirrita autumnata. In: Proceedings, Insect-plant relationships. 5th International Symposium. Wageningen, Netherlands: Pudoc; 199-203.
Haukioja, E. and T. Hakala. 1975. Herbivore cycles and periodic outbreaks. Formulation of a general hypothesis. Kevo. Subarctic Research Station Rep. 12: 1-9.
Haukioja, E., K. Kapiainen, P. Niemelä, and J. Tuomi. 1983a. Plant availability hypothesis and other explanations of herbivore cycles: complementary or exclusive alternatives? Oikos 40: 419-432.
Haukioja, E. and S. Neuvonen. 1985. Induced long-term resistance of birch foliage against defoliators: tests of defensive and non-defensive hypotheses. Ecology 66: 1303-1308.
Haukioja, E. and P. Niemelä. 1976. Does birch defend itself actively against herbivores? Kevo. Subarctic Research Station Rep. 13: 44-47.
Haukioja, E. and P. Niemelä. 1977. Retarded growth of a geometrid larva after mechanical damage to leaves of its host tree. Ann. Zool. Fennici 14: 48-52.
Haukioja, E., P. Niemelä and K. Kapiainen. 1983b. Herbivory and tree-line birches. In: Tree-line ecology, collection nordicana, No. 27 (P. Morriset and S. Payette, Eds.). Quebec: Universite Laval, Centre d'etudes nordiques; 47: 153-158.
Haukioja, E., P. Niemelä and S. Sirén. 1985. Foliage phenols and nitrogen in relation to growth, insect damage, and ability to recover after defoliation in the mountain birch. Betula pubescens ssp. tortuosa. Oecologia (Berlin). 65: 214-222.
Hegnauer, R. 1966. Chemotaxonomie der Pflanzen. Basel: Birkhauser Verlag.
Ikeda, T., F. Matsumura, D. M. Benjamin. 1977. Mechanisms of feeding discrimination between matured and juvenile foliage by two species of pine sawflies. J. Chem. Ecol. 3: 677-694.
Ingestad, T. 1982. Relative addition rate and external concentration; driving variables used in plant nutrition research. Plant Cell Environ. 5: 443-453.
Janzen, D. H. 1974. Tropical black water rivers, animals and mast fruiting by the Dipterocarpaceae. Biotropica 6: 69-103.
Janzen, D. H. and P. G. Waterman. 1984. A seasonal census of phenolics, fibre and alkaloids in foliage of forest trees in Costa Rica: some factors influencing their distribution and relation to host selection by Sphingidae and Saturnidae. Biol. J. Linn. Soc. 21: 439-454.
Jeker, T. B. 1981. Durch Insektenfrass induzierte, resistenzähnliche Phänomene bei Pflanzen. Wechselwirkungen zwishen Grauerle, Alnus incana (L.) und den Erlenblattkäfern Agelastica alni L. und Melasoma aenea L. sowie zwishen Stumpfblättrigem Ampfer, Rumex obtusifolius L. und Ampferblattkäfer, Gastrophysa viridula Deg. Diss. Eidgenoessischen Technishen Hochschule Zürich. Nr. 6895, 107 p.
Karban, R. and J. R. Carey. 1984. Induced resistance of cotton seedlings to mites. Science 225: 53-54.
Larsson, S., A. Wiren, L. Lundgren, and T. Ericsson. 1986. Effects of light and nutrient stress on leaf phenolic chemistry in Salix dasyclados and susceptibility to Galerucella lineola (Col., Chrysomelidae). Oikos 47: 205-210.
Lee, S. and S. Aronoff. 1967. Boron in plants: a biochemical role. Science 158: 798-799.

Lincoln, D. E., T. S. Newton, P. R. Ehrlich, and K. S. Williams. 1982. Coevolution of the checkerspot butterfly Euphydryas chalcedona and its larval food plant Diplacus aurantiacus: larval response to protein and leaf resin. Oecologia (Berlin). 52: 216-223.
Löyttyniemi, K. and N. Piisilä. 1983. Moose Alces alces damage in young pine plantations in the forestry board district Uusimaa-Häme (in Finnish with English summary). Folia For. 553: 1-23.
Margna, U. 1977. Control at the level of substrate supply--an alternative in the regulation of phenylpropanoid accumulation in plant cells. Phytochemistry 16: 419-426.
Mattson, W. J. 1980. Herbivory in relation to plant nitrogen content. Ann. Rev. Ecol. Syst. 11: 119-161.
Mattson, W. J., S. S. Slocum, and C. N. Koller. 1983. Spruce budworm Choristoneura fumiferana performance in relation to foliar chemistry of its host plants. In: Proceedings, Forest defoliator-host interactions: a comparison between gypsy moth and spruce budworms. USDA, Forest Service, Northeastern Forest Experiment Station, Gen. Tech. Rep. NE-85, 53-65.
May, R. M. 1975. Stability and complexity in model ecosystems. 2nd Ed. Princeton: Princeton Univ. Press.
McKey, D. 1979. The distribution of secondary compounds within plants. In: Herbivores: their interaction with secondary plant metabolites (G. A. Rosenthal and D. H. Janzen, Eds.). New York: Academic Press; 55-133.
McKey, D., P. G. Waterman, C. N. Mbi, J. S. Gartlan, T. T. Struhsaker. 1978. Phenolic content of vegetation in two African rain forests: ecological implications. Science 202: 61-64.
Myers, J. H. 1981. Interactions between western tent caterpillars and wild rose: a test of some general plant herbivore hypotheses. J. Anim. Ecol. 50: 11-25.
Myers, J. H. and K. S. Williams. 1984. Does tent caterpillar attack reduce the food quality of red alder foliage? Oecologia (Berlin) 62: 74-79.
Niemelä, P., J. Tuomi, R. Mannila, and P. Ojala. 1984. The effect of previous damage on the quality of Scots pine as food for Diprionid sawflies. Z. Angew. Entomol. 98: 33-43.
Phillips, R. and G. G. Henshaw. 1977. The regulation of synthesis of phenolics in stationary phase cell culture of Acer pseudoplatanus L. J. Exp. Bot. 28: 785-794.
Raupp, M. J. and R. F. Denno. 1984. The suitability of damaged willow leaves as food for the leaf beetle, Plagiodera versicolora. Ecol. Entomol. 9: 443-448.
Rhoades, D. F. 1979. Evolution of plant chemical defence against herbivores. In: Herbivores: their interaction with secondary plant metabolites (G. A. Rosenthal and D. H. Janzen, Eds.). New York: Academic Press; 3-54.
Rhoades, D. F. 1983. Responses of alder and willow to attack by tent caterpillars and webworms: evidence for pheromonal sensitivity of willows. In: Plant resistance to insects (P. E. Hedin, Ed.). Washington DC: Amer. Chem. Soc.; 55-68.
Rhoades, D. F. 1985. Pheromonal communication between plants. Rec. Adv. Phytochem. 19: 195-218.
Rhoades, D. F. and R. G. Cates. 1976. A general theory of plant antiherbivore chemistry. In: Biochemical interaction between plants and insects (J. W. Wallace and R. L. Mansell, Eds.). Recent Adv. Phytochem. 10: 168-213.
Ricklefs, R. E. and K. K. Matthew. 1982. Chemical characteristics of the foliage of some deciduous trees in southeastern Ontario. Can. J. Bot. 60: 2037-2045.
Ryan, C. A. and T. R. Green. 1974. Proteinase inhibitors in natural plant protection. Recent Adv. Phytochem. 8: 123-140.

Schultz, J. C. and I. T. Baldwin. 1982. Oak leaf quality declines in response to defoliation by gypsy moth larvae. Science 217: 149-151.

Swain, T. 1979. Tannins and lignins. In: Herbivores: their interaction with secondary plant metabolites (G. A. Rosenthal and D. H. Janzen, Eds.). New York: Academic Press; 657-682.

Tuomi, J., P. Niemelä, E. Haukioja, S. Sirén, and S. Neuvonen. 1984. Nutrient stress: an explanation for anti-herbivore responses to defoliation. Oecologia (Berlin) 61: 208-210.

Wallner, W. E. and G. S. Walton. 1979. Host defoliation: a possible determinant of Gypsy moth population quality. Ann. Entomol. Soc. Am. 72: 62-67.

Waring, R. H., A. J. S. McDonald, S. Larsson, T. Ericsson, A. Wiren, E. Arwidsson, A. Ericsson, and T. Lohammar. 1985. Differences in chemical composition of plants grown at constant relative growth rates with stable mineral nutrition. Oecologia (Berlin) 66: 157-160.

Warren-Wilson, J. 1966. An analysis of plant growth and its control in arctic environments. Ann. Bot. 30: 383-402.

Wender, S. H. 1970. Effects of some environmental stress factors on certain phenolic compounds in tobacco. Recent Adv. Phytochem. 3: 1-29.

Werner, R. A. 1979. Influence of host foliage on development, survival, fecundity and oviposition of the spear-marked moth Rheumaptera hastata (Lepidoptera: Geometridae). Can. Entomol. 111: 317-322.

White, L. M. 1973. Carbohydrate reserves of grasses: a review. J. Range Manage. 26: 13-18.

Whittaker, R. H. and P. P. Feeny. 1971. Allelochemics: chemical interactions between species. Science 171: 757-770.

Williams, K. S. and J. H. Myers. 1984. Previous herbivore attack of red alder may improve food quality for fall webworm larvae. Oecologia (Berlin) 63: 166-170.

4

Growth Differentiation-Balance Relationships in Pines Affect Their Resistance to Bark Beetles (Coleoptera: Scolytidae)

Peter L. Lorio, Jr.

How trees defend themselves against attack by bark beetles (Coleoptera: Scolytidae) is poorly understood. Because of this, there are diverse theories on the mechanisms of defense. Whatever the specific mechanisms may be, I propose here that normal physiological changes that occur during tree phenology, and in response to environmental conditions, cause regular and predictable changes in resistance/susceptibility to insects. I also propose that the concept of balance between plant growth and differentiation processes provides a useful framework for examining and interpreting knowledge of bark beetle biology in relation to host physiology under ordinary and stressful environmental circumstances. This framework leads one to conclude that moderate environmental stresses (e.g., water deficits) increase tree resistance to bark beetle attack because the production of defensive compounds (secondary metabolites) increases in response to any environmental conditions that do not adversely affect photosynthesis and translocation while reducing the use of available photosynthates in competing growth processes.

INTERACTIONS BETWEEN BARK BEETLES AND HOST TREES

Understanding bark beetle and tree interactions is a significant challenge to students of bark beetle ecology. Reviews by Rudinsky (1962) and Stark (1965) illustrate the great complexity of the problem. This paper focuses on the genus *Dendroctonus*, and specifically the southern pine beetle, *D. frontalis*, and its major host species, loblolly pine, *Pinus taeda*, and related southern pines. I suggest, however, that the relationships discussed here have application to a wide range of insect- and disease-plant interactions.

There are many serious gaps in knowledge about the southern pine beetle and its behavior, associated microorganisms, and host trees.

For example, researchers continue to question the means by which host trees are killed. One hypothesis states that the beetle kills pines by excavating egg galleries in the phloem and thereby girdles the trees over all or most of the clear bole. However, southern pines are well-known to live for long periods following simple girdling. Therefore, some researchers believe that other factors also play a role in the process.

Microorganisms, especially the blue stain fungus, *Ceratocystis minor*, are important in bark beetle biology; some investigators believe that blue stain is the primary killing agent and that the beetle depends upon concomitant fungal colonization for successful attack. However, the mechanism by which the fungus affects the physiology of beetle-attacked trees has not been satisfactorily demonstrated. Further, some southern pine beetle infestations lack *C. minor*, suggesting that the fungus is not always the cause of death of infested trees, nor is it required for successful beetle development. (Bridges *et al*. 1985).

Whatever the process by which trees are killed, it is clear that the oleoresin system in southern pines plays an important role (Hodges *et al*. 1979). Both the primary resin system (the *in situ* network of vertical and radial resin ducts in the xylem) and the secondary resin system (resin produced in response to wounding or fungal infection) influence beetle activity and fungal growth (Berryman 1972). Although there is little agreement on specific mechanisms of tree resistance to beetle attack, there is general agreement that some aspect of the oleoresin system constitutes the primary defense against southern pine beetle attack (Coulson 1980, Cates and Alexander 1982, Matson and Hain 1985, Hain *et al*. 1985). However, much of the research on this problem has concentrated on the hypothesis that some abnormal stress (Berryman 1972, 1976), such as severe water deficit or lightning-strike damage (Coulson *et al*. 1983) is necessary for successful beetle attack and development. Although other factors such as high density of trees, senescence, and root disease are recognized as contributing to southern pine beetle success and the development of outbreaks (Hicks 1980, Belanger 1980), there is little understanding of how site, tree, and stand factors affect southern pine beetle activity and population dynamics. Sharpe and Wu (1985) and Sharpe *et al*. (1985) emphasized the importance of distinguishing among various kinds of stresses and plant responses to them.

Outbreaks

Foresters, entomologists, and researchers in a variety of disciplines have struggled to understand the basic causes of outbreaks (Price and Doggett 1982, Thatcher et al. 1980, Thatcher 1960, Dixon and Osgood 1961). The onset and collapse of southern pine beetle outbreaks have not consistently been linked to climate or weather. Coulson (1980) pointed out that this is not surprising given the enormous complexity of the process.

Hopkins (1892, 1899) proposed that the southern pine beetle swarmed into forests and caused enormous mortality of healthy, vigorous trees, at least partly because of a lack of natural enemies. Later, Craighead (1925), MacAndrews (1926), Hetrick (1949), and others reasoned that factors such as drought, excessive rainfall, and various disturbances such as lightning strikes, ice storms, and wind adversely affected tree physiology and were precursors of southern pine beetle outbreaks.

Stark (1965) implied that water deficit was probably the most important single factor leading to conditions conducive to outbreaks. Rudinsky (1962), on the other hand, considered the abundance of suitable breeding material to be the key factor in bark beetle outbreaks. Both authors attempted to integrate knowledge gathered from a wide range of bark beetle species and host trees, but opinions just as divergent can be found among researchers studying only the southern pine beetle and its primary host species.

Heavy emphasis has been placed on the hypothesis that stress on the host is a requisite for southern pine beetle attack success, brood development, and the onset of outbreaks. Little attention has been given to studying the normal seasonal physiological changes in host trees in relation to beetle behavior and activity to develop a foundation upon which to evaluate the effects of stress as precursors to southern pine beetle outbreaks. Unless such an approach is taken to study interactions among the southern pine beetle, microorganisms, and host trees, the potential to develop a deep understanding of factors that lead to the onset and collapse of outbreaks will remain low.

It appears that abundant food and habitat are necessary for the development of outbreaks (Lorio 1978, Lorio et al. 1982); but they are not sufficient in and of themselves. Much more knowledge is required to predict the actual event. Loomis' (1932) concept of plant growth and differentiation balance has been proposed as a basis for understanding southern pine beetle interactions with southern pines because it provides a rationale for the great difficulties experienced in identifying consistent precursors to southern pine beetle outbreaks and, furthermore, forms a philosophical basis for development of future research (Lorio 1986, Lorio and Hodges 1985).

GROWTH AND DIFFERENTIATION BALANCF AND PLANT BEHAVIOR

Walter E. Loomis' Concept

In his pioneering work, Klebs (1903) proposed that the course of plant development is determined by internal conditions, which may be altered by external factors. Although many advances have been made in plant physiology and biochemistry in the intervening years, Klebs' principle endures (Kramer and Kozlowski 1979).

Kraus and Kraybill (1918) showed the applicability of Klebs' principle to the control of fruiting in commercial crops, and because of the importance of nitrogen in the fertilization of fruit plants, some workers espoused the idea that the mathematical ratio of total nitrogen to total carbohydrates was a determining factor in plant development (Loomis 1932). In Loomis' (1932) opinion, this ratio concept was weak because it considered only two of the important growth and differentiation-balance factors (nitrogen and carbohydrate content). It overlooked the importance of water, other essential nutrients in addition to nitrogen, temperature, and active carbohydrates as opposed to storage forms. His growth and differentiation-balance concept, on the other hand, provides for explicit consideration of these factors in the study of plant behavior.

Loomis (1932), following common practice, divided the development of plants into three more or less distinct but overlapping phases: cell division, cell enlargement, and cell differentiation. The first two are generally considered together as elements of growth involving increase in plant size. The third has to do largely with changes in morphology due to pre-existing chemical conditions in the cells or tissue involved. For the purposes of growth and differentiation balance, Loomis defined differentiation as the sum of the chemical changes that occur in maturing cells and of the morphological changes which result from these chemical conditions. Examples of differentiation processes, as provided by Loomis (1953), are thickening and lignification of secondary cell walls; thickening of leaf cuticle; hardening of the protoplasm; formation of specific flowering substances; and the production of cellular inclusions such as gum, resin, essential oil, or similar products.

Growth, involving cell division and cell enlargement, depends upon an array of internal and external factors, including temperature, water, oxygen, sugar, inorganic nutrients, enzymes, and hormones. As long as all factors are favorable for growth, growth processes predominate over differentiation. Differentiation depends primarily upon temperature and sugars and is dominant only when conditions other than temperature and photosynthate supply are below optimum for growth.

Robert S. Loomis (1983) explained how growth and differentiation-balance relationships are helpful in understanding partitioning of photosynthates. With water not limiting, supplies are used principally in growth and the new tissue consists mostly of proteins and cellulose. Under mild stress, differentiation is favored and tissues have a higher content of lignin, wax, and other materials. If the direct effect of a deficiency is on photosynthesis (e.g., low light or leaf removal), or if the water deficit is severe, then both growth and differentiation are limited. In a nutshell, plants tend to grow fast and differentiate little when conditions are optimal for growth, and they grow slowly and differentiate more when conditions are suboptimal for growth, but temperature and carbohydrate supply are not limiting.

Plant Behavior in Relation to Growth and Differentiation Balance

A few examples of plant behavior are offered to illustrate the apparent utility of the concept without proposing that its application can in any way explain all aspects of plant behavior.

The work on guayule, *Parthenium argentatum* (Wadleigh *et al*. 1946), dramatically illustrates how inadequate consideration for growth and differentiation-balance relationships led to the failure of early attempts to cultivate guayule because of excessive irrigation (Kramer 1969). Heavy watering increased total vegetative growth and decreased the rubber content of guayule. Subsequently, Veihmeyer and Hendrickson (1961) reported that the absolute yield of rubber increased in response to soil dryness, and Black (1968) pointed out that time is a factor because the rubber content increases slowly.

Mooney and Chu (1974) reported that growth processes and secondary metabolism processes (differentiation) in the evergreen sclerophyll shrub, *Heteromeles arbutifolia*, compete for available photosynthates and that carbon allocation to all functions cannot be met simultaneously. During growth periods, large amounts of carbon go to compounds involved in metabolism and to the formation of new cell wall materials.

During nongrowth periods, large amounts of carbon go to storage and to synthesis of phenolic and nonsaponifiable compounds.

Other examples show that water stress increased the nitrogen and nicotine content of cigarette tobacco (van Bavel 1953), and that rubber production in *Hevea* seems to depend on the alternating conditions favorable to growth with conditions favorable to the accumulation of sugars and the differentiation of latex (Loomis 1953, Buttery and Boatman 1976).

Gardner, *et al.* (1985) emphasized that the production of quality crop products often requires strategies that achieve an appropriate balance between growth and differentiation. They noted that growth is essential but generally should not be favored to the point of precluding differentiation as can happen when inappropriate irrigation and nitrogen fertilization leads to low sugar accumulation in sugar beet, *Beta vulgaris*. In recognition of these relationships, sandy soils are used in the commercial production of melons in humid areas so that levels of water and nitrogen can be controlled during ripening. Melons produced on heavy soils in humid areas will normally be larger than those produced on sandy soils, but they lack the sweetness that develops with differentiation.

The competition between wood formation and the biogenesis of oleoresin in pines is another example of growth and differentiation balance (Loomis 1953). For southern pines growing in the Southeastern United States, the most common limiting growth factor is water. The effects of water deficits on tree growth and development have long been a subject of major interest in forest science (Zahner 1968, Kozlowski 1968-1981). However, water deficit has been given only little attention in terms of its possible beneficial effects on the formation of differentiation products, such as the oleoresin of pines. Growth and differentiation balance influences when and where resin ducts are formed and oleoresins are produced. Factors that affect tree crown development and radial growth also affect the synthesis and flow of oleoresin from wounds. For example, large-crowned trees that produce large supplies of photosynthates usually demonstrate fast stem radial growth as well as the ability to produce copious defensive chemicals compared to smaller crowned trees, such as those in intermediate and suppressed crown classes (Wyman 1932, Clements 1974).

GROWTH AND DIFFERENTIATION-BALANCE AND BARK BEETLE/HOST INTERACTIONS

A Proposed Hypothesis for the Southern Pine Beetle

A general hypothesis has been proposed, based on growth and differentiation-balance relationships in southern pines, and the seasonal activity of the southern pine beetle, based on knowledge from experimentation and observations reported in the literature (Lorio 1986). The hypothesis suggests that the spring is particularly favorable to successful beetle attack because of the strong demand for available photosynthates by growth processes at that time, whereas, in the summer, strong resin flow increases the potential resistance of trees to attack. It is proposed that southern pine beetle behavior changes seasonally in relation to growth and differentiation-balance relationships of host trees in such a way that successful colonization of well-hydrated, fast-growing trees is always enhanced.

Supporting Evidence from Research and Observations

If the southern pine beetle has evolved in response to characteristics of southern pines (Futuyma 1983), one might expect to find some close relationships between beetle behavior and the physiological changes associated with host tree phenology.

Seasonal Behavior of the Southern Pine Beetle. Southern pine beetles apparently behave differently in different seasons of the year (Payne 1980). For example, autumn, winter, and spring are periods of dispersal, whereas summer is a period of strong tendency for beetles to remain within a locale, infesting trees in the immediate vicinity.

Hedden and Billings (1977) suggested that long-range dispersal of southern pine beetle in east Texas, followed by the initiation of new infestations, occurs primarily during the spring and autumn when fat reserves of beetles are high, environmental conditions are optimal for flight, and intermittent cool weather interrupts pheromone production in old infestations. Moser and Dell (1979) trapped large numbers of southern pine beetles in January, May, and October of 1975, with peak catches occurring in October. In another study, more beetles were trapped in the first week in January than any other week of the year (Moser and Dell 1980). Least numbers of beetles were trapped during very cold periods of January and February and during the hot summer months.

During the summer, the southern pine beetle rapidly mass attacks trees on the periphery of existing infestations. This may indicate behavioral responses to elevated levels of oleoresins (Vité 1970, Billings 1985) that typically occur in pines at that season. Such behavior would enhance the potential success of attacking beetles at a time when the general population of trees, in the absence of severe stress such as intense drought or lightning strike, would be most resistant to attack.

Thatcher (1974) concluded, on the basis of studies in southeast Texas and central Louisiana (Thatcher and Pickard 1964; Thatcher 1967, 1971), that the highest southern pine beetle survival occurs in trees infested during the autumn through early spring, whereas survival and activity are lowest in the summer. Severity of outbreaks is greatest in the spring.

Seasonal Changes in Host Characteristics. Based on the anatomical characteristics of southern pine wood (especially the earlywood/ latewood transition, including the development of vertical resin ducts), oleoresin synthesis would be expected to occur primarily in the summer or whenever water deficit checks growth and favors differentiation. Data of Harper and Wyman (1936) support this because maximum first-day oleoresin yields for 70 longleaf pines, *Pinus palustris*, in central Florida, occurred in July when monthly potential evapotranspiration had maximized, presumably checking growth (Moser and Dell 1980).

Fourteen-day yields of oleoresin from 315 slash pines, *P. elliottii* var. *elliottii* (Barrett and Bengtson 1964), and first-day yield from 10 loblolly pines in central Louisiana (Lorio and Sommers 1986) followed similar trends, with peak yields in late summer (Fig. 1). Lorio and Sommers (1986) attributed the late summer increase in oleoresin yield to the influence of moderate water deficits that limited growth but were not sufficient to significantly affect photosynthesis or translocation (Fig. 2).

Research conducted on red pine, *P. resinosa*, by Gordon and Larson (1968) suggests a close relationship between maturation of the current season's needles and the transition from earlywood to latewood formation. Gordon and Larson (1968) concluded that because demand for photosynthate in the new shoot decreases at a time when photosynthesis is high in the whole plant, a sharply increased amount of photosynthate becomes available for wall synthesis by cambial derivatives. It is reasonable to expect that such an increase in photosynthate would also

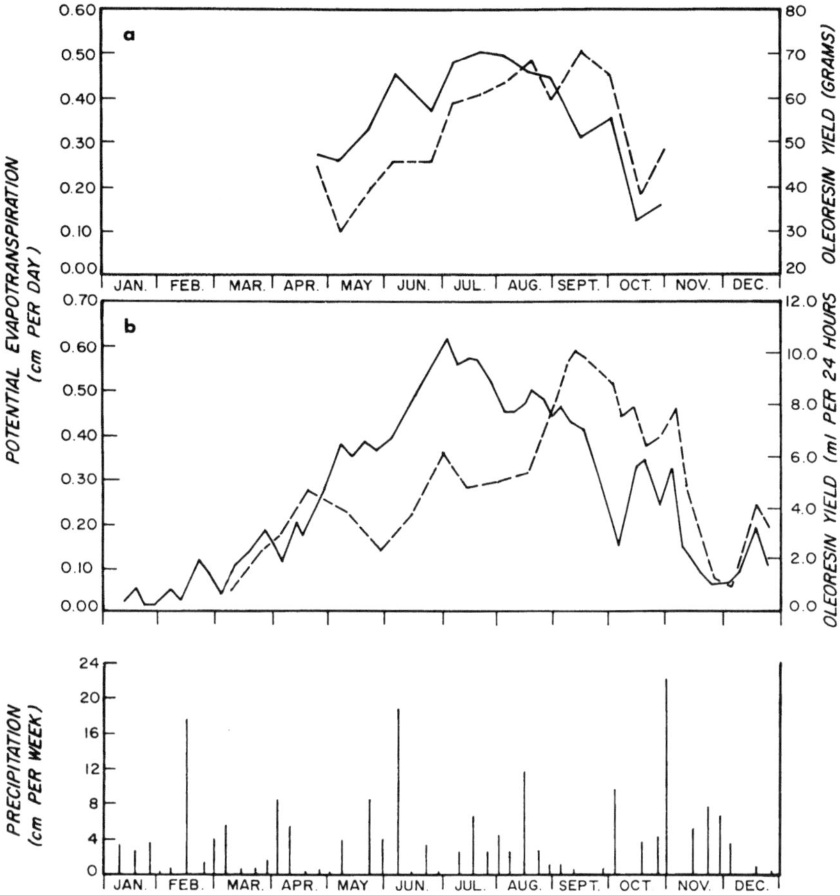

Figure 1. Seasonal trends in potential evapotranspiration and average oleoresin yield per tree. (a) Oleoresin yield (----) is the average for 315 slash pines over 2 weeks following wounding. Average potential evapotranspiration per day (——) was calculated from mean daily temperature data for each 2-week period. (Modified from Barrett and Bengston 1964.) (b) Oleoresin yield (----) is the average for 10 loblolly pines over 24 hours following wounding; average potential evaportranspiration per day (——) was calculated from mean daily temperature data for each 1-week period; precipitation is summed weekly. (Modified from Lorio and Sommers 1986.)

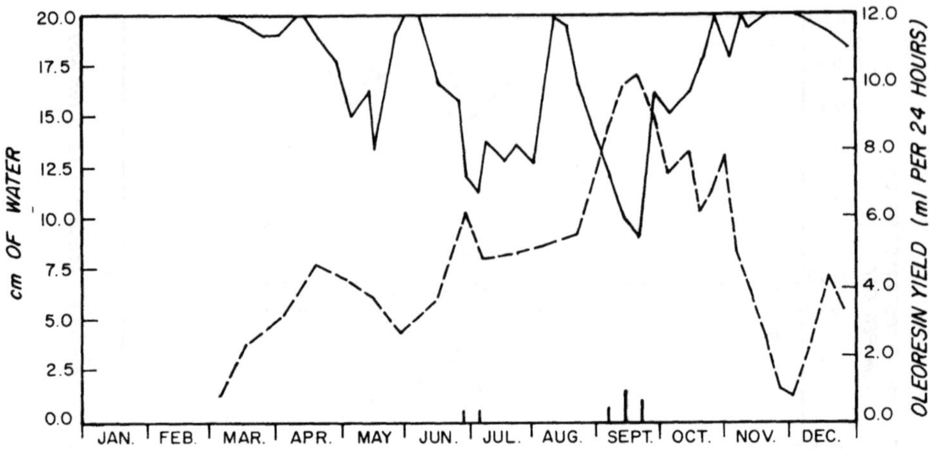

Figure 2. Calculated soil water storage (——), water deficits (vertical bars), and loblolly pine oleoresin yield (----) per 24 hours in 1984 for 10 loblolly pines and 30 sampling dates. Water balance was calculated assuming a loam-textured soil with a water-holding capacity of 20 cm in top meter (modified from Lorio and Sommers 1986).

favor synthesis of oleoresin, if environmental or internal conditions limit growth.

Loblolly pine, unlike red pine, produces multiple flushes of shoot growth within a year, but similar relationships may exist among development of the current year's needles, production and transport of photosynthate, latewood formation, and the potential for oleoresin synthesis.

Lorio and Hodges (1985) reported that control trees in a study of loblolly pine responses to induced soil water deficits (Hodges and Lorio 1969) showed marked changes in nitrogen and carbohydrates of the inner bark in relation to diameter growth rates. The changes suggest that in the spring months, tree growth places a preferential demand on both current and reserve energy sources (Fig. 3). In the summer months when growth slows, photosynthesis continues at a high rate, and there is an excess of carbohydrates over that required, or which can be used, for growth. This energy then becomes available for other uses, one of which is the production of oleoresin. Amino compounds also increase

Figure 3. Tree diameter growth in relation to inner-bark carbohydrate and nitrogen fractions: (a) cross-sectional growth of 40-year-old loblolly pines, (b) changes in total carbohydrates and starch content in inner bark, (c) changes in sugar content, and (d) changes in nitrogen fractions of the same trees. (Modified from Hodges and Lorio 1969.)

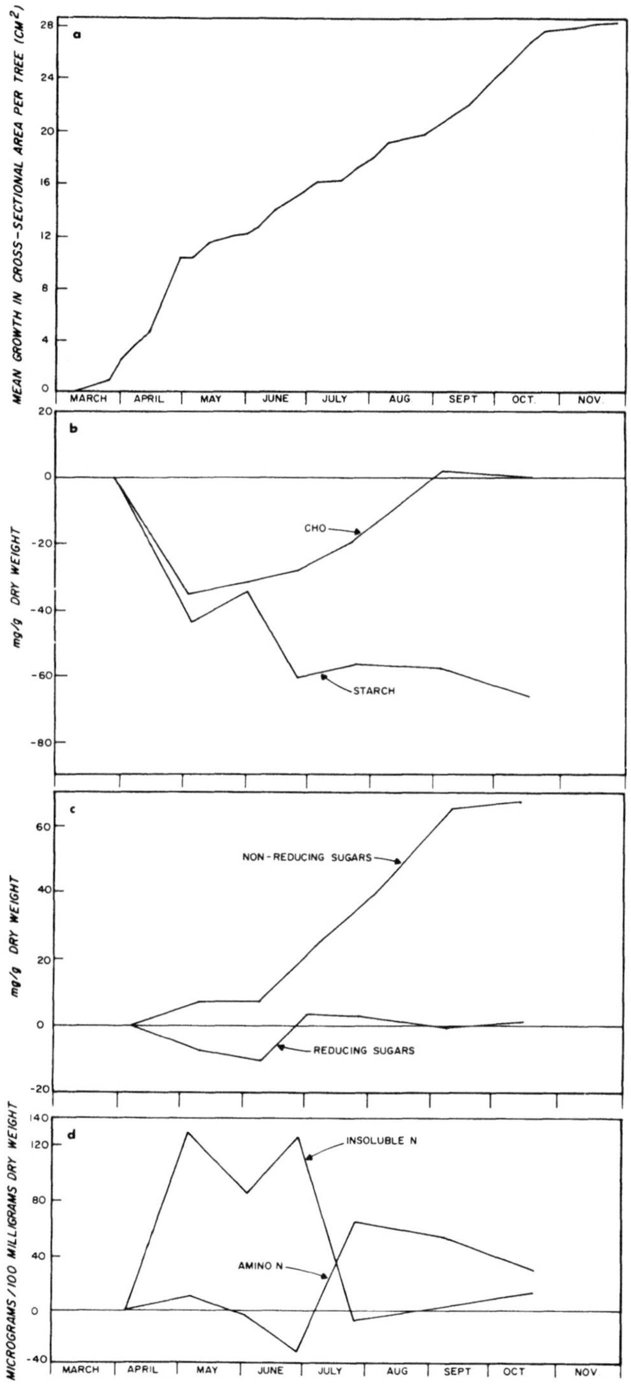
MEAN GROWTH IN CROSS-SECTIONAL AREA PER TREE (CM²)
a
28
24
20
16
12
8
4
0
MARCH
APRIL
MAY
JUNE
JULY
AUG
SEPT
OCT.
NOV.
b
20
0
-20
-40
-60
-80
mg/g DRY WEIGHT
CHO
STARCH
c
60
40
20
0
-20
mg/g DRY WEIGHT
NON-REDUCING SUGARS
REDUCING SUGARS
d
140
120
80
40
0
-40
MICROGRAMS/100 MILLIGRAMS DRY WEIGHT
INSOLUBLE N
AMINO N
MARCH
APRIL
MAY
JUNE
JULY
AUG
SEPT
OCT
NOV

during the summer months and, although not components of oleoresin, they are important in its synthesis. All of these studies strongly support an inverse relationship between growth processes and the synthesis of oleoresin and its flow from wounds. Competition for available photosynthates, as described by the growth and differentiation-balance concept, appears to be the basis for the inverse relationship.

In the lower West Gulf Coastal Plain of Louisiana and Texas, pines on flat, poorly drained sites commonly are attacked first in the development of southern pine beetle infestations. However, trees on slightly elevated mounds in these sites are not attacked at all or are attacked only later as an infestation grows (Lorio 1968, Thatcher 1971). Lorio and Hodges (1971) found widely different growth patterns for loblolly pines on or between mounds. Those growing between mounds continued fast diameter growth much longer in the spring than neighbors on mounds. Furthermore, the intermound pines also demonstrated strong growth responses to intermittent rainfall in the mid- to late summer and tended to produce false rings within annual rings. The prolonged accelerated growth of trees on intermound sites extended their period of high susceptibility to beetle attack, thus enhancing the success of the spring surge in activity of the southern pine beetle (Thatcher 1971, Billings and Kibbe 1978).

<u>Lightning</u>. Lightning is recognized universally as an important factor in southern pine beetle ecology (Blanche <u>et al</u>. 1983), and some researchers believe that a fundamental relationship exists between epidemiology of the southern pine beetle and the occurrence of lightning (Coulson <u>et al</u>. 1983). However, the literature also strongly suggests that the relationship between lightning-damaged trees and the southern pine beetle varies with seasons (Thatcher 1971, Hodges and Pickard 1971, Lorio and Bennett 1974, Lorio and Yandle 1978, Flamm and Coulson in this volume). For example, data show a strong association between southern pine beetle infestations and lightning-struck trees in southwest Louisiana during mid- to late-summer months but only a weak association during the winter and spring months (Lorio and Yandle 1978) (Fig. 4).

Growth and differentiation-balance relationships in southern pines predict that the strongest resin flows should occur in summer months and weaker flows in the autumn, winter, and spring. Experience and literature on the subject support this and indicate that lightning-struck trees should be most important to southern pine beetles during the summer months when undamaged trees have the highest potential for

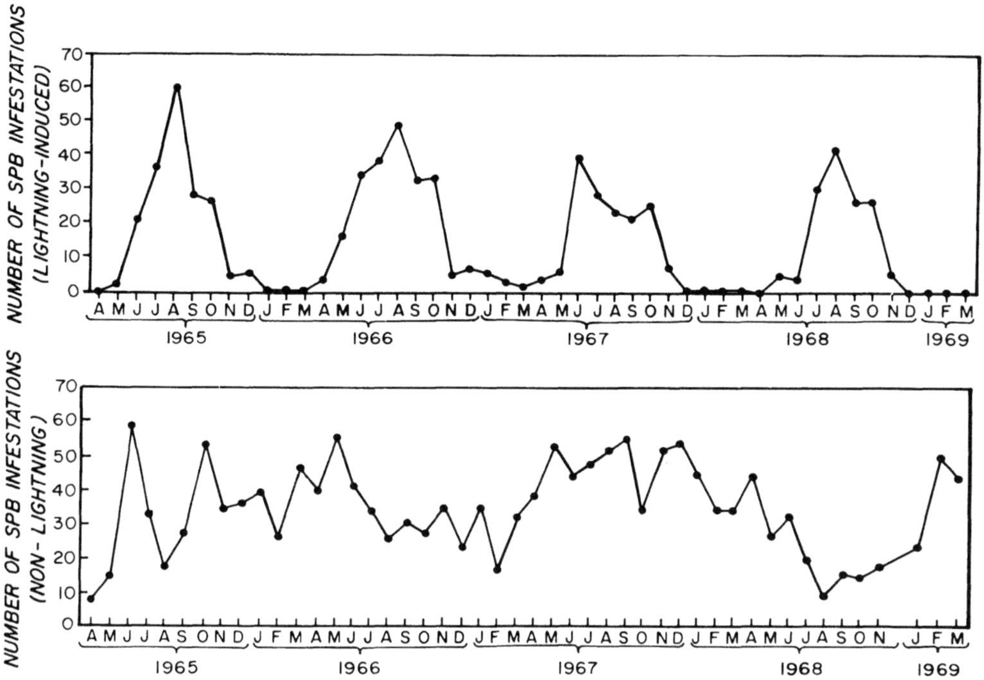

Figure 4. Seasonal trends in association of southern pine beetle infestations with lightning-strike damage in Allen Parish, Louisiana, over 4 years. (From Lorio and Yandle 1978.)

resin flow. Conversely, lightning-struck trees should be considerably less important in the late autumn, winter, and spring when phenological changes in all host trees enhance the potential success of southern pine beetle attacks.

<u>Testing the Hypothesis</u>

Preliminary results of one study developed to test the general hypothesis appear supportive (Lorio and Sommers 1986), but they are clearly preliminary and but a part of an ongoing effort which includes integrated studies of oleoresin flow; diameter growth; earlywood/ latewood transition; timing of resin duct formation; resin duct number, density, and distribution; and the carbohydrate and nitrogen status of inner bark within the same trees through the seasons of the year. Also in progress are studies to determine the relative resistance of trees to beetle attack in relation to host physiological conditions and environmental factors known to affect growth and differentiation-balance relationships.

RELEVANCE TO ECOLOGICAL AND EVOLUTIONARY THEORIES

Understanding of plant growth and development in response to environmental conditions is facilitated by considering the concept of balance between growth and differentiation activities, and this concept seems to apply directly to the development of ecological and evolutionary theories of plant defenses against herbivores.

Environmental Influences on Plant/Herbivore Interactions

Coley *et al*. (1985) proposed that resource availability is the major factor influencing the evolution of both the amount and type of plant defense. After reviewing a large body of evidence that apparently supported their theory, they suggested that resource availability better explains observed patterns of plant defense than the plant "apparency" model developed by Feeny (1976) and Rhoades and Cates (1976). Because habitat disturbance and successional stages are often associated with extremes of resource availability, Coley *et al*. (1985) stated that the theories of resource availability and plant apparency can sometimes lead to the same predictions. However, some studies separate the effects of apparency from availability of resources. Grime (1977, 1979), for example, was one of the first to identify an increase in defenses of plants associated with an increase in environmental stress, an apparent example of growth and differentiation-balance relationships in ecological or physiological time.

Mooney *et al*. (1983) hypothesized that a genetically determined time schedule of resource allocation, modified to a degree by environmental conditions, results in "windows" of susceptibility to herbivores. Limitations in supply of nitrogen and carbon and their allocation to a variety of functions in plants, including the development of defense against herbivores, could result in "priorities" of use within plants in order to maximize fitness. Examination of priorities in the allocation of carbon in the temperate deciduous forest indicates that trees are especially vulnerable to attack by herbivores during the period of canopy development.

Based on growth and differentiation-balance relationships in southern pines, a similar "window of vulnerability" to the southern pine beetle appears during the spring growth flush. This leads one to recognize the importance of physiological changes associated with phenology of pines in relation to their resistance to bark beetle attack (Kozlowski 1969). Conversely, the need for special behavioral mechanisms for identifying relatively rare susceptible hosts by "pioneer" southern pine beetles (Heikkenen 1977, Coulson 1980) seems to decrease as a requisite for bark beetle attack success and survival of the species.

Cost of Defensive Compounds

The "cost" to produce defensive chemicals is a major issue in the study of the evolution of plant defenses against herbivores. Matson and Hain (1985) consider cost a major factor in the evolution of host conifer defense mechanisms against bark beetles. Coley et al. (1985) argue that there is a causal relationship between inherent growth rates and antiherbivore defenses of plants, and they present a mathematical model of the relationship. Their rationale indicates that cost is a major factor in determining the optimal level of defense investment in relation to potential growth rate. Mattson (1980), however, points out that the apparent cost of producing allelochemics may be negligible. He suggests, for example, that if nitrogen limits growth processes, and the plant has carbohydrates in excess of what can be used to maximize growth under those conditions, then there is no growth-enhancing benefit to the plant by producing storage carbohydrates instead of allelochemics. It seems that the cost is more apparent than real and that differences in the utilization of photosynthates for growth or secondary metabolism can be more satisfactorily explained by an understanding of growth and differentiation-balance relationships.

According to McDermitt and Loomis (1981), the relative cost of producing carbohydrates or other compounds needs to be considered from an energetic point of view. They illustrate that although the weight yield for lipids is low, most of the energy to form them is stored in the product and can be recovered by the organism. Considering recoverability, carbohydrates are nearly as expensive to form as lipids. These considerations may have significance in calculating the cost of monoterpene and resin acid synthesis in pines. Loomis and Croteau (1980) provide ample evidence that monoterpenes are both rapidly synthesized and catabolized and conclude that they play a dynamic role in plant metabolism. Lawrence (1971) also presented evidence that suggests the metabolic turnover of monoterpenes but not resin acids in longleaf pine. Hence, estimates of the relative cost of synthesis of allelochemics should consider the energy which is recoverable in catabolism and its potential use in growth or other processes.

REFERENCES

Barrett, J. P. and G. W. Bengtson. 1964. Oleoresin yields for slash pines from seven seed sources. For. Sci. 10: 159-164.

Belanger, R. P. 1980. Sivicultural guidelines for reducing losses to the southern pine beetle. In: The southern pine beetle (R. C. Thatcher, J. L. Searcy, J. E. Coster, and G. D. Hertel, Eds.). USDA, Forest Service, and Science and Education Administration, Tech. Bull. 1631; 165-177.

Berryman, A. A. 1972. Resistance of conifers to invasion by bark beetle-fungus associations. BioScience 22(10): 598-602.

Berryman, A. A. 1976. Theoretical explanation of mountain pine beetle dynamics in lodgepole pine forests. Environ. Entomol. 5: 1225-1233.

Billings, R. F. 1985. Southern pine bark beetles and associated insects: effects of rapidly-released host volatiles on response to aggregation pheromones. Z. Angew. Entomol. 99: 483-491.

Billings, R. F. and A. Kibbe. 1978. Seasonal relationships between southern pine beetle brood development and loblolly pine foliage color in east Texas. Southwest. Entomol. 3(2): 89-95.

Black, C. A. 1968. Soil-plant relationships. New York: John Wiley and Sons, 792 p.

Blanche, C. A., J. D. Hodges, T. E. Nebeker, and D. M. Moehring. 1983. Southern pine beetle: the host dimension. Mississippi Agricultural Forest Experiment Station Bull. 917, 29 p.

Bridges, J. R., W. A. Nettleton, and M. D. Connor. 1985. Southern pine beetle (Coleoptera: Scolytidae) infestations without the bluestain fungus, Ceratocystis minor. J. Econ. Entomol. 78: 325-327.

Buttery, B. R. and S. G. Boatman. 1976. Water deficits and flow of latex. Vol. 4. In: Water deficits and plant growth (T. T. Kozlowski, Ed.). New York: Academic Press; 223-289.

Cates, R. G. and H. J. Alexander. 1982. Host resistance and susceptibility. In: Bark beetles in North American conifers: evolution and ecology (J. B. Mitton and K. B. Sturgeon, Eds.). Austin, TX: Univ. of Texas Press; 212-263.

Clements, R. W. 1974. Modern gum naval stores methods. USDA, Forest Service, Gen. Tech. Rep. SE-7, 29 p.

Coley, P. D., J. P. Bryant, and F. S. Chapin, III. 1985. Resource availability and plant antiherbivore defense. Science 230: 895-899.

Coulson, R. N. 1980. Population dynamics. In: The southern pine beetle (R. C. Thatcher, J. L. Searcy, J. E. Coster, and G. D. Hertel, Eds.). USDA, Forest Service, and Science and Education Administration, Tech. Bull. 1631; 71-105.

Coulson, R. N., P. B. Hennier, R. O. Flamm, E. J. Rykiel, C. L. Hu, and T. L. Payne. 1983. The role of lightning in the epidemiology of the southern pine beetle. Z. Angew. Entomol. 96(2): 182-193.

Craighead, F. C. 1925. The Dendroctonus problems. J. For. 23: 340-359.

Dixon, J. C. and E. A. Osgood. 1961. Southern pine beetle: a review of present knowledge. USDA, Forest Service, Res. Pap. SE-128, 34 p.

Feeny, P. P. 1976. Plant apparency and chemical defense. Rec. Adv. Phytochem. 10: 1-40.

Futuyma, D. J. 1983. Evolutionary interactions among herbivorous insects and plants. In: Coevolution (D. J. Futuyma and M. Slatkin, Eds.). Sanderland, MA: Sinauer; 201-231.

Gardner, F. P., R. B. Pearce, and R. L. Mitchell. 1985. Physiology of crop plants. Ames, IA: Iowa State Univ. Press, 327 p.

Gordon, J. C. and P. R. Larson. 1968. Seasonal course of photosynthesis, respiration, and distribution of ^{14}C in young pinus resinosa trees as related to wood formation. Plant Physiol. 43: 1617-1624.

Grime, J. P. 1977. Evidence for the existence of three primary strategies in plants and its relevance to ecological and evolutionary theory. Am. Nat. 111: 1169-1194.

Grime, J. P. 1979. Plant strategies and vegetative processes. Chichester, England: John Wiley and Sons, 222 p.

Hain, F. P., S. P. Cook, P. A. Matson, and K. G. Wilson. 1985. Factors contributing to southern pine beetle host resistance. In: Proceedings, Integrated pest management research symposium (S. J. Branham and R. C. Thatcher, Eds.); 1985 April 15-18; Asheville, NC. New Orleans, LA: USDA, Forest Service, Southern Forest Experiment Station, Gen. Tech. Rep. SO-56; 154-160.

Harper, V. L. and L. Wyman. 1936. Variations in naval-stores yields associated with weather and specific days between chippings. USDA, Tech. Bull. 510, 35 p.

Hedden, R. L. and R. F. Billings. 1977. Seasonal variations in fat content and size of the southern pine beetle in East Texas. Ann. Entomol. Soc. Am. 70: 876-880.

Heikkenen, H. J. 1977. Southern pine beetle: a hypothesis regarding its primary attractant. J. For. 75: 412-413.

Hetrick, L. A. 1949. Some overlooked relationships of southern pine beetle. J. Econ. Entomol. 42: 466-469.

Hicks, R. R., Jr. 1980. Climatic, site, and stand factors. In: The southern pine beetle (R. C. Thatcher, J. L. Searcy, J. E. Coster, and G. D. Hertel, Eds.). USDA, Forest Service, and Science and Education Administration, Tech. Bull. 1631; 55-68.

Hodges, J. D., W. W. Elam, W. F. Watson, and T. E. Nebeker. 1979. Oleoresin characteristics and susceptibility of four southern pines to southern pine beetle (Coleoptera: Scolytidae) attacks. Can. Entomol. 111: 889-896.

Hodges, J. D. and P. L. Lorio, Jr. 1969. Carbohydrate and nitrogen fractions of the inner bark of loblolly pines under moisture stress. Can. J. Bot. 47: 1651-1657.

Hodges, J. D. and L. S. Pickard. 1971. Lightning in the ecology of the southern pine beetle, _Dendroctonus frontalis_ (Coleoptera: Scolytidae). Can. Entomol. 103(1): 44-51.

Hopkins, A. D. 1892. Notes on a destructive forest tree scolytid. Science 20(495): 64-65.

Hopkins, A. D. 1899. Report on investigations to determine the cause of unhealthy conditions of the spruce and pine from 1880-1893. West Virginia Agricultural Experiment Station Bull. 56: 197-461.

Klebs, Georg. 1903. Willkurliche entwickelungsanderungen bei pflanzen. Jena: Gustav Fischer.

Kozlowski, T. T. (Ed.). 1968-1981. Water deficits and plant growth. Vol. I-VI. New York: Academic Press.

Kozlowski, T. T. 1969. Tree physiology and forest pests. J. For. 67: 118-123.

Kramer, P. J. 1969. Plant and soil water relationships: a modern synthesis. New York: McGraw-Hill, 482 p.

Kramer, P. J. and T. T. Kozlowski. 1979. Physiology of woody plants. New York: Academic Press, 811 p.

Kraus, E. J. and H. R. Kraybill. 1918. Vegetation and reproduction with special reference to the tomato. Oregon Agricultural College Experiment Station, Station Bull. 149, 89 p.

Lawrence, R. H., Jr. 1971. Biosynthesis and metabolism of terpenoids in _Pinus elliotti_, engelm, and _Pinus palustris_, Mill. Athens, GA: Univ. of Georgia; Ph.D. Dissertation, 117 p.

Loomis, R. S. 1983. Crop manipulations for efficient use of water: An overview. Chapter 8. In: Limitations to efficient water use in crop production (H. M. Taylor, W. R. Jordan, and T. R. Sinclair, Eds.). Madison, WI: ASA-CSSA-SSSA; 354-374.

Loomis, W. E. 1932. Growth-differentiation balance vs carbohydrate-nitrogen ratio. Proc. Am. Soc. Hortic. Sci. 29: 240-245.

Loomis, W. E. 1953. Growth correlation. In: Growth and differentiation in plants (W. E. Loomis, Ed.). Ames, IA: Iowa State College Press; 197-217.

Loomis, W. D. and R. Croteau. 1980. Biochemistry of terpenoids. Chapter 13. In: The biochemistry of plants (P. K. Stumpf and E. E. Conn, Eds.). New York: Academic Press; 4: 364-418.

Lorio, P. L., Jr. 1968. Soil and stand conditions related to southern pine beetle activity in Hardin County, Texas. J. Econ. Entomol. 61: 565-566.

Lorio, P. L., Jr. 1978. Developing stand risk classes for the southern pine beetle. USDA, Forest Service, Res. Pap. SO-144, 9 p.

Lorio P. L., Jr. 1986. Growth-differentiation balance: a basis for understanding southern pine beetle-tree interactions. For. Ecol. Manage. 14: 259-273.

Lorio, P. L., Jr., and W. H. Bennett. 1974. Recurring southern pine beetle infestations near Oakdale, Louisiana. USDA, Forest Service, Res. Pap. SO-95, 6 p.

Lorio, P. L., Jr. and J. D. Hodges. 1971. Microrelief, soil water regime, and loblolly pine growth on a wet, mounded site. Soil Sci. Soc. Am. Proc. 35: 795-800.

Lorio, P. L., Jr. and J. D. Hodges. 1985. Theories of interactions among bark beetles, associated microorganisms, and host trees. In: Proceedings, Third Biennial Southern Silvicultural Research Conference (E. Shoulders, Ed.); 1984 November 7-8, Atlanta, GA. USDA, Forest Service, Southern Forest Experiment Station, Gen. Tech. Rep. SO-54; 485-492.

Lorio, P. L., Jr., G. N. Mason, and G. L. Autry. 1982. Stand risk rating for the southern pine beetle: integrating pest management with forest management. J. For. 80: 212-214.

Lorio, P. L., Jr. and R. A. Sommers. 1986. Evidence of competition for photosynthates between growth processes and oleoresin synthesis in Pinus taeda L. Tree Physiology 2: 301-306.

Lorio, P. L., Jr. and D. O. Yandle. 1978. Distribution of lightning-induced southern pine beetle infestations. South. Lumberman Jan.: 12-13.

MacAndrews, A. H. 1926. The biology of the southern pine beetle. Syracuse, NY: New York State College of Forestry. Master's Thesis, 112 p.

Matson, P. A. and F. P. Hain. 1985. Host conifer defense strategies: a hypothesis. In: The role of the host in the population dynamics of forest insects (L. Safranyik, Ed.); Proceedings, IUFRO Conference; 1983 September 4-7; Banff, Alberta. Victoria, BC: Canadian Forestry Service and USDA, Forest Service; 33-42.

Mattson, W. J. 1980. Herbivory in relation to plant nitrogen content. Ann. Rev. Ecol. Syst. 11: 119-161.

McDermitt, D. K. and R. S. Loomis. 1981. Elemental composition of biomass and its relation to energy content, growth efficiency, and growth yield. Ann. Bot. 48: 275-290.

Mooney, H. A. and C. Chu. 1974. Seasonal carbon allocation in Heteromeles arbutifolia, a California evergreen shrub. Oecologia, 14: 295-306.

Mooney, H. A., S. L. Gulmon, and N. D. Johnson. 1983. Physiological constraints on plant chemical defenses. In: Plant resistance to insects (P. A. Hedlin, Ed.). Washington, DC: American Chemical Society; 21-36.

Moser, J. C. and T. R. Dell. 1979. Predictors of southern pine beetle flight activity. For. Sci. 25: 217-222.

Moser, J. C. and T. R. Dell. 1980. Weather factors predicting flying populations of a clerid predator and its prey, the southern pine beetle. In: Dispersal of forest insects (A. A. Berryman and L. Safranyik, Eds.); Proceedings, Second IUFRO Conference; 1979 August; Sandpoint, ID, Conference Office, Cooperative Extension Service. Pullman, WA: Washington State Univ.; 266-278.

Payne, T. L. 1980. Life history and habits. In: The southern pine beetle (R. C. Thatcher, J. L. Searcy, J. E. Coster, and G. D. Hertel, Eds.). USDA, Forest Service, and Science and Education Administration, Tech. Bull. 1631; 7-28.

Price, T. S. and C. Doggett. 1982. A history of southern pine beetle outbreaks in the southeastern United States. Macon, GA: Georgia Forestry Commission, 35 p.

Rhoades, D. F. and R. G. Cates. 1976. Toward a general theory of plant antiherbivore chemistry. Rec. Adv. Phytochem. 10: 168-213.

Rudinsky, J. A. 1962. Ecology of Scolytidae. Annu. Rev. Entomol. 7: 327-348.

Sharpe P. J. H. and H. Wu. 1985. A preliminary model of host susceptibility to bark beetle attack. In: The role of the host in the population dynamics of forest insects (L. Safranyik, Ed.); Proceedings, IUFRO Conference; 1983 September 4-7; Banff, Alberta. Victoria, BC: Canadian Forestry Service and USDA, Forest Service; 108-127.

Sharpe, P. J. H., H. Wu, R. G. Cates, and J. D. Goeschil. 1985. Energetics of pine defense systems to bark beetle attack. In: Proceedings, Integrated pest management research symposium (S. J. Branham and R. C. Thatcher, Eds.); 1985 April 15-18; Asheville, NC. New Orleans, LA: USDA, Forest Service, Southern Forest Experiment Station, Gen. Tech. Rep. SO-56; 206-223.

Stark, R. W. 1965. Recent trends in forest entomology. Annu. Rev. Entomol. 10: 303-324.

Thatcher, R. C. 1960. Bark beetles affecting southern pines: a review of current knowledge. USDA, Forest Service, Southern Forest Experiment Station, Occas. Pap. 180, 25 p.

Thatcher, R. C. 1967. Winter brood development of the southern pine beetle in southeast Texas. J. Econ. Entomol. 60: 599-600.

Thatcher, R. C. 1971. Seasonal behavior of the southern pine beetle in central Louisiana. Auburn, AL: Auburn Univ.; Ph.D. Dissertation, 102 p.

Thatcher, R. C. 1974. Past and present approaches to southern pine beetle research--an overview. In: Proceedings, southern pine beetle symposium (T. L. Payne, R. N. Coulson, and R. C. Thatcher, Eds.); 1974 March 7-8; College Station, TX: Texas A & M Univ., 57 p.

Thatcher, R. C. and L. S. Pickard. 1964. Seasonal variations in activity of the southern pine beetle in east Texas. J. Econ. Entomol. 57: 840-842.

Thatcher, R. C., J. L. Searcy, J. E. Coster, and G. D. Hertel (Eds.). 1980. The southern pine beetle. USDA, Forest Service, and Science and Education Administration, Tech. Bull. 1631, 267 p.

Van Bavel, C. H. M. 1953. Chemical composition of tobacco leaves as affected by soil moisture conditions. Agron. J. 45: 611-614.

Veihmeyer, F. J. and A. A. Hendrickson. 1961. Response of a plant to soil-moisture changes as shown by guayule. Hilgardia 30(20): 621-637.

Vité, J. P. 1970. Pest management systems using synthetic pheromones. Contrib. Boyce Thompson Inst. 24(13): 343-350.

Wadleigh, C. H., H. G. Gauch, and O. C. Magistad. 1946. Growth and rubber accumulation in guayule as conditioned by soil salinity and irrigation regime. USDA, Tech. Bull. 925, 34 p.

Wyman, L. 1932. Experiments in naval-stores practice. USDA, Bull. 298, 60 p.

Zahner, R. 1968. Water deficits and growth of trees. In: Vol II. Water deficits and plant growth (T. T. Kozlowski, Ed.). New York: Academic Press; 191-254.

5

Seasonal Variations in Energy Sources and Biosynthesis of Terpenes in Maritime Pine

C. Bernard-Dagan

Plant defensive reactions are commonly discussed in terms of their energy cost. However, little is known about the energy content of tree tissues when under attack by insects (or fungi) or the energy sources necessary for synthesis of the allelochemicals involved in defense.

The available energy content of tree tissues is related to the amounts of different kinds of molecules present in cell structures and to the ability of organisms to degrade and use these molecules. The first part of this report will address the distribution of the common sugars and storage substances in maritime pine, *Pinus pinaster*.

Among the secondary substances involved in plant/insect interactions, lower terpenoids are important because they serve as attractants, repellents, and toxins. The biosynthesis and cell localization of these molecules were, until recently, poorly known. The second part of this report will address the distribution of terpenes in different organs in various populations of *Pinus pinaster* and define the rules of their biosynthesis in normal conditions. Mechanical and chemical stresses induce quite different mechanisms that will be discussed elsewhere (see Cheniclet *et al*. in this volume).

SEASONAL NUTRIENT VARIABILITY IN DIFFERENT ORGANS AND TISSUES OF *PINUS PINASTER*

Methods

The geographic distribution of maritime pine is limited to South-Western Europe (France, Iberian peninsula, Italy) and Northern Africa (Fig. 1). This study used trees occurring naturally in four ecologically different sites in the Landes area of France. Each month, over several years, we harvested various organs (needles, lateral and main

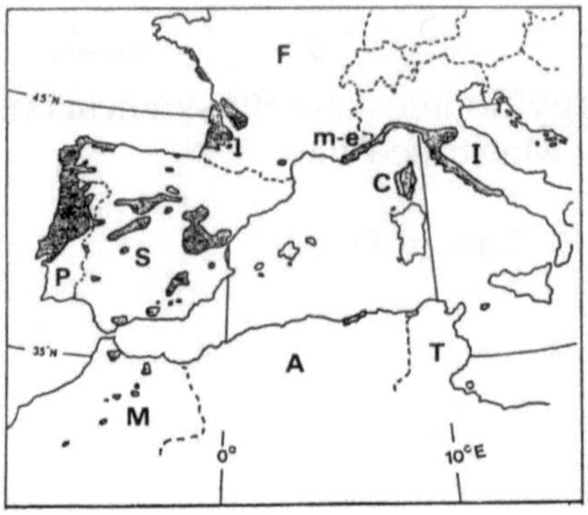

Figure 1. Natural distribution of the maritime pine, Pinus pinaster.

shoots, stems, and roots) for nutrient analyses (water soluble carbohydrates, starch, and lipids). For each collection, shoots and needles of different ages were separated. Root and stem samples were immediately separated into phloem and xylem tissues (Fig. 2).

Plant organs and tissues were immediately weighed and then soaked in boiling alcohol followed by ethanol-water (70:30) extraction in a soxlhet apparatus for 6 hours. After vacuum evaporation and elimination of phenols, hydrosoluble sugars were measured by the Nelson method (1944). Total reducing carbohydrates were directly estimated, nonreducing carbohydrates were first liberated by acid hydrolysis and then estimated. Isolation of the different components was performed by paper chromatography according to the method described by Pauly (1968).

Water Soluble Carbohydrates in Maritime Pine

The types of sugars were roughly the same in all parts of the tree. The main reducing sugars were fructose and glucose, the proportions of which varied according to the season. Hexoses are involved in cell metabolic functions and are renewed with a very rapid turnover. Trace amounts of pentoses (xylose as well as galactose, melibiose, maltose, cellobiose, and arabinose) were found mainly in stem and roots. These are often linked to phenolic molecules.

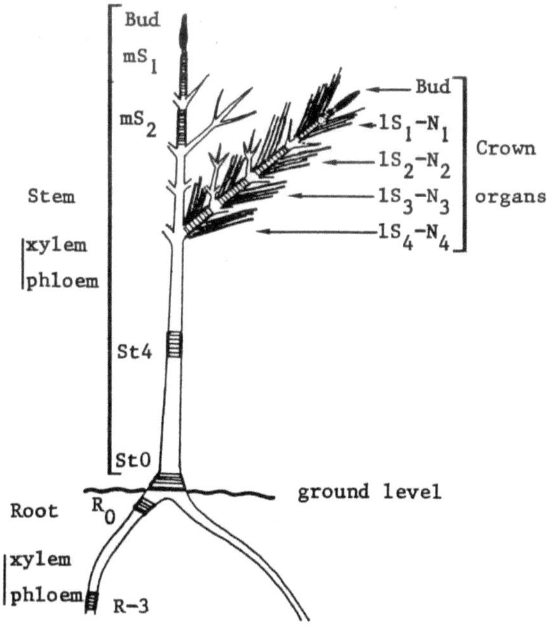

Figure 2. Nature and position of the different organs and tissues harvested. The crown organ study was performed on mature trees. Each month, three 4-year-old branches were collected and separated into bud; 1-, 2-, 3-, and 4-year-old needles (N_1, N_2, N_3, N_4); and the corresponding lateral shoots (lS_1, lS_2, lS_3, lS_4). To study stem and root tissues, trees were felled monthly from a homogeneous population. Xylem and phloem tissues were carefully separated at the following levels: terminal bud, 1- and 2-year-old main shoots (mS_1, mS_2), stem at 4 m and 0 m above ground level (St_4, St_0), and root at 0 m and 3 m below ground level (R_0, R_{-3}).

Sucrose is the primary transfer form of carbohydrates. Only a few minutes after photosynthetic CO_2 fixation, sucrose is loaded into sieve tubes and distributed by the sap stream throughout the entire plant. Raffinose and stachyose, which are the higher homologues of sucrose with one and two galactosyl units added, are commonly found in phloem sap during the cold season. They can be rapidly hydrolysed and thereby increase the osmotic pressure of the cells to increase resistance to freezing.

Variations in Sugars Within Crown Organs of Maritime Pine. In maritime pine, the buds start elongating in early spring (March to April). The first green needles appear in May and grow until September. Fully elongated needles are about 20 cm long and remain on twigs for 3 or 4 years.

Sugar concentrations in 1-, 2-, 3-, and 4-year-old needles (N_1, N_2, N_3, N_4) and in corresponding twigs ($1S_1$, $1S_2$, $1S_3$, and $1S_4$) were estimated for 5 years at Talence, Marcheprime, Hourtin, and Ares (the Landes area in France). Values shown on Fig. 3 represent data collected from the Talence trees during 2 consecutive years for buds and 1- and 2-year-old organs (Bernard-Dagan 1958, Besson-Cloarec 1962).

Comparisons of the same-aged needles and lateral shoots reveal that they contain roughly similar amounts of sugars. This result is

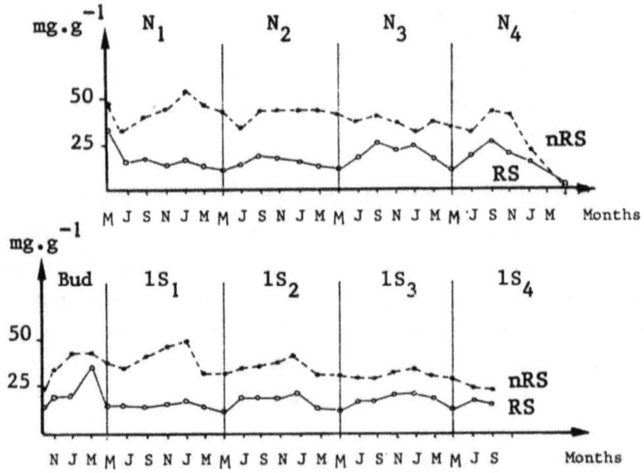

Figure 3. Variations in reducing sugars (RS) and nonreducing sugars (nRS) within the 1-, 2-, 3-, and 4-year-old needles (N_1, N_2, N_3, N_4), the bud; and the 1-, 2-, 3-, and 4-year-old lateral shoots ($1S_1$, $1S_2$, $1S_3$, $1S_4$), according to the different months for each concerned organ. Results are presented in mg/g dry weight.

the same for both reducing and nonreducing carbohydrates (Fig. 3). According to the analysis of variance, the age of an organ is more important than the kind of an organ on tissue sugar levels. There is a general decrease in carbohydrates going from the youngest to the oldest organ. For example, at the extreme, sugar concentrations reach zero in senescent needles.

Furthermore, there is a strong seasonal change in carbohydrate levels, but the values measured on the same dates during two different years are often very different, especially for sucrose. This occurs because sucrose levels are closely related to the current intensity of photosynthesis, especially during the few days immediately preceding sampling.

However, sucrose changes in twigs can be clearly defined as accumulation during winter (December, January, February) and as depletion around May. Considering all the data, this date effect is highly significant. There is also a highly significant date effect for foliar concentrations of glucose and fructose with a maximum occurring in August and September and a minimum occurring in May. This can be related to an active intermediary metabolism just before the late summer storage accumulation (see "Changing Starch and Lipid Levels in the Stem Xylem") and the spring/summer flushing periods.

Variations in Sugars Within Stem and Root Phloem and Xylem. We felled 5 to 30 trees monthly at Marcheprime (Fillon 1963), Hourtin (Bezard 1967), Le Barp (Gleizes 1964) and Ares (Pauly 1968) to collect tissue samples at different levels of the main shoots, stems, and roots (Fig. 2). Xylem and phloem were always carefully separated.

Concentration of sugars was always higher in phloem than in xylem tissues, except for an important accumulation in the xylem at the upper part of the stem in June at the moment of the shoot elongation and differentiation of new tissues (Table 1). At this time, the main sugars are fructose and glucose.

Amounts of sugars found in phloem varied significantly ($p \leq .01$) according to the position along the stem: sugar concentration in lower parts was two to four times higher than in upper parts. This result pertains mainly to the hexoses. An accumulation of reducing sugars (glucose and fructose) started in September and reached a maximum in February. However, in the case of sucrose in phloem, the seasonal effect was rather small compared to the level effect.

Assimilates elaborated by the chloroplasts are rapidly translocated out of the photosynthetic donors towards the "sinks" represented by growing parts and storage organs. When radioactive carbon dioxide is supplied to illuminated needles, direction and rate of sugar transport can be evaluated by estimating the ^{14}C-labelled assimilates found in tissues.

Two experiments performed in June and November consisted of feeding needles with the same quantity of $^{14}CO_2$ and then measuring the radioactive sugars in phloem and xylem at various levels on the shoot.

Table 1. Reducing and nonreducing sugar contents (mg/g dry weight) in xylem and phloem tissues of stems at different levels (1- and 2-year-old main shoots mS_1 and mS_2, stems at 0 and 4 m above ground and root) on three characteristic dates (in June, September, and February).

Date	Level	Reducing sugars		Nonreducing sugars	
		Xylem	Phloem	Xylem	Phloem
June	mS_1	140	88	31	38
	mS_2	17	44	6	21
	Stem 4	6	107	4	58
	Stem 0	7	78	4	55
	Root	9	24	5	34
September	mS_1	38	34	17	33
	mS_2	10	34	9	42
	Stem 4	6	130	6	89
	Stem 0	5	127	5	66
	Root	5	75	4	55
February	mS_1	16	48	14	48
	mS_2	8	60	10	43
	Stem 4	4	209	4	70
	Stem 0	4	190	5	52
	Root	3	103	6	59

The photosynthesis in pine needles remained quite efficient in November (Fig. 4). The direction of assimilate translocation was very different according to season. In June, the assimilates were mainly translocated towards the upper part of the shoots and were measurable in both the phloem and the xylem. This is the first cause of the high level of sugars in the xylem of shoots during their elongation.

In November, the main transfer of sugars was downward. These translocated sugars were transformed into storage foods within all plant tissues and were later used to initiate the growth of organs in the spring.

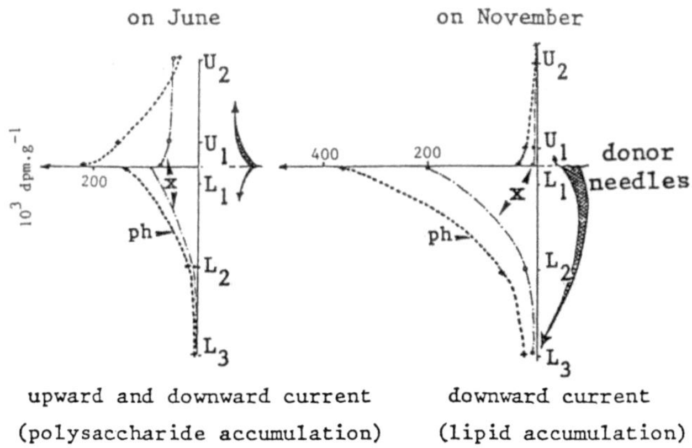

Figure 4. Values of radioactive assimilates (presented as 10^3 dpm g^{-1}) found in xylem (x) and phloem (ph) of the shoot at 3 cm and 40 cm above the donor needles (U_1 and U_2) and 3 cm, 40 cm, and 120 cm under the donor needles (L_1, L_2, and L_3) 2 days after photosynthetically feeding the needles with $^{14}CO_2$ (9.25 MB_g).

Variations in Storage Substances

Large quantities of water insoluble substances are found in pine tissues. Some of them accumulate in specialized structures and stay there permanently, such as tannins in vacuoles or oleoresin terpenes in the secretory system. Some others present a transient accumulation for only a few hours to several months (or years) and then are used again for the plant's energy needs. In pine, these storage substances are mainly starch and lipids, which play a very important role as nutrients. Starch grains accumulate within plastids and can be found in all leaf, root, and stem phloem parenchyma cells and also in stem xylem rays. Lipids also occur within living cells as droplets scattered in cytoplasm or as globules enclosed in plastids.

Analytical Methods. Because starch evaluation is rather tricky owing to the complex structure of the starch molecule, we used two comparative methods: estimation of reducing power released after β-amylase treatment and polarimetric measurement according to Steiner and Guthrie (1944) and Clendenning (1945). Absolute values given by the two methods are somewhat different, but the relative variations remain quite similar, leading therefore to consistent conclusions (Bernard-Dagan 1958, Besson-Cloarec 1962, Philip de Laborie 1962, and Gleizes 1964).

Lipids and resins were extracted together using light petroleum and then anhydrous diethylether (Bernard-Dagan 1958) on samples free of sugars as described earlier. Selective methylation by 2-naphtalenesulfonic acid-methanol was done to separate resin acids and fatty acids which were then estimated by the pH-meter method.

Changing Starch and Lipid Levels in Crown Organs. Generally, amounts of starch and lipids found in crown organs vary greatly according to the period of the year. However, in this study, these seasonal variations were quite similar during 7 years of study. Lipids reached their highest amount during winter (a maximum in February), then they decreased, with a concomitant rapid accumulation of starch. Starch content was very high (up to 10 percent dry weight) in May and June and then it declined and remained at a low level during the following summer/autumn period with a minimum (which was sometimes near zero) occurring from November to February. This date effect is highly significant ($p \leq .01$) for both needles and twigs.

As shown on Fig. 5, this negative relationship between starch-storage food during spring and lipid-storage food during winter was true for 1-, 2-, 3-, and 4-year-old needles (N_1, N_2, N_3, N_4) and twigs ($1S_1$, $1S_2$, $1S_3$, $1S_4$). However, lipids appear as the main storage substances in twigs where their concentration is two-fold higher than in needles. On the contrary, the transient starch accumulation during spring is always more abundant in needles. If all results are considered, we note that the precise date when the maximum is reached varies within a 15-day interval. The magnitude of this maximum may vary according to the climatic conditions.

Changing Starch and Lipid Levels in the Stem Xylem. As occurred for crown organs, the same balance between lipids and starch also occurred at the different levels of the stem xylem (Table 2).

At the end of summer (in September) the normal, non-photosynthetic sink tissues are empty. They are filled during the autumn by the downwards movement of sugar through the sieve tubes. The winter form of energy storage is lipids; indeed lipid droplets are found within the living cells of the whole tree (see "Formation of the Secretory Cell"). In early spring, lipids are rapidly used and transformed into starch within the roots and the upper parts of the tree. At that time, the plastids in the elongating buds become distended by numerous big starch grains. Before the new needles become functional photosynthetic sources and before the new phloem is formed, a fast upward movement of hexoses (from the hydrolysis of root starch) can occur through the xylem pathway. Therefore, a high concentration of reducing sugars is observed during June in the xylem of the youngest shoots (Table 1).

Later, the chemical energy available from storage substances is no longer used because sucrose from needle photosynthesis is actively loaded into the sieve tubes and translocated and distributed through the phloem system by a mainly downward flow to the whole tree.

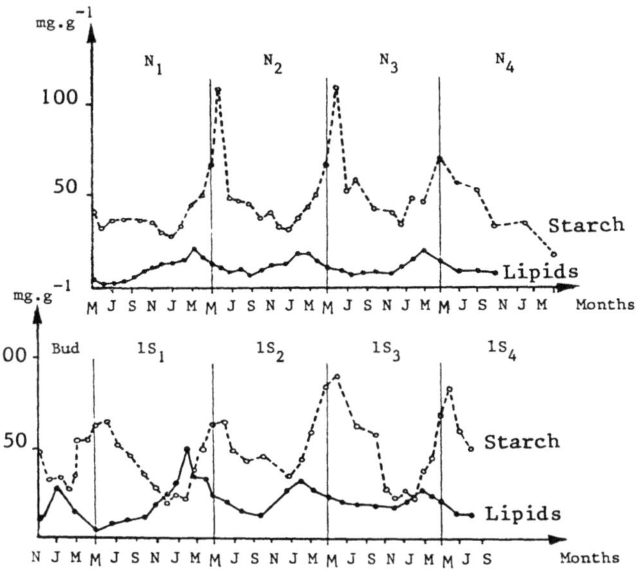

Figure 5. Variation in starch and lipids within the 1-, 2-, 3-, and 4-year-old needles (N_1, N_2, N_3, N_4), the bud, and the 1-, 2- 3-, and 4-year-old lateral shoots ($1S_1$, $1S_2$, $1S_3$, $1S_4$) throughout a year. Results are presented in mg/g dry weight.

Furthermore, the balance between lipids and starch and the rapid disappearance of starch which is observed in May and June is directly related to cell reorganizations leading to terpene biosynthesis.

TERPENE BIOSYNTHESIS UNDER NORMAL PHYSIOLOGICAL CONDITIONS

Resin ducts are found throughout the whole tree. They are located within the parenchyma of buds, leaves, and cortex, and in phloem (only horizontal ones), and xylem (horizontal and vertical

Table 2. Lipid and starch contents (mg/g dry weight) in xylem and phloem tissues at different levels (1- and 2-year-old main shoots mS_1 and mS_2, stems at 4 m and 0 m above ground and root) on three characteristic dates (in April, September, and February).

Level	April		September		February	
	Lipids	Starch	Lipids	Starch	Lipids	Starch
mS_1	5	65	12	14	38	18
mS_2	17	60	15	4	26	14
Stem 4	2	17	4	4	14	2
Stem 0	3	25	7	3	14	2
Root	4	34	7	1	11	4

interconnected systems). Oleoresin is composed of resin acids (diterpenes with 20 atoms of carbon) dissolved in volatile monoterpenes (C_{10}) and sesquiterpenes (C_{15}). In an individual tree, the nature and the relative amount of these major components vary according to the kind of organ (buds, leaves, twigs) and the age of the organ. Furthermore, there are important tree-to-tree variations which are the consequence of some physiological and genetic properties that control the biosynthesis of terpenes.

Variability in Terpene Composition in Pinus Pinaster

Within an individual tree, the oil composition exhibits an increasing complexity going from wood to cortical tissues, to buds, and then to leaves (Table 3). In the stem and twig tissues,

monoterpene hydrocarbons represent 80 to 95 percent of volatile terpenes.
Their composition is rather stable throughout the year, apart from the short period of shoot elongation. In the leaves, there are numerous sesquiterpene hydrocarbons and oxygenated compounds (Pauly et al. 1973). The amounts of oxygenated compounds (geranyl-, bornyl-, linalylacetate) are higher in the young than in the older leaves. On the contrary, the sesquiterpene level increases during organ aging (Zimmermann-Fillon and Bernard-Dagan 1977). The chemical diversification of oil components is related to specialization of

Table 3. Comparing the terpene composition of different organs (leaves, buds) and tissues of the shoots (wood, cortical tissues) of maritime pine (+ = present, - = absent, tr = trace).

Oleoresin volatiles		Wood	Cortex tissues	Buds	Leaves
Monoterpenes	α-pinene	+	+	+	+
	β-pinene	+	+	+	+
	delta-3-carene	-	+	+	+
	myrcene	-	+	+	+
	limonene	tr	+	+	+
	terpinolene	-	+	+	+
Sesquiterpenes	longifolene	tr	+	tr	+
	caryophyllene	tr	+	tr	+
	germacrene	-	-	-	+
	cadinene	-	-	-	+
	muurolene	-	-	-	+
Oxygenated monoterpenes		-	-	+	+

secretory structures, but the changes during leaf development may affect some sequential transformations of metabolites.

Between individual trees, the composition of the oil in leaves and cortical tissues exhibits an important variability. Compounds such as delta-3-carene, longifolene or caryophyllene can be absent in one tree but present in large amounts in another tree. This clear absence/abundance pattern suggests a simple hereditary control for the ability to synthesize terpene hydrocarbons.

Genetic Control and Inheritance of Terpene Hydrocarbons. Using selected clones with known terpene composition and fullsib families obtained by controlled pollination of these clones as parents, monogenic control of the biosynthesis of four monoterpenes has been demonstrated: delta-3-carene, terpinolene (Bernard-Dagan _et al_. 1971, Baradat _et al_. 1972), myrcene (Baradat _et al_. 1975), limonene (Marpeau _et al_. 1983) and two sesquiterpenes: longifolene and caryophyllene (Marpeau _et al_. 1975). Monogenic control of β-pinene biosynthesis is also highly probable. Except for caryophyllene, the allele controlling high concentration is dominant or codominant over the allele controlling low concentration. The terpene concentrations of heterozygous individuals compared with the homozygous individuals depend on the dominance of one allele over the other. Consequently, studies involving the role of terpenes in plant/insect relationships ought to be performed with individuals or clones whose terpene composition is well-known.

Gene Frequency and Geographical Variability. The frequency of the genes controlling the biosynthesis of the different terpenes varies according to their populations and their geographical origins. Mean terpene composition can be highly different for different samples of the same species (Fig. 6). Factorial discriminant analysis of terpenes from different populations leads to a good discrimination of geographical groups of maritime pine over its natural area (Baradat _et al_. 1978).

Biosynthesis of Terpenes--Biochemical Data

General Scheme of Terpene Biosynthesis. All terpenoid compounds originate from the C_5 unit, isopentenyl pyrophosphate (IPP) which is formed by a well-known biosynthetic pathway involving acetate, mevalonate, and dimethylallyl pyrophosphate (DMAPP). The sequential elongation of this first C_5 unit by a regular addition of one or more other C_5 units leads to the different intermediary components: geranyl pyrophosphate GPP (C_{10}), farnesyl pyrophosphate FPP (C_{15}), geranylgeranyl pyrophosphate GGPP (C_{20}) and so on--up to the very long, regular chains of polyterpenoids as rubber (Fig. 7). These successive additions of IPP are enzymatically activated by prenyl transferases.

During this regular elongation, two shunts involving an addition of two FPP or two GGPP lead to the sterols and carotenoids, respectively. Many of these reactions are common to both animals and plants, but some of them are specific to plant metabolism, especially

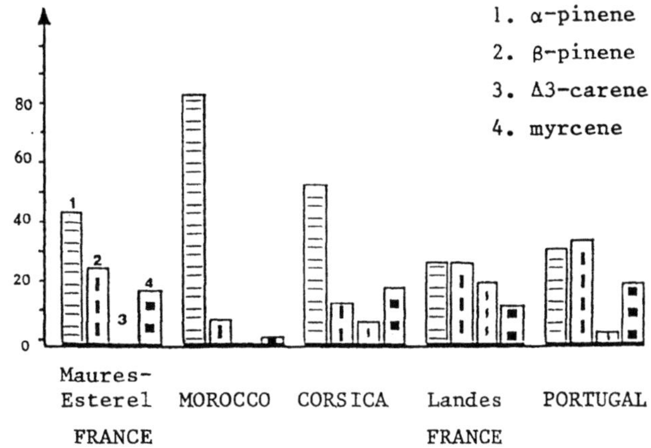

Figure 6. Percentages of major monoterpene hydrocarbons in cortical tissues of maritime pines from five geographical origins.

the formation of monoterpenes, sesquiterpenes, and diterpenes from GPP, FPP and GGPP. The biosynthesis of these lower terpenoids is rather poorly known, so I will present the main biochemical and ultrastructural data obtained from maritime pine.

Physiological Conditions of Terpene Biosynthesis. In pine, volatile and non-volatile components of oleoresin accumulate within the lumen of resin ducts which are located in various tissues. As a matter of fact, monoterpene and diterpene compounds form during a very short time when the secretory cells surrounding the lumen are young and active. This fact is supported by various experiments using ^{14}C-labelled molecules (Bernard-Dagan et al. 1982). For example, when needles are fed with $^{14}CO_2$ in November as described on Fig. 4, it is impossible to detect any radioactive monoterpene (and diterpene) in needles or in upper and lower adjacent shoots. On the contrary, labelled terpenes can be so detected in June, but they are located only at the bases of the needles and near the top of the elongating bud. These two sites correspond exactly to the meristematic zones

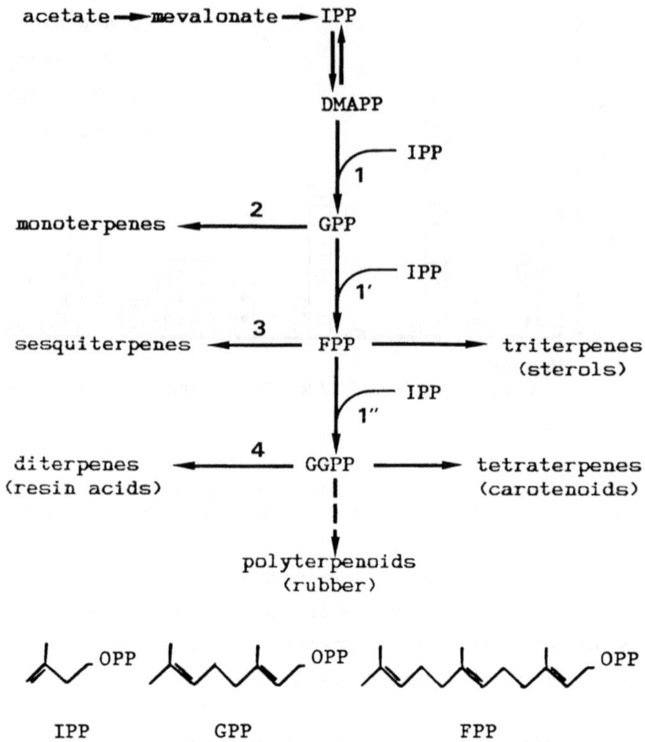

Figure 7. Main steps of terpene biosynthesis. The regular addition of isopentenyl pyrophosphate (IPP) on the different precursors dimethylallyl pyrophosphate (DMAPP), geranyl pyrophosphate (GPP), farnesyl pyrophosphate (FPP) is enzymatically activated by prenyl transferases 1, 1', 1". The transformations of the C_{10} (GPP), C_{15} (FPP) and C_{20} (GGPP) precursors into cyclic hydrocarbons and resin acids involve processes of dephosphorylation, deprotonation, and specific cyclisations. Cyclases 2 are found in leucoplasts, cyclases 3 are found in endoplasmic reticulum, and cyclases 4 are likely present in leucoplasts.

where new cells of needles and shoots are actively differentiating from May to July. From ultrastructural studies of the growing needles (Bernard-Dagan et al. 1979) and shoots (Charon 1983, Charon et al. 1986), it is obvious that the structural organization of the secretory cells varies according to their position in the young organs. Secretory cells located near the meristematic zones are in an active secretory stage and present a typical aspect characterized by large amoeboid leucoplasts (see "Characteristics of the Secretory Cell in its Active Stage"). As tissues become older, the activity of secretory cells progressively decreases and eventually disappears. Thus, the biosynthesis of monoterpenes and diterpenes takes place only in young secretory cells and is directly related to the presence of specific leucoplasts. Furthermore, it has been shown that the biosynthesis of these compounds is a photodependent phenomenon (Gleizes et al. 1980).

On the contrary, the biosynthesis of sesquiterpenes in the leaves is a permanent process which takes place within the entire needles throughout the year. The amount of C_{15} compounds increases continuously during the aging of these organs, and the formation of these compounds is not a light-dependent process (Bernard-Dagan et al. 1982).

Cell Compartmentation of Terpene Biosynthesis. Using subcellular fractions isolated and purified by differential centrifugation, it is possible to obtain more accurate information on mono- and sesquiterpenes biosynthesis. Three important facts have thus been demonstrated.

The water soluble (or easily solubilized) enzymes remaining in the supernatant after centrifugation are able to transform the C_5 unit IPP into GPP and FPP and then to use these C_{10} and C_{15} precursors for hydrocarbon biosynthesis. But the hydrocarbons so formed are mainly acyclic compounds such as farnesene (Bernard-Dagan et al. 1982).

The formation of cyclic hydrocarbons, which are the main constituents of essential oils from pine, requires specific membrane supports. A light membrane fraction, probably endoplasmic reticulum, performs the reactions generating the cyclic sesquiterpenes, such as caryophyllene (see Cheniclet et al. in this volume).

The leucoplasts have the specific ability to use the C_5-precursor and to direct its transformation towards the cyclic monoterpenes (Gleizes et al. 1982, 1983; Pauly et al. 1986).

The Secretory System--Ultrastructural Data

The differentiation of resin ducts takes place very early and close to the meristems. The future secretory cells are first arranged concentrically, then successive radial divisions lead to the formation of the resin duct and the enlargement of the central lumen. At the same time, the cells undergo substantial structural modifications which result in highly specialized secretory cells.

Formation of the Secretory Cell. During winter, the future secretory cells are full of lipid droplets (Fig. 8a). In early spring, lipid droplets become smaller because lipids are disappearing and starch grains arise inside the plastids (Fig. 8b). A few weeks later, the starch is completely lysed and amyloplasts are subjected to spectacular structural reorganization. The plastids enlarge rapidly, and soon most of the cell volume is filled by large amoeboid plastids involved in terpene secretion (Fig. 9a).

Characteristics of the Secretory Cell in its Active Stage. Secretory cells of pine needles (or buds) in an active secretory stage are characterized by large leucoplasts wrapped by a sheath of fenestrated endoplasmic reticulum (Wooding and Northcote 1965, Carde *et al*. 1980, Charon 1983, Charon *et al*. 1986). These plastids contain only few inner membranes and their very dense stroma is devoid of ribosomes (Fig. 9a). The envelope and some invaginations of the inner membrane contain osmiophilic droplets assumed to be terpenes. The plastid outer membrane and endoplasmic reticulum are connected by luminal continuities which allow the translocation of terpenes from their elaboration site to their accumulation site. The extracellular outflow of terpenes is carried out by endoplasmic reticulum tubules budding into plasma membrane evaginations and giving rise to membrane bounded terpene vesicles. After breaking the bounding membranes, the terpene material flows across the loosened wall into the lumen of the resin duct.

These typical structures are located in very young secretory cells which are functional during an extremely short time (a few days) just after their differentiation from the meristem.

Decrease of the Secretory Activity to a Quiescent State. The wall lining the resin duct rapidly becomes more compact and prevents the diffusion of elaborated terpenes which disappear in lytic vacuoles. The plastid system, endoplasmic reticulum membranes, and cytoplasm

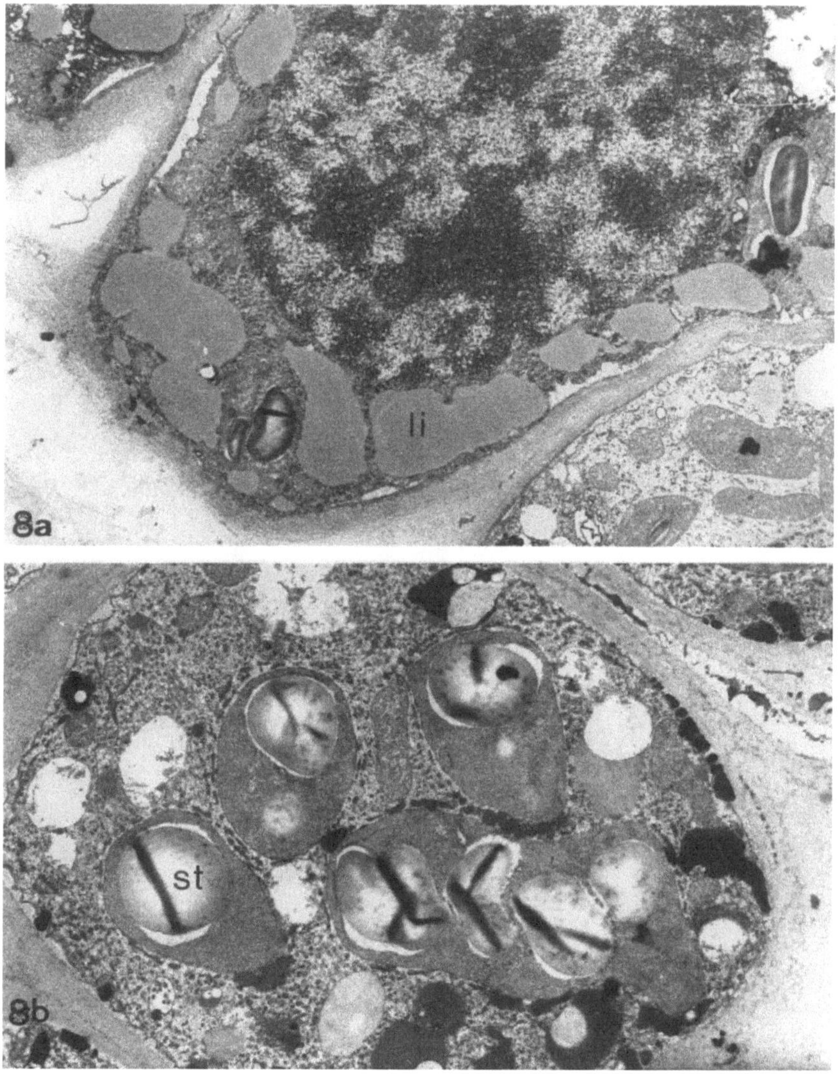

Figure 8. 8a. Bud secretory cell containing large lipid droplets (li) during the quiescent phase (winter) (x 9,500). 8b. Bud secretory cell at the prosecretory stage (early spring); large starch grains (st) are present in the plastid stroma (x 14,300).

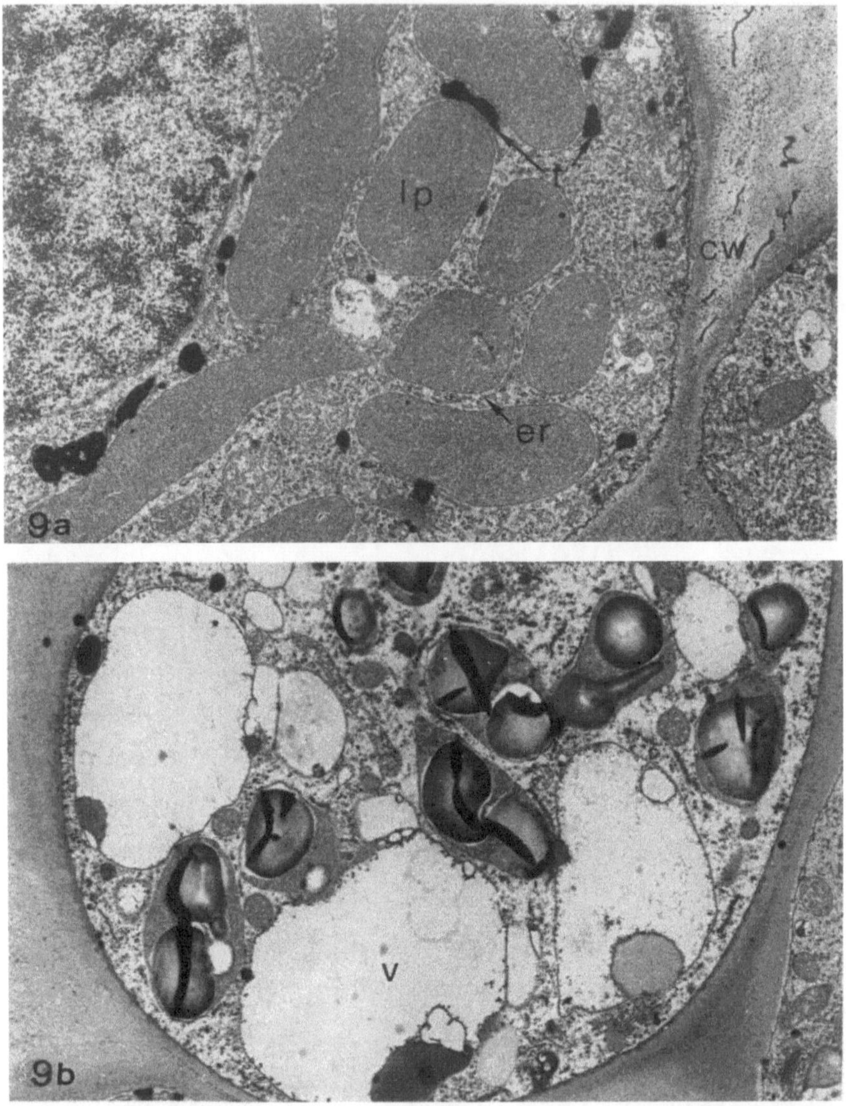

Figure 9. 9a. Bud secretory cell during the active secretory stage (spring). The dense cytoplasm contains many leucoplast transections (lp), endoplasmic reticulum membranes (er) and osmiophilic terpene material (t). The cell wall (cw) lining the duct is loosened (x 12,800). 9b. Bud secretory cell at the end of the secretory stage (summer). The cytoplasm is clearer and highly vacuolated (v), the plastids contain starch grains (x 11,500).

undergo a regressive process as illustrated by Fig. 9b. Then quiescent cells with clear cytoplasm and numerous vacuoles surround a resin duct filled up with substances previously excreted. Green upper parts of the needles and cortex of the fully grown shoots present these various stages of partial, then total, degeneration with loss of secretory activity.

The structural events described for the primary meristems of buds and needles occur also in the secondary resin ducts of the stem in phloem and xylem originating in the division of the cambial cells (see Cheniclet et al. in this volume).

CONCLUSIONS

Behavior of Nutrient Substances

In pine needles, photosynthesis is active all year, but the allocation of the sugars so formed varies according to season. In the photosynthetic organs, sucrose, raffinose, stachyose, and lipids reach their highest levels during winter. During other periods, sucrose is actively loaded into the phloem system; its flow is mainly upward when new organs are growing, but there is also permanent downward flow toward all tree organs. But during spring and summer, sugars are consumed as rapidly as they are produced and as a result the "sinks" are empty at this time.

Filling of sinks begins in early autumn. At this time, the amount of sugars (sucrose and some higher osides) is very high in sieve tubes of the whole tree with an important flow towards the lowest parts of the trunk. Most of these sugars are then converted into lipids which are the main storage form of energy during winter. They accumulate in the parenchyma cells of the whole plant (phloem and xylem rays of root and stem, twigs, and leaves). Suddenly from February to March, all these lipids are lyzed, transformed into starch, and then into hexoses which are translocated throughout the xylem up to the new elongating shoots. This sequence of events is observed in the early spring throughout whole plant.

Electron microscopy shows that these phenomenona are particularly active in new cells where proplastids are differentiating into amyloplasts and then into leucoplasts in secretory cells or into chloroplasts in leaf mesophyll cells.

This general mobilization of the storage resources can be correlated with the transient formation of oleoresin and also with the formation of proteins and polysaccharides in new cells.

Rates of Available Energy in Tissues

We have attempted to evaluate the consequences of these events on the rate of chemical energy available as nutrients in the tree tissues. The values are given in Fig. 10. At each time period, the caloric value has been calculated from the amounts of carbon nutrients (sugars, lipids, starch) and the amounts of proteins and amino acids estimated in maritime pine organs by David (1966).

Lateral shoots and leaves offer roughly the same amount of calories to herbivores, but there is a strong seasonal effect for the shoots, ranging from a minimum in September to a maximum in March to May. This spring maximum has to be correlated with the transient accumulation of starch. In regard to the age of organs, it appears that the available energy increases only slightly as organs age except

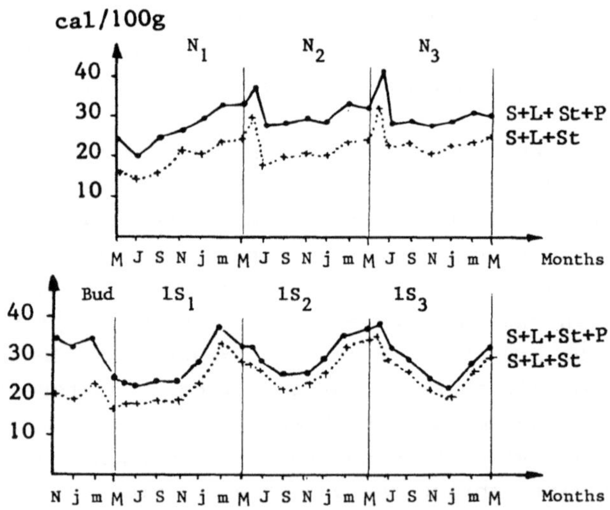

Figure 10. Evaluations of chemical energy contents of 1-, 2-, and 3-year-old needles (N_1, N_2, N_3), the bud, and 1-, 2-, and 3-year-old lateral shoots ($1S_1$, $1S_2$, $1S_3$) during the growing season. The caloric values (cal/100 g fresh weight) take into account either the amounts of sugars, lipids, starch, proteins and amino acids (S+L+St+P) or the amounts of sugars, lipids, starch without proteins (S+L+St).

for buds. This high level of calories in buds is due to the presence of abundant proteins. In shoots, the amounts of amino acids and proteins decrease with age. In stem tissues, especially in xylem, it is well-known that the amount of protein is very low.

Figure 10 also shows that the total energy values of sugars, lipids, and starch give a good estimation of the nutritive content of plant tissue with a possible correction when proteins are taken into account. When the same measurements are performed for the xylem at different levels, very low values are obtained except for the young main shoots during the early spring--their caloric power is about 30 cal/100 g of fresh weight. Unfortunately, we cannot extrapolate the estimation to the stem phloem because we have not evaluated the insoluble substances (starch and lipids) there. Ultrastructural observations show a significant accumulation of starch in phloem which has to be taken into account. However, the values found by Pauly (1968) show that the energy level of phloem is very high and can be more than 400 cal/100 g of fresh weight in the lower trunk. In this tissue, the available energy is highly variable according to season and level.

Biosynthesis of Terpenes: Their Sequestration, a Vital Requirement

Results of the two biochemical and ultrastructural approaches lead to the same conclusions. The oleoresin which is enclosed inside resin ducts is synthesized by the secretory cells during a very short period. This secretory activity involves specific organelles. These organelles are large leucoplasts which support the synthesis of lower terpenes, mainly monoterpenes and resin acids. They are closely associated with the endoplasmic reticulum which allows the translocation of newly formed terpenes into the lumen of resin ducts. The capacity for elaborating each terpene is genetically controlled and the composition of oleoresin depends on the genotype of each individual. Because the terpenes so enclosed are only poorly renewed, monoterpenes can be efficiently used as chemotaxonomic markers.

Besides its involvement in the transfer of terpenes from the leucoplasts to the lumen of the resin duct, the endoplasmic reticulum is also involved in the synthesis of cyclic sesquiterpenes which are mainly formed in needles whatever their age and the environmental conditions. Thus oleoresin components are always strictly sequestered in cell compartments: within leucoplasts or endoplasmic reticulum during their biosynthesis, in membrane-bounded vesicles during their transfer, and within lumen of resin duct during their accumulation.

It is of interest to note that this sequestration is absolutely necessary for cell survival (see Cheniclet et al. in this volume). Indeed, when β-pinene is released during cell fractionation, an inhibition of mitochondrial or chloroplast electron transfer occurs immediately (Douce et al. 1978, Pauly et al. 1981). All of this should be taken into account when interpretating the effects of different stresses (wounding, fungus or insect attacks, chemical treatments) on oleoresin production.

REFERENCES

Baradat, P., C. Bernard-Dagan, C. Fillon, A. Marpeau, and G. Pauly. 1972. Les terpènes du Pin maritime: aspects biologiques et génétiques. II. Hérédité de la teneur en monoterpènes. Ann. Sci. For. 29: 307-334.

Baradat, P., C. Bernard-Dagan, G. Pauly, and C. Zimmermann-Fillon. 1975. Les terpènes du Pin maritime: aspects biologiques et génétiques. III. Hérédité de la teneur en myrcène. Ann. Sci. For. 32: 29-54.

Baradat, P., A. Marpeau, and C. Bernard-Dagan. 1978. Variation of terpenes within and between populations of maritime pine. In: Biochemical genetics of forest trees (D. Rudin, Ed.). Umea, Sweden; 151-169.

Bernard-Dagan, C. 1958. Contribution l'étude de l'oléorésinogénése : l'évolution des principaux glucides, lipides et résines au cours de la vie des pseudophylles de Pin maritime. Thèse Doctorat d'Etat Sciences Nat., Univ. Bordeaux, France, 150 p.

Bernard-Dagan, C., J. P. Carde, and M. Gleizes. 1979. Etude des composés terpéniques au cours de la croissance des aiguilles de Pin maritime: comparaison des données biochimiques et ultrastructurales. Can. J. Bot. 57: 255-263.

Bernard-Dagan, C., C. Fillon, G. Pauly, P. Baradat, and G. Illy. 1971. Les terpènes du Pin maritime. I. Variabilité de la composition monoterpénique dans un individu, entre individus et entre provenances. Ann. Sci. For. 28: 223-258.

Bernard-Dagan, C., G. Pauly, A. Marpeau, M. Gleizes, J. P. Carde, and P. Baradat. 1982. Control and compartmentation of terpene biosynthesis in leaves of Pinus pinaster Ait. Physiol. Veg. 20: 775-795.

Besson-Cloarec, A. 1962. Evolution des principaux glucides, lipides et résines dans les bourgeons et les rameaux du Pin maritime: relation avec la teneur en potassium, magnésium, calcium. Thése Doctorat d'Etat Sciences Nat., Univ. Bordeaux, France; 87-114.

Bezard, A. 1967. Influence de l'annélation du tronc sur le métabolisme glucidique du Pin maritime. Thèse Phytobiol., Univ. Bordeaux, France, 162 p.

Carde, J. P., C. Bernard-Dagan, and M. Gleizes. 1980. Membrane systems involved in synthesis and transport of monoterpene hydrocarbons in pine leaves. In: Biogenesis and functions of plant lipids (P. Mazliak, P. Benveniste, C. Costes, and R. Douce, Eds). Amsterdam: Elsevier/North Holland Biomedical Press; 441-444.

Charon, J. 1983. Différenciation et fonctionnement des canaux sécréteurs dans les bourgeons de Pin maritime (Pinus pinaster Ait.). Etudes structurale et ultrastructurale. Thèse Cytol. et morphol. vég., Univ. Paris VI, France, 127 p.

Charon, J., J. Launay, and E. Vindt. 1986. Ontogénèse des canaux sécréteurs d'origine primaire dans le bourgeon de Pin maritime. Can. J. Bot. 64: 2955-2964.

Clendenning, K. A. 1945. Polarimetric determination of starch in cereal products. II. Factors affecting the specific rotary power of wheat starch in aqueous calcium chloride solution. Can. J. Res. 23B: 765.

David, H. 1966. Variations de la teneur en composés azotés des bourgeons, aiguilles et pousses du Pin maritime. Thèse Phytobiol., Univ. Bordeaux, France, 137 p.

Douce, R., M. Neuburger, R. Bligny, and G. Pauly. 1978. Effects of β-pinene on the oxidative properties of purified intact flaut mitochondria. In: Plant mitochondria (E. Ducet and C. Lance, Eds.). Elsevier: North Holland Biochemical Press; 207-214.

Fillon, C. 1963. Variations saisonnières des glucides dans la tige principale du Pin maritime. D. E. S., Bordeaux, France, 42 p.

Gleizes, M. 1964. Evolution des glucides, lipides et résines dans le bois de la tige principale et les racines du Pin maritime. Thèse Phytobiol., Univ. Bordeaux, France, 129 p.

Gleizes, M., C. Bernard-Dagan, J. P. Carde, G. Pauly, and A. Marpeau. 1982. Function of plastids in terpene biosynthesis. In: Biochemistry and metabolism of plant lipids (J. F. G. M. Wintermans and P. J. C. Kuiper, Eds.). Elsevier: North Holland Biomedical Press; 511-514.

Gleizes, M., G. Pauly, C. Bernard-Dagan, and R. Jacques. 1980. Effects of light on terpen hydrocarbon synthesis in Pinus pinaster. Physiol. Plant. 50: 16-20.

Gleizes, M., G. Pauly, J. P. Carde, A. Marpeau, and C. Bernard-Dagan. 1983. Monoterpene hydrocarbons biosynthesis by isolated leucoplasts of Citrofortunella mitis. Planta 159: 373-381.

Marpeau, A., P. Baradat, and C. Bernard-Dagan. 1975. Les terpènes du Pin maritime: aspects biologiques et génétiques. IV. Hérédité de la teneur en deux sesquiterpènes: le longifolène et le caryophyllène. Ann. Sci. For. 32: 185-203.

Marpeau, A., P. Baradat, and C. Bernard-Dagan. 1983. Les terpènes du Pin maritime. V. Hérédité de la teneur en limonène. Ann. Sci. For. 40: 97-216.

Nelson, N. 1944. A photocolorimetric adaptation of the Somogyi method for the determination of glucose. J. Biol. Chem. 153: 375-380.

Pauly, G. 1968. Contribution à l'etude du metabolisme glucidique Pin maritime: évolution des principaux glucides solubles dans la racine, les aiguilles, la tige principale et la racine. Thèse Doctorat d'Etat Sciences Nat., Univ. Bordeaux, France, 186 p.

Pauly, G., L. Belingheri, A. Marpeau, and M. Gleizes. 1986. Monoterpene formation by leucoplasts of Citrofortunella mitis and Citrus unshiu: steps and conditions of their biosynthesis. Plant Cell Rep. 5; 19-22.

Pauly, G., R. Douce, and J. P. Carde. 1981. Effects of β-pinene on spinach chloroplast photosynthesis. Z. Pflanzenphysiol. 104: 199-281.

Pauly, G., M. Gleizes, and C. Bernard-Dagan. 1973. Identification des constituants de l'essence des aiguilles de Pinus pinaster. Phytochemistry 12: 1395-1398.

Philip de Laborie, J. 1962. Recherches sur la teneur eu amidon de la tige et des pseudophylles de Pin maritime. Thèse Phytobiol. Bordeaux, France, 100 p.

Steiner, E. T. and J. D. Guthrie. 1944. Determination of starch in sweet potato products and other plant materials. Ind. Eng. Chem. 16: 736.

Wooding, F. B. P. and D. H. Northcote. 1965. The fine structure of the mature resin canal cells of Pinus pinea. J. Ultrastruct. Res. 13: 233-244.

Zimmermann-Fillon, C. and C. Bernard-Dagan. 1977. Variations qualitatives et quantitatives des carbures terpéniques au cours de la croissance des rameaux et des aiguilles du Pin maritime: étude comparée de huit phénotypes. Can. J. Bot. 55: 1009-1018.

6

Terpene Biosynthesis Under Pathological Conditions

C. Cheniclet, C. Bernard-Dagan, and G. Pauly

It is well-known that various stresses on resinous trees can induce an oleoresin flow, which is often considered to be a defensive mechanism (Raffa and Berryman 1983). The cellular phenomena of terpene synthesis under normal physiological conditions have been the subject of numerous investigations, but synthesis occurring under stress is largely unstudied. Herein we propose an explanatory model for terpene synthesis taking into account the results obtained by several different research approaches. We performed three types of *in vivo* experiments on a single clone of maritime pine, *Pinus pinaster*: wounding, mycelium inoculation, and insect infestation. Responses were evaluated by terpene analysis and ultrastructural observations. Finally, we compared these investigations with *in vitro* experiments on enzymatic activity present in isolated organelles involved in terpene biosynthesis.

EFFECTS OF WOUNDING, MYCELIUM, AND INSECT INOCULATION ON TERPENE CONTENT

Materials and Methods

At the end of February (swarming time for *Tomicus piniperda*, the bark beetles under study), three 25-year-old grafted ramets (Pinus pinaster) of the same clone, growing next each other, were treated by boring 20 to 30 holes with a punch into the trunk just up to the sapwood (Fig. 1). On the first tree, the holes were plugged with the outcut tissues (simple wounding). On the second tree, the holes were inoculated with sporulating mycelium from cultures of *Verticicladiella*, a fungus isolated from *Tomicus piniperda* (Scolytidae). On the third tree, females of *T. piniperda* were introduced into the holes.

During the ensuing 4 weeks, samples were periodically collected and processed for terpene analysis. Samples consisted of a piece of tissue of a similar size surrounding the hole, including the brownish reaction zone (Fig. 1). In the case of fungus inoculation, an area of translucent tissue appeared after 7 days beyond the brownish area (Fig. 1, zone B). It enlarged steadily and mainly in the vertical direction. It was 10 to 20 cm long on the 28th day. This translucent tissue was entirely removed and processed separately from the brown tissue (zone A).

Terpenes were extracted by pentane maceration and fractionated on a silica-gel column by elution with pentane:ether (98:2) for the recovery of hydrocarbons and with pentane:ether (50:50) for oxygenated compounds. Hydrocarbons (mainly mono- and sesquiterpenes) were separated by gas chromatography on a CP-Sil 5 capillary column (60 ^{o}C to 200 ^{o}C, 6 ^{o}C/min) using dodecane as the internal standard. Oxygenated compounds (mainly resin acids) were methylated by diazomethane (Schlenk and Gellerman 1960) and chromatographed on the same column (190 ^{o}C to 220 ^{o}C, 4 ^{o}C/min., 15 min. initial temporization) using heptadecanoate as the internal standard. Major constituents were identified by retention time and/or mass spectrometry.

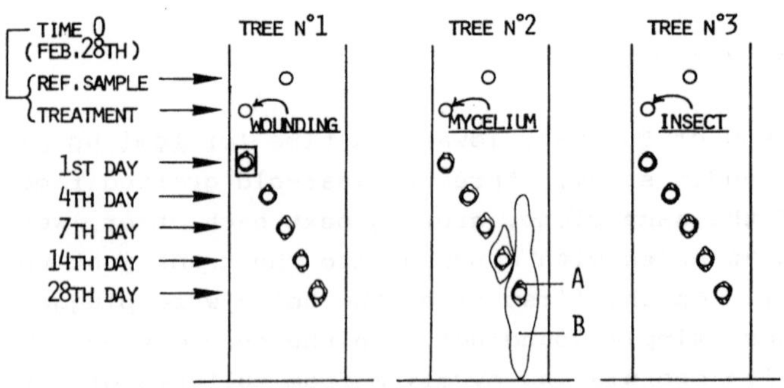

Figure 1. Diagrammatic representation of the experimental procedure.

Analytical Results

All three types of wound treatments resulted in a terpene enrichment within phloem (Fig. 2). During the first week, total terpene content increased 2-fold and thereafter stabilized. However, the fungus inoculation induced an additional reaction: after the regular enrichment during the first week, there followed an exponential increase in tapenes, which led to a 60-fold enrichment in the zone A 28 days after inoculation. Additionally, a vertical extension of the translucent resin-enriched tissue occurred, indicating a diffusive process.

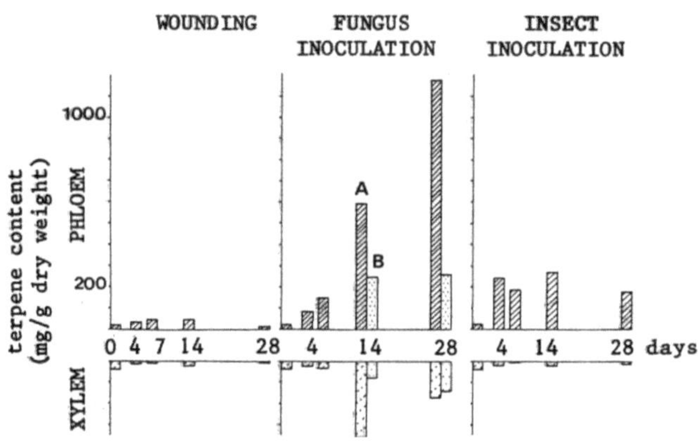

Figure 2. Evolution of total terpene contents (mono- and sesquiterpene hydrocarbons plus resin acids) in phloem (upper part, box with diagonal lines: zone A, box with dots: zone B) and xylem (lower part) in the three experimental conditions.

The tree responses to insect infestation were highly variable from one hole to another both with respect to visible extension of the reaction zones and its terpene content. The average response was a fast enrichment followed by a stabilization. In most cases, the final terpene accumulation induced by insects was less than that induced by mycelium inoculation. It seems that the response resulting from insects themselves was weak and that the major effect was due to the spores they carried. Their number and pathogenicity are variable according to the insect (Lieutier in this volume).

In the xylem tissue located just behind the holes, terpene content was only slightly affected by wounding and insect introduction. However, fungus inoculation increased it significantly. This was probably due to an elicitor diffusing from the phloem.

Total resins are comprised of volatile terpenes (mono- and sesquiterpenes) and resin acids (diterpenes). In the case of wounding and insect inoculation, the ratio of volatile terpenes/non-volatile terpenes remained roughly constant (≈1:3) and the percentages of major constituents in each fraction were affected by the treatments. However, the fungal inoculation induced an accumulation of mainly volatile hydrocarbons, thus suggesting a deviation in terpene metabolism from the other two treatments.

EFFECTS OF WOUNDING AND MYCELIUM INOCULATION ON THE SECRETORY SYSTEM

During the experiments, we also collected samples on the same days for ultrastructural study. Taking the analytical results into account, we chose to look forstructural events occurring in proximal phloem (zone A, Fig. 1) after simple wounding and after mycelium inoculation.

Tissue Processing for Ultrastructural Observations

Samples (1.2 cm x 0.4 cm pieces cut with a punch close to the holes) were fixed with 2.5 percent glutaraldehyde and postfixed with 1 percent osmium tetroxide, then gradually dehydrated in ethanol. Each piece of tissue was divided into eight parts which were embedded in Epon (Luft 1961) in a labeled mould in order to keep the identification of the position of each specimen in comparison with the hole.

Semi-thin (1.5-2μm) transverse, radial, and tangential sections were stained with toluidine blue. Ultrathin sections (60 to 90 nm) were stained with uranyl acetate and lead citrate (Reynolds 1963).

Cytological Observations

Reference situation. The secondary phloem of maritime pine does not contain vertical resin ducts but only horizontal ones, located within some parenchyma rays (Fig. 3a). At the end of winter before the treatments, the secretory ducts are in resting phase. Epithelial cells present a clear cytoplasm containing scarce proplastids and organelles and numerous large lipid drops (Fig. 3b).

Response to simple wounding. Rapidly after wounding (1 to 4 days), resin ducts located near the hole display obvious changes indicating that metabolic activities started again: densification of cytoplasm; multiplication of ribosomes, dictyosomes, and mitochondria; development of endoplasmic reticulum; decrease of lipids; and high increase of plastid number and size. The latter ones transiently accumulate large amounts of starch (Fig. 3c).

The next step is characterized by evolution of the plastids into typical leucoplasts with starch regression (Fig. 3d). Osmiophilic droplets, assumed to be terpene compounds, are visible within the plastid envelope and inner membranes and within some endoplasmic reticulum membranes and piroplasmic spaces. These features are similar to those observed in primary ducts during the secretory stage (Charon 1983, Bernard-Dagan in this volume).

In addition, new secondary resin ducts are differentiated from the cambial cells near the hole. Figure 3c illustrates this and demonstrates two newly formed resin ducts within the same ray, a feature which is rarely observed in intact phloem.

It is of interest to note that the effect of simple wounding appears as a limited one: the cells bounding the holes undergo a necrotic process with a collapse of their walls leading to the formation of a barrier preventing underlying tissues from further dehydration and degradation (Fig. 4a).

Response to mycelium inoculation. The first structural changes occurring in the resin ducts are similar to those described for wounding response. But there are further changes which differentiate the two responses. Lysis occurs in various cell types.

In resin canal cells, the stroma of leucoplasts becomes clearer and their envelope disappears, many organelles are disrupted and it is obvious that these cells are finally unfunctional (Fig. 4c). These phenomena of resin canal cell decay are not synchronous in the same zone. Different stages can be simultaneously observed. But 2 to 4 weeks after inoculation, all the resin canals within the zone A are completely disorganized (Fig. 4b)

The decay process not only affects resin ducts. The walls of parenchyma and sieve cells undergo more or less severe degradations: they become thinner, less rigid (Fig. 5a), and finally are disrupted (Fig. 5b). The lysis of walls, concomitant with the degeneration of cell contents, leads to the formation of large cavities (Figs. 5a and 5c). These spaces very likely represent sites of terpene accumulation. But it was until now impossible to visualize terpenes by the techniques used for electron microscopy observations.

Additionally, transformations of polyphenolic compounds occur in several parenchyma cells (Fig. 5d). These cells, as well as some ray cells and sieve tubes, transiently accumulate a polysaccharide-like material which is pink-colored by toluidine blue.

In contrast to the wounding response, the necrotic barrier surrounding the immediate hole does not prevent the extensive decay of tissues far from the treated hole. This probably represents the existence of an elicitor diffusing from the original wound area.

INTERPRETATION OF BIOCHEMICAL AND ULTRASTRUCTURAL OBSERVATIONS

From these observations, two types of responses can be defined: (1) In the case of simple wounding and during the first phase of the response to fungal inoculation, the moderate increase of terpene content can be correlated with the reactivation of preexisting quiescent resin ducts and with the differentiation of new resin ducts; (2) The 60-fold increase of terpene content induced by mycelium inoculation cannot simply be explained by the reactivation of the functional secretory structures because this enrichment occurs after a general decay of all cell compartments (Figs. 4b and 4c).

We have to assume that the terpene accumulation induced by the fungus results from other processes, involving activation of some water-soluble enzymes, without intact membrane requirements. As it is yet impossible to perform any biochemical experiment with specific elicitors extracted from fungus or from reacting plant tissue, a possible explanation can be proposed with the help of some results obtained with chemicals.

Figure 3a. Cross section of reference phloem tissue showing sieve tubes, sieve areas, and polyphenolic vertical parenchyma cells; a resin duct of the horizontal system is surrounded by phloem ray cells (x 450). 3b. Epithelial cell of a resin canal in resting phase (x 6,000). 3c. Response of phloem resin canals to wounding. Tangential section in newly differentiated phloem showing two horizontal resin canals containing many amyliferous plastids (x 900). 3d. Epithelial cell of a resin canal 28 days after the wounding; leucoplasts are well-differentiated, and osmiophilic droplets are observed within leucoplast membranes (▸) and envelopes and in the piroplasmic space (→), indicating a reactivation of the secretory process (X 30,000). Abbreviations: li: lipid droplet, lp: leucoplast, lu: lumen, p: plastid, po: polyphenolic parenchyma cell, rc: ray cell, s: starch, sa: sieve area, sc: secretory cell.

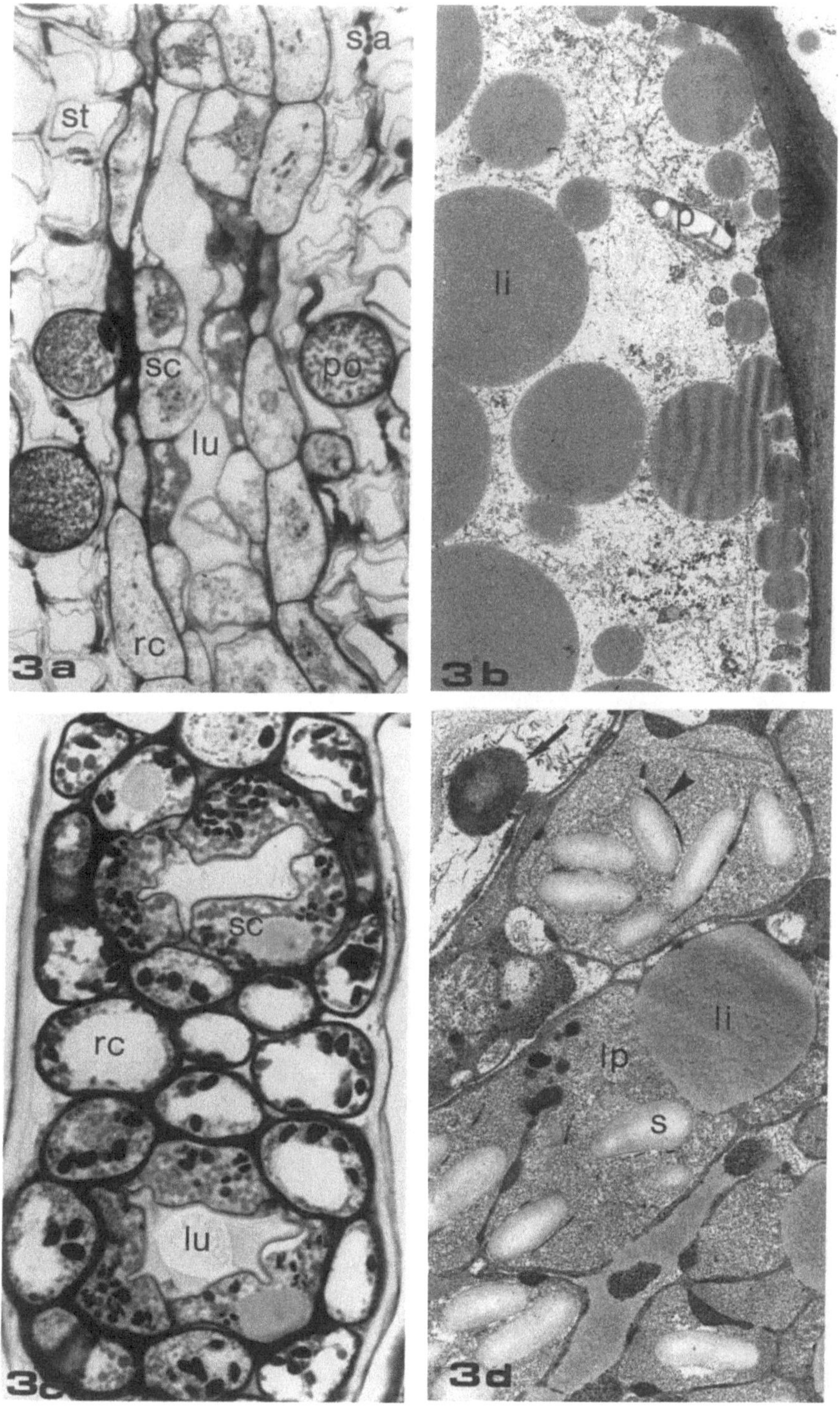
st
s a
sc
po
lu
rc
3a
p
li
3b
sc
rc
lu
li
lp
s
3d

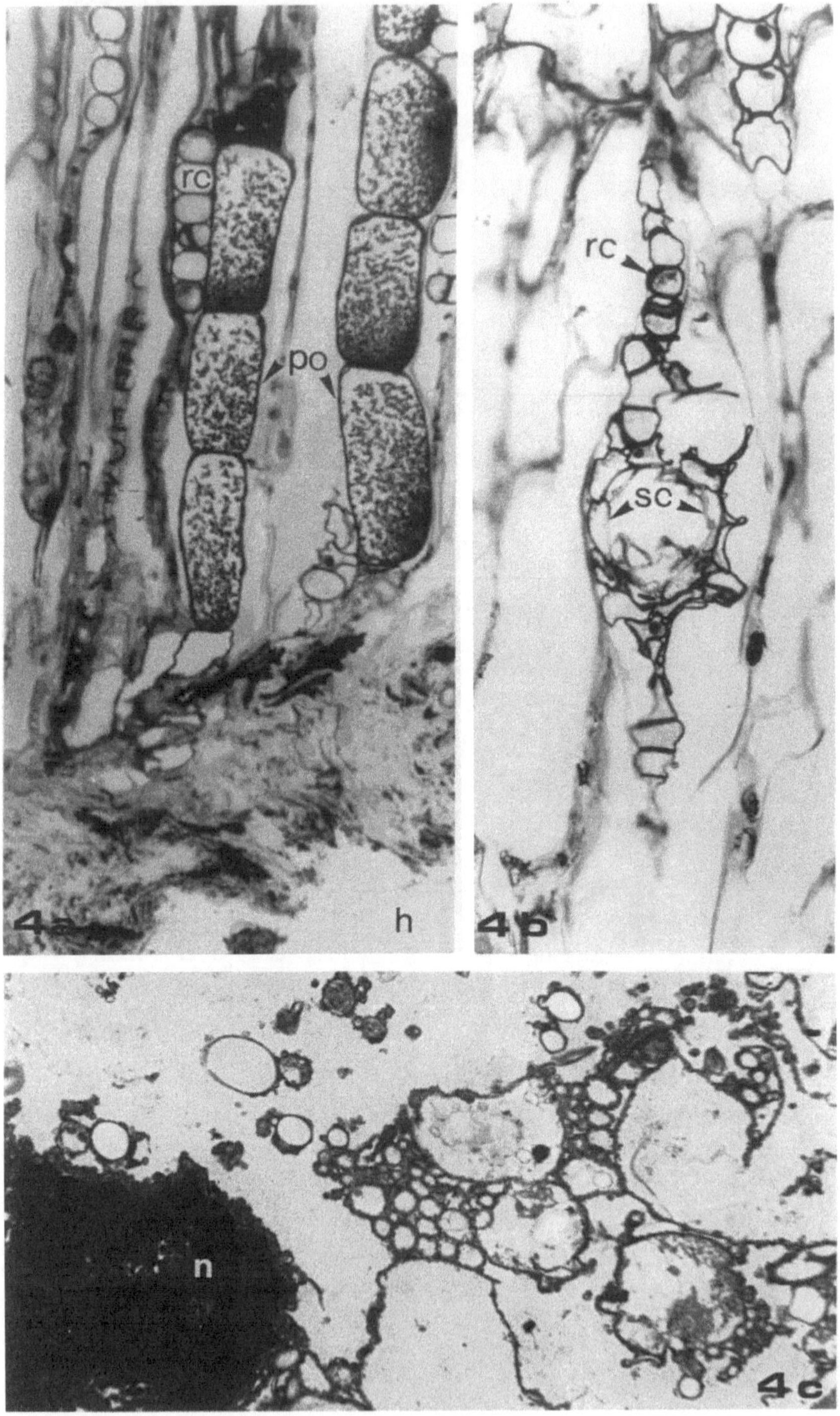
rc
po
h
4a
rc
sc
4b
n
4c

Action Of Paraquat On Isolated Leucoplasts

The bipryridilium molecules such as paraquat are well-known as herbicides. However, when paraquat is applied to living pine wood, large amounts of terpenes are formed (Stone 1977), and at the same time, active structures are progressively destroyed. Fungus inoculation and paraquat application seem to induce similar *in vivo* responses. We have therefore used paraquat solutions as elicitor-like substances for performing some *in vitro* experiments on isolated leucoplasts (Pauly, unpublished results).

Under normal conditions, without paraquat, isolated active leucoplasts (Gleizes *et al*. 1983) are able to transform the C_5 terpene precursor isopentenyl pyrophosphate (IPP) into the C_{10} precursor geranyl pyrophosphate (GPP). The enzyme which performs this condensation is a water-soluble system, prenyl transferase. The subsequent transformation of GPP into cyclic monoterpene hydrocarbons is carried out by specific cyclases, which are assumed to be associated with the leucoplast envelope according to the possible following compartmentation:

```
      prenyl transferase          cyclases
IIP ----------------------> GPP --------------> cyclic monoterpenes
  C5  water-soluble enzyme   C10 membrane linked       C10
                                  enzymes
```

Without paraquat (Table 1), IPP is equally transformed into GPP and β-pinene: the two enzyme systems are active. With a concentration of about 0.2 mM paraquat, a high activation of prenyl transferase is observed, resulting in a significant transformation of GPP into β-pinene. But higher concentrations of paraquate inhibit cyclase activity which is fully inactivated by 0.3 mM paraquat. At the same time however, IPP is still actively transformed into GPP.

According to these experimental data, it appears clearly that an activation of the two steps of terpene biosynthesis (elongation and cyclization) is induced only by the lowest concentrations of paraquat. With high concentration, cyclases are no longer active, whereas

Figure 4a. Tangential section of the phloem tissue 28 days after the wounding, showing the limited necrosis near the hole and the intactness of the underlying cells (x 200). 4b and 4c. Response to fungus inoculation: decay of phloem resin canals 14 and 28 days after inoculation (Fig. 4b: x 300; Fig. 4c: x 11,500). Abbreviations: h: hole, n: nucleus, po: polyphenolic parenchyma cell, rc: ray cell, sc: secretory cell.

Table 1. Amounts of β-pinene and GPP synthesized from the same quantity of IPP by isolated leucoplasts in the presence of various concentrations of paraquat.

	Paraquat (mM)						
	0	0.19	0.23	0.27	0.31	0.35	0.38
β-pinene	0.3	0.4	0.4	0.1	0.0	0.0	0.0
Geraniol[a]	0.4	3.3	7.3	8.2	8.0	8.1	8.1

[a]released after enzymatic hydrolysis of GPP.

soluble prenyl transferases are still highly active, thereby leading to an important accumulation of monoterpene pyrophosphate.

It is very likely that somewhat similar reactions are induced by diffusing substances produced by fungus or by reactant plant tissue.

CONCLUSION AND POSSIBLE EXPLANATIONS

As a summary of the data obtained by the three different approaches, we propose the following schemes for terpene biosynthesis under normal conditions or under pathological conditions following wounding or fungus infestation.

Secretory cells in active phase (Fig. 6.1) are characterized by large leucoplasts with dense stroma. Assimilates from photosynthesis are brought towards these cells and are transformed by cytoplasmic water-soluble enzymes that synthesize the primary precursors of terpenes and then cause sequential additions of these C_5 units. Prenyl transferases are found in cytoplasm and within leucoplast. Monoterpenes are formed by cyclization of GPP by specific cyclases probably located on/in the leucoplast envelope. The so-formed C_{10} hydrocarbons (pinenes, limonene, delta-3-carene) are translocated by endoplasmic

Figure 5a to 5d. Changes in phloem tissue after fungus inoculation (tangential sections). 5a. Some cell walls become thinner and some ray cells get out of shape. The sieve tube walls are locally disrupted (arrow) (x 300). 5b. Disruption of the walls of the ray cells (x 500). 5c. Disruption of a sieve tube wall, leading to the formation of a cavity. Adjacent ray cells and phenolic parenchyma cells do not seem affected (x 500). 5d. Modification of the polyphenolic content of affected parenchyma cells (compare with 5c) (x 500). For abbreviations, see Fig. 3.

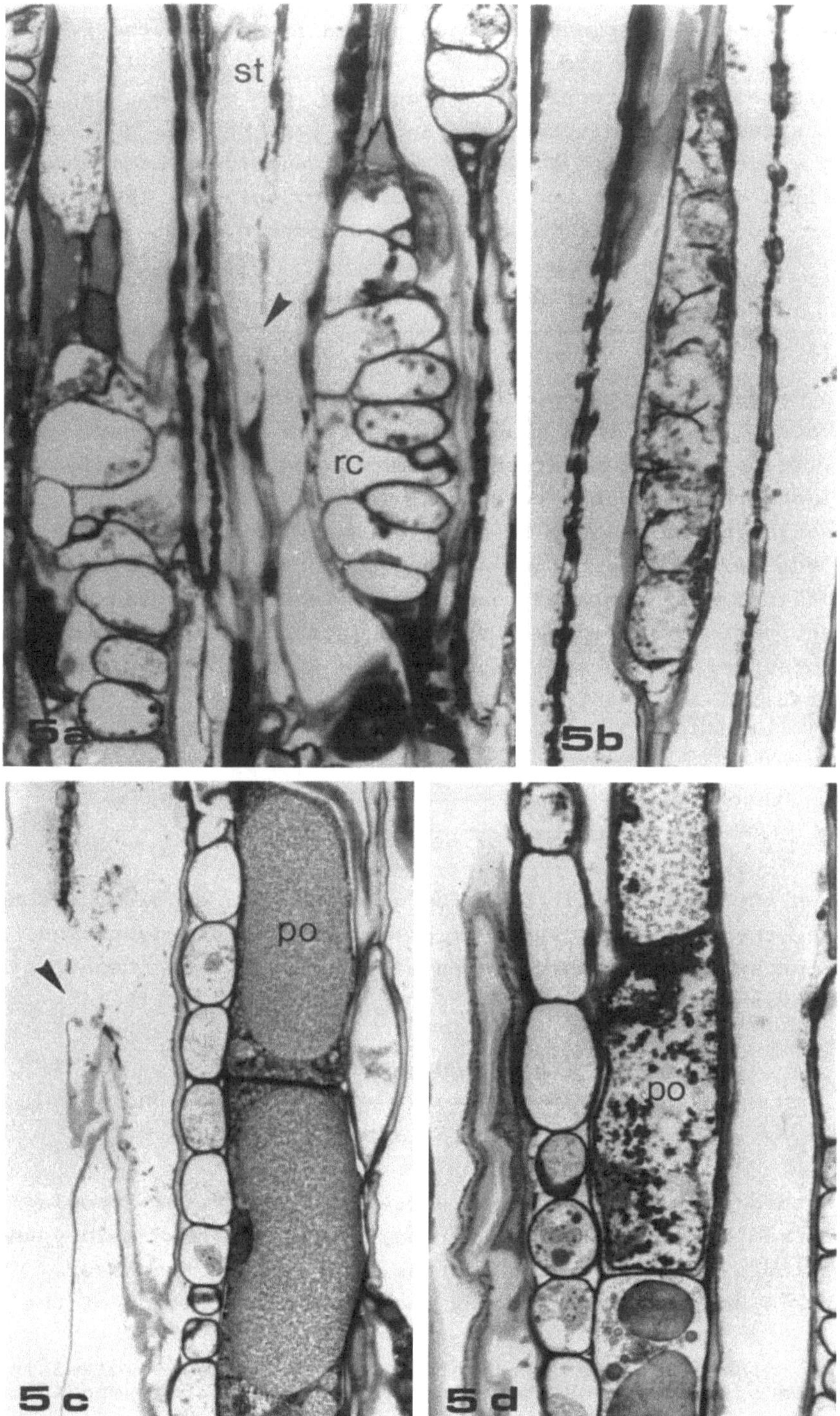
st
rc
5a
5b
po
5c
po
5d

reticulum to the periplasm and then they diffuse into the resin duct lumen where oleoresin accumulates.

This secretory process is a transitory phenomenon. Rapidly this typical structure is disorganized and the cell becomes quiescent. Resting secretory cells (Fig. 6.2) present numerous large vacuoles and large lipid droplets scattered in a clear cytoplasm. These resting cells are no longer able to synthesize oleoresin.

in normal conditions
Stage 1 ------------------------------> Stage 2

In certain conditions, the resting secretory cells can be reactivated. During this reactivation, three events occur: lysis of lipids, transient accumulation of starch, and differentiation of new leucoplasts that are able to carry out terpene biosynthesis. These reactivation phenomena can be observed a few days after wounding and during the first phase following fungus inoculation. According to the data obtained with isolated leucoplasts (Table 1), we can suppose that the reactivation from stage 2 to stage 1 is induced either by wounding (stress factor?) or by some water-soluble diffusing elicitor in low concentration.

wounding
Stage 2 ----------------------------------> Stage 1
low concentration of elicitor

When the concentrations of the water-soluble elicitor further increase, then cell structures of phloem are rapidly destroyed, leading to the stage 3, which concerns secretory cells in stage 1 or 2 as well as every cell type.

high concentration
Stage 1 or 2 ------------------------------> Stage 3
of elicitor

In this stage cell, walls are damaged, lipids and cytoplasm proteins are lysed, and the so-formed metabolites are rapidly used by water-soluble systems for the synthesis of terpene precursors. This activity is strongly increased by the high concentration of the

Figure 6. Intracellular localization of the enzymes involved in the main steps of monoterpene biosynthesis in physiological conditions.

6.1 - State 1 : active secretory cell

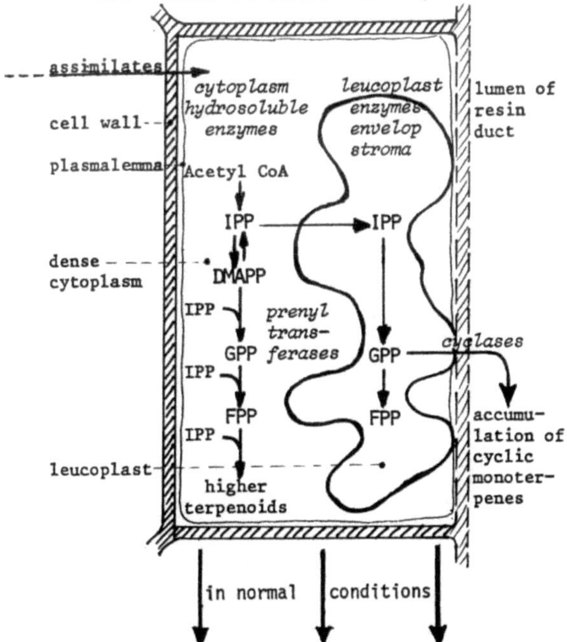

6.2 - State 2 : resting secretory cell

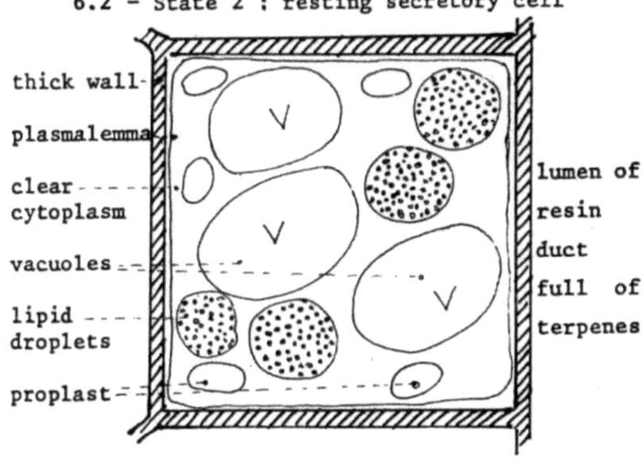

elicitor. The observed accumulation of oleoresin (mainly α-pinene and β-pinene) within inoculated tissues is due to a disordered and delocalized biosynthesis from this high amount of precursors in aqueous medium. This random biosynthesis could be performed by cyclases released from degraded leucoplasts and/or by additional cyclases resulting from the stimulation of the plant genome by the elicitor in non-specialized cells. Such stimulation of expression of nuclear genes has been demonstrated in the case of viral infection (Fritig, unpublished results). Many questions have therefore to be resolved in order to explain the action of elicitors on monoterpene enzymes: activation? neoformation? loss of the regulation of the prenyl transferase/cyclase equilibrium? inhibition of higher terpenoid synthesis?

REFERENCES

Charon, J. 1983. Différenciation et fonctionnement des canaux sécréteurs dans les bourgeons de Pin maritime (Pinus pinaster Ait.): etudes structurales et ultrastructurales. Thèse 3ème cycle Cytol. et morphol. vég., Paris VI, France.

Gleizes, M., G. Pauly, J. P. Carde, A. Marpeau and C. Bernard-Dagan. 1983. Monoterpene hydrocarbons biosynthesis by isolated leucoplasts of Citrofortunella mitis. Planta 159: 373-381.

Luft, J. H. 1961. Improvements in epoxy resin embedding methods. J. Biophys. Biochem. Cytol. 9: 409-414.

Raffa, K. F. and A. A. Berryman. 1983. Physiological aspects of Lodgepole pine wound responses to a fungal symbiont of the mountain pine beetle, Dendroctonus ponderosae (Coleoptera: Scolytidae). Can. Entomol. 115: 723-734.

Reynolds, E. S. 1963. The use of lead citrate at high pH as an electronopaque stain in electron microscopy. J. Cell Biol. 17: 208-212.

Schlenk, H. and J. L. Gellerman. 1960. Esterification of fatty acids with diazomethane on a small scale. Anal. Chem. 32: 1412-1414.

Stone, R. N. 1977. A critique of completed research on paraquat-induced lightwood. TAPPI Conference Papers, Madison, WI.

7

Resistance of Plants at the Population Level to Attack by Phytophagous Insects

Jörg Lunderstädt

THE SYSTEMIC CHARACTER OF FORESTS

In all cases of possible linkages between plants and animals, a state of order establishes itself and a system is formed; for example, the boreal coniferous forest or the mixed forest of the cool, moderate climate. There are flows of energy and mass in any kind of forest between a finite number of system components which can be registered in a system's inventory. They are determined qualitatively by their vector qualities and quantitatively by their individual fluxes, which are variable. Their state at any arbitrary time depends on the age of the system relative to the climax stage. The duration of the climax phases of the respective plant species is determined by the collective population-level resistance to abiotic and biotic environmental factors.

RESISTANCE AS A POPULATION QUALITY

Resistance against pathogens is achieved by the capacity of the population on a metabolic level to keep the costs for breaking down this resistance very high. Because of this tight metabolic bond, resistance is not a static trait. It is oscillating constantly at the population level according to the different pressures of overcoming resistance among the different individuals, each with differential resistance in the plant population. The expression by individual plants of their genetically fixed ability for resistance into the actual phenotype of resistance depends largely on their physiological age, but it is also affected by site, climate, and silvicultural practices.

THE CONTROL OF THE RELATION BETWEEN PLANT AND PHYTOPHAGOUS INSECTS

Within the system, host plant and insect form biomass pools in which the flux of mass is retained for a certain time depending on the kind of mass (e.g., glucose or cellulose). In both cases, the pool capacity for a certain biochemical form of mass is genetically controlled, while the duration of forms within pools at different levels is modified by environmental conditions. Therefore, at any given time there are changing relations between the concentrations of the individual compounds such as proteins or phenols, each of which affects insect development differently.

In order to investigate the control mechanism, a pilot-experiment was designed as follows: The physiological performance of insects and trees was determined with genetically identical material of _Gilpinia hercyniae_ and _Picea_ _abies_, respectively. The physiological performance was classified under four different aspects by means of nine parameters acting in a positive or negative manner on the insect population dynamics (e.g., number of eggs per female, larval mortality, etc.) (Lunderstädt and Ahlers 1984, Lunderstädt 1987). At the same time, the fluxes of individual compounds were determined as rates. For this purpose, at 2-day intervals, the differences between concentration of 16 protein amino acids and 9 non-amino-compounds including phenols and carbohydrates in needles and feces, respectively, were related to the concentration of this compound in the needles at the beginning of the respective interval of intake. The study lasted for the duration of the sawfly's larval stage. It was learned that (1) The changes in insect development as controlled by environmental conditions are reflected by the relations of the rates of intake of protein-bound amino acids (his: tyr: arg); and (2) The relation of the rates of intake as controlled by external conditions can be described semiquantitavely as conic sections (Lunderstädt and Küster 1985). In the case of the plant constituents mentioned above, there was no constant relation between the changes in their concentrations in the needles as influenced by the season or age and the rates of intake by _Gilpinia_ as influenced by the same factors. However, minimum or maximum values of the rates of intake of some of these compounds coincide with the insects' molting, and changes in the period of their occurrence are paralleled by changes in the rate of intake of protein-bound amino acids. All changes of the larval fresh weight as influenced by the different time of the year can be described as a function of the rates of intake of the sum of protein-bound amino acids (Lunderstädt and Ahlers 1985).

We may explain the results as shown in Fig. 1 which represents the interaction of the same insect population with the same food plant under the two different external conditions 5 and 9. External conditions control (by means of the food plant) the physiological performance of the insects to a remarkable extent. For example, they constantly change the ratio of individual plant constituents (e.g., proteins and phenols) to each other in an annually recurring cycle which is superimposed on the major process of plant growth. In contrast to late summer (Fig. 1, situation 9), in spring (Fig. 1, situation 5) a larger amount of the C_2-units synthesized by the plant are channeled into proteins, and a smaller amount into phenols. This variation in the ratios of plant constituents to one another is due to the genetical make-up of the individual trees and to external environmental differences within the stand. It leads to a continuously changing utilizability of those individual plant constituents suitable as food for insects. The degree of utilizeability obeys a regulatory function function (r_f) which describes the potential range of interaction within the respective genetic frames of plant and insect under all realistic external conditions (Lunderstädt and Küster 1985). Its level above the x-z-plane is considered as a function of different physiological age of clones of the same plant at different sites, or of different individuals of one tree population at one site, each under attack by insects under a given external situation of certain duration. All partial situations during this period of observation are represented by the intercept (r_{fi}) on the regulatory function (r_f). Its extension is determined by of minor variations in the external conditions and by the amount of variation within the attacked tree population and the insect population.

The insects' metabolism is directed onto the corresponding intercept (r_{fi}) of the regulatory function (r_f) according to the control function (s_f). Two main parameters of this function are the insect's assimilating capacity (a) and its the detoxifying capacity (e). Both enzyme systems, by nature, adjust their effectiveness to the actual concentrations of assimilable, inhibiting, or toxic compounds in the food plant. The control effect is expressed by changes in the sequence of the extrema of the rates of intake of plant-born compounds (Lunderstädt and Ahlers 1985). The assimilation (A) can be related to the insect development (ϑ) (Lunderstädt 1987).

The degree of resistance or susceptibility of a given plant population at any arbitrary moment of the observed ecosystem can be understood as the positions of as many points (M_n) in the three-dimensional system of co-ordinates as there are functional individual plant-insect relationships at this moment. They result from the respective detoxifying (e_n) and assimilating (a_n) capacities and of all members of the insect population. This cloud of points (M_n) will change its position during the lifetime of the ecosystem. It can be identified as the pattern of mass propagations which results after recording its sequence in time and space (Lunderstädt 1987).

THE EFFECTS OF THE CONTROL OF THE RELATIONS BETWEEN PLANTS AND PHYTOPHAGOUS INSECTS

As in all self-controlled systems, the control in natural forests occurs according to the principle of optimization. The conservation of a steady-state equilibrium is achieved at any moment by feedback-control which favors those system links that build up by their pool-capacity mass potentials of different energy content in such a way that after their breakdown, sufficient chemically bound energy is released to maintain the system in time. This flow of system mass by a controlled shift of relations of different compounds in plant and animal fulfills the requirements of living systems which are thermodynamics and kinetics, design of biochemical processes, and evolution of design and control (Hess 1983). It is reflected in the respective population dynamics.

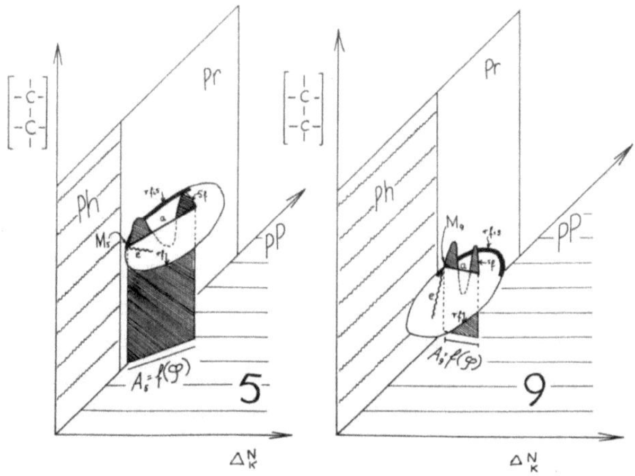

Figure 1. Schematic presentation of the insect/plant interrelationship:

y-axis : production of plant constituents, expressed in C_2-units
x-axis : rate of intake of plant constituents (delta $\frac{N}{K}$)
z-axis : external conditions, expressed as photoperiod (PP)
Ph : inhibiting compounds (phenolics)
Pr : assimilable compounds (proteins)
5,9 : two possible situations at different times of existence of the interrelationship
A : assimilated plant constituents (proteins)
r_f : regulatory function
r_{fi} : intercept on the regulatory function
s_f : control function
e : detoxifying capacity of the insect
a : assimilating capacity of the insect
φ : insect development

For further details, see text.

EFFECTS OF THE TRANSFORMATION OF NATURAL FORESTS INTO COMMERCIAL FORESTS

The relationship between plants as producers and the phytophagous insects as "ecological growth regulators" (due to their position as first level consumers in the food chain) is optimized in old coevolutionary systems. In the commercial forests derived from these systems, man tries to maximize the biomass of a relatively few plant species which he calls commercial timber and to minimize competitors for this plant biomass. This causes small deviations in the average numerical and physiological age of the stand and changes in the natural distribution of variability among individuals, thereby creating more uniformity, which is evidenced by a concentration of the same species of a single age.

Elimination of the senescent age-classes and homogenizing the average age of a population can cause changes in the potential defense alternatives on a physiological basis only necessary in ecological borderline cases, e.g., drought. Spatial and temporal synchronization of stand growth causes spatial and temporal synchronization of states of disposition of individual trees for attack by phytophagous insects and may provoke mass propagations. Synchronizing the state of disposition of a few species and, consequently, intensifying the potential mass fluxes between these species and insects reduces the partial fluxes between the other plant species of the system and their consumers. With polyphagous insect species, this can lead to an unwanted preference for host species which were little affected until then.

CONSEQUENCES FOR THE MANAGEMENT OF FORESTS

It becomes clear from these considerations that there remains relatively little room for action for the maximization of plant mass if the costs for destroying the system resistance are to be economically bearable and ecologically justifiable.

The widespread extension of uniform forests in space and time prohibits the use of control techniques that work in small-scale, confined environments such as in the glass culture of vegetables or the agricultural use of the best soils and of an intensive breeding management of short-lived plants.

Classical measures of forest management promise the best way towards the maximization of wood production without fundamental damage to ecological rules of nature. They include a medium but broadly effective level of resistance by maintaining a sufficient number of species and/or age classes, adaptation to the site, spatial rectification and management on small areas of genetically related high-capacity species, assuming the ecological function of phytophagous insects by removing damaged individuals, recycling of biomass, and last, but not least, tolerating some levels of phytophagous insects.

ACKNOWLEDGEMENT

I thank Dr. William J. Mattson for helpful criticism.

REFERENCES

Hess, B. 1983. Non-equilibrium dynamics of biochemical processes. Hoppe-Seyler's Z. Physiol. Chem. 364: 1-20.

Lunderstädt, J. (1987). Zur Steuerung der Populationsdichte von phytophagen Insekten durch ihre Wirtspflanze. 4. Der Ablauf der Wechselwirkung zwischen Pflanze und Insekt. Z. Angew. Entomol. 103: 29-46.

Lunderstädt, J. and S. Ahlers. 1984. Zur Steuerung der Populationsdichte von phytophagen Insekten durch ihre Nahrungspflanze. 1. Physiologische Leistung der Insekten. Z. Angew. Entomol. 98: 448-462.

Lunderstädt, J. and S. Ahlers. 1985. Zur Steuerung der Populationsdichte von phytophagen Insekten durch ihre Wirtspflanze. 3. Steuerung der physiologischen Leistung der Insekten. Z. Angew. Entomol. 100: 513-522.

Lunderstädt, J. and E. Küster. 1985. Zur Steuerung der Populationsdichte von phytophagen Insekten durch ihre Nahrungspflanze. 2. Regelung der physiologischen Leistung der Insekten. Z. Angew. Entomol. 99: 333-340.

II. Defenses Against Free-Feeding Insects

8

Induced Defenses in Ponderosa Pine Against Defoliating Insects

Michael R. Wagner

The observation that trees manage to persist in spite of seemingly endless insect pressure has prompted scientists to investigate the characteristics in trees that protect them from insect attack. It has also been observed that when insect outbreaks occur, they usually do not persist for long periods. Again the question is raised, "What factors in trees allow for defense against insect herbivores?"

Of the many possible mechanisms that could be responsible for protecting trees from herbivores, one prominent hypothesis is induced defenses. Kogan and Paxton (1983) define induced defense as the qualitative or quantitative enhancement of a plant's defense mechanism against pests in response to extrinsic physical or chemical stimuli. One biologically important extrinsic stimuli is feeding injury by an insect herbivore.

There might be strong selective advantages for plants having induced defense capabilities. Presumably, under some circumstances an induced defense response confers higher fitness to a plant than does a constitutive defense. Some examples of induced defense that have been observed in forest trees are given in Table 1.

If induced defense is a metabolically more efficient defense against insect herbivores, then trees which utilize this defensive strategy have more energy to allocate to biomass accumulation than trees which utilize alternative strategies. Utilization of induced defense in forest management has the potential to increase total forest productivity provided the factors which influence the induced resistance response in forest trees are understood.

In this chapter, I summarize much of the current research on induced defense in forest trees. The evidence suggests that induced defenses are more common in deciduous trees than in conifers. However, I present additional evidence that induced defenses occur in

Table 1. Examples of induced resistance responses in forest tree species as a result of previous damage.

Host	Damage agent	Effect on host
Deciduous trees		
Acer saccharum[a]	Mechanical damage to nearby plant	Increased phenolics, hydrolyzable tannins, condensed tannin
Alnus glutinosa[b]	Mechanical	--[v]
Alnus incana[b]	Mechanical	--
Alnus rubra[c]	Malacosoma californicum pluviale	--
Betula allegheniensis[d]	Mechanical damage to nearby trees	Increased phenols
Betula pendula[e]	Mechanical	Increased tannins
Betula populifolia[f]	Lymantria dispar	--
Betula populifolia[g]	Lymantria dispar	--
Betula pubescens[e]	Mechanical	Increased tannins
Betula pubescens[h]	Mechanical	--
Betula pubescens[b]	Mechanical	--
Betula pubescens[i] ssp. pubescens	Mechanical	--
Betula pubesçens spp. totuosa[j,k,l]	Oporinia autumnata	Phenolic increase
Carpinus betulus[b]	Mechanical	--
Corylus avellana[b]	Mechanical	--
Crataegus monogyna[b]	Mechanical	--
Populus x euroamericana[a]	Mechanical damage to nearby plant	Increased phenolics
Prunus serotina[m]	Magicicada spp.	Increased gum deposition

Table 1. Continued.

Host	Damage agent	Effect on host
Quercus emoryi[n,o]	*Stilbosis juvantis*, mechancial	Increased condensed tannins, lower protein
Querus robur[b]	Mechanical	--[v]
Quercus rubrum[p]	*Lymantria dispar*	Increased tanning coefficient, total phenols hydrolyzable and condensed tannins, dry matter and toughness
Quercus velutina[f]	*Lymantria dispar*	--
Quercus velutina[g]	*Lymantria dispar*	Reduced sugar
Salix alba[q]	Mechanical	--
Salix babylonica[q]	*Plagiodera versicolora*	--
Salix cinerea[b]	Mechanical	--
Sambucus nigra[b]	Mechanical	--
Sorbus aucuparia[b]	Mechanical	--
Coniferous trees		
Larix decidua[r]	*Zeiraphera diniana*	Lower nitrogen, higher fiber
Pinus ponderosa[s]	Mechanical (seedlings)	Increased phenols, procyanidins, proteins
Pinus ponderosa[t]	Mechanical (mature)	Lower nitrogen and tannin
Pinus sylvestris[u]	*Neodiprion setifer*	Increased phenolics

[a]Baldwin and Schultz 1983
[b]Edwards *et al*. 1986
[c]Myers and Williams 1984
[d]Baldwin and Schultz 1984
[e]Wratten *et al*. 1984
[f]Wallner and Walton 1979
[g]Valentine *et al*. 1983
[h]Haukioja and Hanhimaki 1985
[i]Edwards and Wratten 1982
[j]Haukioja and Niemelä 1976
[k]Haukioja and Niemelä 1977
[l]Haukioja 1980
[m]Karban 1983
[n]Faeth 1985
[o]Faeth 1986
[p]Schultz and Baldwin 1982
[q]Raupp and Denno 1984
[r]Baltensweiler *et al*. 1977
[s]Wagner and Evans 1985
[t]Wagner 1986
[u]Thielges 1968
[v]Response unknown

ponderosa pine, Pinus ponderosa. Finally, I discuss some experimental design considerations in induced defense research and potential application of induced defenses in forestry.

CONCEPT OF INDUCED DEFENSE

Much of the early conceptual work on induced defense comes from work on plant diseases by Kuc and Caruso (1977), and Kuc (1982). These pioneers referred to this phenomenon as plant immunity or immune response. More recently induced resistance or induced defense has been used to describe this plant response to damage. I prefer the use of induced defense because resistance implies that this phenomenon evolved specifically as a mechanism of plant protection against herbivores or pathogens. Plant defense, on the other hand, may have evolved as a rather generalized response to environmental damage. Many scientists prefer the term "induced response" for similar reasons.

There are two critical components to the concept of induced defense: (1) the response is induced by damage and (2) the response has a negative effect on herbivores. A third component is that the plant must ultimately benefit by the response. Benefit to the plant is difficult to demonstrate, especially for long-lived plants like forest trees. Demonstrating a long-term benefit to plants from induced defense is important in understanding the evolutionary basis, as well as in its application for reducing damage by insects and pathogens.

My discussion is limited to induced defenses in forest trees to defoliators, but this phenomenon is widespread among plants (Edwards et al. 1985, Green and Ryan 1972, Harrison and Karban 1986a, Karban 1986, Karban and Carey 1984, Tallamy 1985, McNaughton et al. 1985), and the response is not specific to defoliators (Ericsson et al. 1985, Paine et al. 1985, Karban et al. 1987). In general, the induced defense response is much more common among deciduous trees than among conifers (Table 1). No explanation is offered at this point except perhaps that fewer conifers have been studied. It is important to note that induced defenses have not been demonstrated in all tree species tested (Niemelä et al. 1984, Fowler and Lawton 1985, Chapin et al. 1985, Myers 1981, Williams and Myers 1984, Myers and Williams 1984 --induction only after 3 years). Tuomi et al. (1984) suggested that long-lasting induced responses may not be defensive responses (but see Haukioja and Neuvonen 1985 for comments).

The lack of induced defensive reactions in some tree species may be a reflection of between-species variability in this phenomenon or it may be the result of not knowing the unique requirements necessary for stimulating induced defense in those species. Factors that influence the induced defensive reaction are the following: nearby feeding or damage (Rhoades 1983, Baldwin and Schultz 1983, 1984), timing of damage (Haukioja and Niemelä 1979, Wratten et al. 1981, Wratten et al. 1984), time since damage (Wratten et al. 1984, Wagner and Evans 1985, Edwards et al. 1986), and extent and amount of damage (Wagner and Evans 1985) (see Table 2 for summary).

EVIDENCE FOR INDUCED DEFENSE IN PONDEROSA PINE

Results from my current studies provide strong evidence of significant changes in ponderosa pine foliage following defoliation. For example, mechanical defoliation of pine seedlings significantly increased the levels of phenols, procyanidins (tannins), and protein following 50 percent defoliation (Wagner and Evans 1985). Similar treatment of pole-sized ponderosa pine trees significantly reduced levels of procyanidins and nitrogen, both when trees were water stressed and when they were not (Table 3). Damaged foliage was a significantly poorer food for the pine sawfly, Neodiprion fulviceps complex (Hymenoptera: Diprionidae), than was undamaged foliage from the same tree (Table 3). Different water stress levels did not change the herbivore's response to the induction treatment. Reductions in nitrogen content and procyanidin were best correlated with the reduced food quality. Detailed chemical analysis methods and experimental designs are provided in Wagner and Evans (1985) and Wagner (1986).

VARIABILITY IN THE INDUCED RESPONSE BETWEEN TREES

I found substantial between-tree variability in the change in nitrogen content of individual pole-sized ponderosa pine trees 10 days following mechanical defoliation (Fig. 1). The average response by most trees was to decrease foliar nitrogen content in damaged trees and to increase the nitrogen content in undamaged trees (Fig. 1, trees 8, 10, 13, 14, 16, 19). However, nitrogen content of damaged needles increased in tree 12. Although the average response in the control trees was to increase nitrogen content over time, some trees stayed the same (tree 5) or decreased (trees 17, 20) over that same period (Fig. 1).

Table 2. Examples of the extent of damage, time lapse from damage to effect on herbivore, and age of tissue/tree for reported induced defensive responses in forest trees.

Extent of damage age (%)	Time lapse from damage to effect on herbivore	Tissue age/Tree
Deciduous trees		
100 (in 3 stages)[a]	1, 2 years	Current season/sapling
100 (in 3 stages)[a]	1, 2 years	Current season/sapling
20[b]	2, 14 days	Early season/mature
?[c]	2 days, 2 years	Unknown
100[d]	1 year	Mid-season/ saplings
50[e]	75 hours	Young leaves/ seedlings
~ 5 of total leaves--mechanical; 25--insect[f]	months ?	?/saplings
25[g]	6 hours - 14 days	3 periods in current season/ mature
50[h]	4-7 days	Unknown
10-90[h]	4-7 days	Unknown
~ 100[i]	3 years	Early season/ saplings
7[j]	52 hours	Seedling
7[j]	36 hours	Seedling
25[k]	4-17 days	Early season/mature
Coniferous trees		
Heavy[l]	?	1-year-old needles/?
?[m]	1 year	Early season/mature

Table 2. Continued.

Extent of damage age (%)	Time lapse from damage to effect on herbivore	Tissue age/Tree
25, 50, 75[n]	7, 14 days	1-year-old needles/ seedlings
50[o]	11 days	1-year-old needles/ mature

[a]Wallner and Walton 1979
[b]Edwards *et al*. 1986
[c]Haukioja and Niemelä 1977
[d]Schultz and Baldwin 1982
[e]Baldwin and Schultz 1984
[f]Faeth 1985
[g]Wratten *et al*. 1984
[h]Raupp and Denno 1984
[i]Myers and Williams 1984
[j]Baldwin and Schultz 1983
[k]Edwards and Wratten 1982
[l]Thielges 1968
[m]Baltensweiler *et al*. 1977
[n]Wagner and Evans 1985
[o]Wagner 1986

Changes in the procyanidin content of ponderosa pine needles following mechanical defoliation were also highly variable (Fig. 2). Defoliated (induced) trees showed significantly smaller average increases in procyanidin content than did non-defoliated trees. Even greater between-tree variability occurred in the effect of induction on changes in procyanidin than in the effect on changes in nitrogen. For example, the effect of induction on trees 1, 7, and 10 was to increase the procyanidin content when the average effect was a decrease (Fig. 2). Likewise there was considerable between-tree variation in the control treatment group.

The nitrogen and procyanidin analyses were based on pooled foliage samples taken from individual trees. My experience with these analysis techniques suggests that the variability was not associated with variance in the analysis technique. The trees were located within 100 m of each other and were selected for their homogeneity in age, size, and general conditions; therefore site was probably not a significant factor.

Genetic differences between individual trees is a possible explanation for the highly variable response. I am currently developing asexual propagation techniques in an attempt to establish clones of ponderosa pine with widely variable induced responses. Clonal material should permit testing of genetically related differences in induced response.

AGE EFFECT ON INDUCED RESPONSE

When ponderosa pine seedlings and pole-sized trees were mechanically defoliated, protein and procyanidin increased in seedlings and decreased in pole trees (Fig. 3). Perhaps different defensive strategies exist in pole-sized trees and seedlings. Whatever the explanation, it appears that age influences the induced resistance response in ponderosa pine and should be carefully considered in the

Table 3. Effect of water stress and previous mechanical defoliation (induction) of mature ponderosa pines on feeding parameters of <u>Neodiprion</u> <u>autumnalis</u> and foliage quality factors.[a,b]

Induction treatment	Insect response		Foliage factor			
	RGR[c]	ECI[d]	Moisture content	Nitrogen	Phenol	Tannin
Stressed						
Induced	.03b	2.82a	50.8a	0.95a	7.50a	36.9ab
Not-induced	.08b	5.00b	51.1a	1.02a	8.10b	42.4c
Not-stressed						
Induced	.07a	3.62a	51.3a	1.04b	7.43a	34.6a
Not-induced	.08a	5.60b	51.3a	1.15c	7.62ab	38.2a

p for two-way ANOVA

Induction treatment	Insect response		Foliage factor			
	RGR[c]	ECI[d]	Moisture content	Nitrogen	Phenol	Tannin
Stress level	.15	.23	.48	.000	.20	.03
Induction level	.05	.001	.70	.002	.25	.02
Interaction	.07	.90	.71	.45	.49	.26

[a]Means with a column followed by the same letter are not significantly different at $p = 0.05$ (Duncan's new multiple range test).
[b]n = 20 for each treatment.
[c]RGR = Relative growth rate (mg/mg larval wt/day).
[d]ECI = Efficiency of conversion of ingested food (mg biomass/mg ingested/day).

Modified from Wagner (1986).

design of future experiments. There were slight differences in the experimental methods used between seedlings and pole-sized trees. Consequently, the results should be viewed for trends only.

EXPERIMENTAL DESIGN CONSIDERATIONS

It should be clear that many factors must be considered in designing induced-defense experiments. Fowler and Lawton (1985) and Neuvonen and Haukioja (1985) have suggested some important factors to consider. In addition, careful attention to the extent of damage required to cause induction and the time lapse from damage to bioassay are very important. In general, too much emphasis has been placed on the long-term (years) responses while neglecting the very short-term (hours/days) responses.

It is also appropriate to test, for each host/herbivore system, the suitability of mechanical vs. herbivore damage. Mechanical damage offers greater flexibility in experimental manipulation but may

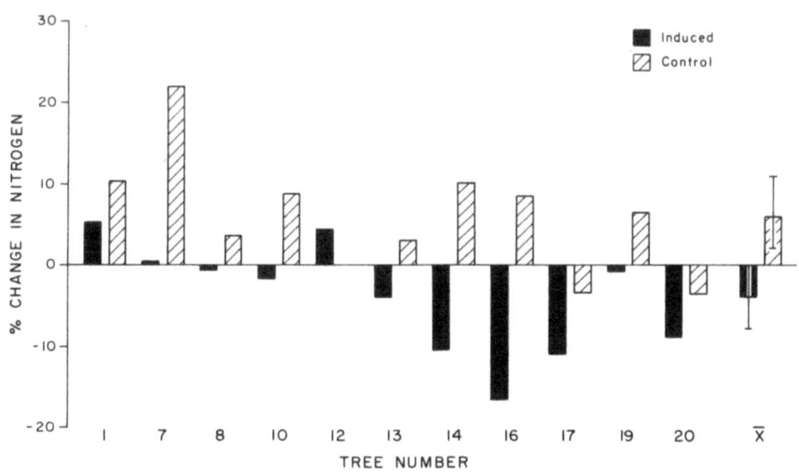

Figure 1. Between-tree variation in percent change (over a 10-day period) in nitrogen content of foliage with and without mechanical damage (induction). Bar about the mean indicates 95 percent confidence interval.

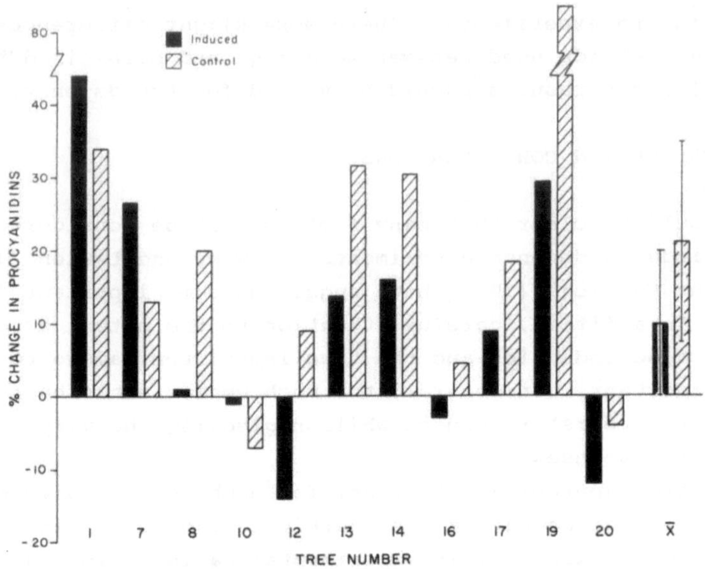

Figure 2. Between-tree variation in percent change (over a 10-day period) in procyanidin content of foliage with and without mechanical damage (induction). Bar about the mean indicates 95 percent confidence interval.

(Harrison and Karban 1986b) or may not (Risch 1985) be similar to the effect of herbivores. The use of herbivores to stimulate the induced response offers much less flexibility in design and may make it difficult to detect very short-term responses. A high density of herbivores, especially in colonial feeding species such as sawflies, may consume the foliage faster than the host can modify its allelochemical or nutritional status. Consequently, the number of herbivores or rate of damage may also be important.

POTENTIAL APPLICATION OF INDUCED DEFENSES IN FORESTRY

Evidence that plants have inducible defense responses may lead to new and effective approaches to pest management. This is particularly important if induced defense is a metabolically less costly defensive strategy than constitutive resistance. Less energy spent by the tree on insect defense results in greater total productivity.

Several hypothetical approaches are outlined below that may be used to apply the induced resistance phenomenon to managing forest insect pests.

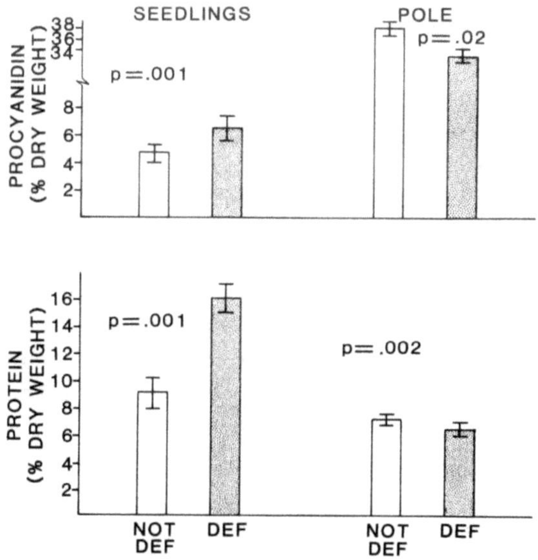

Figure 3. Comparison of changes (over a 10-day period) in protein and procyanidin content of foliage from defoliated (def) and undefoliated (not def) needles of pole-sized trees and seedlings of ponderosa pine. Bar about the mean is ± one standard deviation. Experimental design and chemical analysis methods vary slightly between seedling and pole-sized trees.

Incorporate Induced Resistance into Traditional Tree Breeding Programs.

To accomplish this, trees that show the ability to respond to attack by insects would be propagated through traditional asexual techniques. Select individuals for propagation that respond to specific stimuli (i.e., specific insect herbivores). Highly sensitive plants might not be preferred because of their tendency to respond too quickly to a variety of non-specific stimuli. It would also be desirable to select for plants that relax induced mechanisms very quickly, thereby minimizing the metabolic energy spent on defense. Of key importance in this approach is a thorough understanding of the host factors that are responsible for the induced reaction and the impact this has on the pest herbivore.

Apply Elicitors of Induced Resistance to Plants Threatened by Insect Attack.

Presumably the induced resistance response is communicated to appropriate cells and tissues by some biochemical signal. If the signal could be identified and synthesized, it would be possible to "turn on" defense mechanisms on short notice. It would also seem advisable to be able to "turn off" defensive mechanisms and thereby avoid unnecessary expenditure of metabolic energy. Elicitors could be natural compounds or compounds generally available that stimulate the induced defense response. Insect frass (Haukioja et al. 1985) and chitosan (Walker-Simmons and Ryan 1984, Miller et al. 1986) have been implicated as elicitors of defense responses in plants.

Incorporate Induced Resistance as a Factor in Increasing Variability in Forest Stands. Genotypes representing a range of induced resistance types could be incorporated into forest plantations. A forest plantation, genetically diverse because of variation in induced resistance response, would likely be more stable when faced with an uncertain array of insect pest. A modest number of genotypes (7 to 25) as suggested by Libby (1980) would be preferred. Hopefully, this variability could be found within trees that have other genetically preferred characteristics.

CONCLUSION

Induced resistance is a relatively new and exciting aspect of the complex interaction between forest trees and their herbivores. Several examples exist that indicate induced resistance is found in forest tree species. With a thorough understanding of the factors that may influence the induced reaction, it may be possible to select and breed for trees that respond quickly to herbivore attack. Appropriate application of induced resistance technology may enhance the management of damaging forest pests.

ACKNOWLEDGEMENTS

I thank Karen M. Clancy for critical review of this manuscript and the NAU Organized Research Committee and McIntire Stennis Program for financial support.

REFERENCES

Balwin, I. T. and J. C. Schultz. 1983. Rapid changes in tree leaf chemistry induced by damage: evidence for communication between plants. Science 221: 277-279.

Baldwin, I. T. and J. C. Schultz. 1984. Damage and communication induced changes in yellow birch leaf phenolics. In: Eighth North American forest biology workshop; 25-33.

Baltensweiler, W., G. Genz, P. Beovey, and V. Delucchi. 1977. Dynamics of larch bud moth populations. Annu. Rev. Entomol. 22: 79-100.

Chapin, F. S., J. P. Bryant, and J. F. Fox. 1985. Lack of induced chemical defense in juvenile Alaskan woody plants in response to simulated browsing. Oecologia 67: 457-459.

Edwards, P. J. and S. D. Wratten. 1982. Wound induced changes in palatability in birch (Betula pubescens Ehrh. spp. pubescens). Am. Nat. 120(6): 816-817.

Edwards, P. J., S. D. Wratten, and H. Cox. 1985. Wound induced changes in the acceptability of tomatoe to larvae of Spodoptera littoralis: a laboratory bioassay. Ecol. Entomol. 10: 155-158.

Edwards, P. J., S. D. Wratten, and S. Greenwood. 1986. Palatability of British trees to insects: constitutive and induced defences. Oecologia 69: 316-319.

Ericsson, A., C. Hellquist, B. Långström, S. Larsson, and O. Tenow. 1985. Effects on growth of simulated and induced shoot pruning by Tomicus piniperda as related to carbohydrate and nitrogen dynamics in Scots pine. J. Appl. Ecol. 22: 105-124.

Faeth, S. H. 1985. Host selection by leafminers: interactions among three trophic levels. Ecology 66(3): 870-875.

Faeth, S. H. 1986. Indirect interactions between temporally separated herbivores mediated by the host plant. Ecology 67(2): 479-494.

Fowler, S. V. and J. H. Lawton. 1985. Rapidly induced defenses and talking trees: the devil's advocate position. Am. Nat. 126(2): 181-195.

Green, T. R. and C. A. Ryan. 1972. Wound induced proteinase inhibitor in plant leaves: a possible defense mechanism against insects. Science 175: 776-777.

Harrison S. and R. Karban. 1986a. Behavioral response of spider mites (Tetranychus urticae) to induced resistance of cotton plants. Ecol. Entomol. 11(2): 181-188.

Harrison, S. and R. Karban. 1986b. Effects of an early season folivorous moth on the success of a later-season species, mediated by a change in the quality of the shared host, Lupinus arboreus Sims. Oecologia 69: 354-359.

Haukioja, E. 1980. On the role of plant defences in the fluctuation of herbivore populations. Oikos 35: 202-213.

Haukioja, E. and S. Hanhimaki. 1985. Rapid wound-induced resistance in white birch (Betula pubescens) foliage to the geometrid Epirrita autumnata: a comparison of trees and moths within and outside the outbreak range of the moth. Oecologia 65: 223-228.

Haukioja, E. and S. Neuvonen. 1985. Induced long term resistance of birch foliage against defoliators: defensive or incidental? Ecology 66(4): 1303-1308.

Haukioja, E. and P. Niemelä. 1976. Does birch defend itself actively against herbivores? Kevo. Subarctic Research Station Rep. 13: 44-47.

Haukioja, E. and P. Niemelä. 1977. Retarded growth of a geometrical larva after mechanical damage to its host tree. Ann. Zool. Fenn. 14: 48-52.

Haukioja, E. and P. Niemelä. 1979. Birch leaves as a resource for herbivores: seasonal occurrence of increased resistance in foliage after mechanical damage of adjacent leaves. Oecologia 39: 151-159.

Haukioja, E., J. Suomela, and S. Neuvonen. 1985. Long-term inducible resistance in birch foliage: triggering cues and efficacy on a defoliator. Oecologia 65: 363-369.

Karban, R. 1983. Induced responses of cherry trees to periodical cicada oviposition. Oecologia 59: 226-231.

Karban, R. 1986. Interspecific competition between folivorous insects on Erigeron glaucus. Ecology 67(4): 1063-1072.

Karban, R., R. Adamchak, and W. C. Schinathorst. 1987. Induced resistance and interspecific competition between spider mites and a vascular wilt fungus. Science 235: 678-680.

Karban, R. and J. R. Carey. 1984. Induced resistance of cotton seedlings to mites. Science 225: 53-54.

Kogan, M. and J. Paxton. 1983. Natural inducers of plant resistance to insects. In: Plant resistance to insects. American Chemical Society Series 208; 153-171.

Kuc, J. 1982. Induced immunity to plant disease. BioScience 32(11): 854-860.

Kuc, J. and F. L. Caruso. 1977. Activated coordinated chemical defense against disease in plants. In: Host plant resistance to pests. American Chemical Society Symposium Series 62; 78-89.

Libby, W. J. 1980. What is a safe number of clones per plantation? In: Resistance to diseases and pests in forest trees (H. M. Heybroek, B. R. Stephan, and K. von Weissenberg, Eds.). Wageningen, Netherlands: Pudoc.

McNaughton, S. J., J. L. Tarrants, M. M. McNaughton, and R. H. Davis. 1985. Silica as a defense against herbivory and a growth promotor in African grasses. Ecology 66(2): 528-535.

Miller, R. H., A. A. Berryman, and C. A. Ryan. 1986. Biotic elicitors of defense reactions in lodgepole pine. Phytochem. 25(3): 611-612.

Myers, J. H. 1981. Interactions between western tent caterpillars and wild rose: a test of some general plant herbivore hypotheses. J. Anim. Ecol. 50: 11-25.

Myers, J. H. and K. S. Williams. 1984. Does tent caterpillar attack reduce the food quality of red alder foliage? Oecologia 62: 74-79.

Neuvonen, S. and E. Haukioja. 1985. How to study induced plant resistance? Oecologia 66: 456-457.

Niemelä, P., J. Tuomi, R. Mannila, and P. Ojala. 1984. The effect of previous damage on the quality of Scots pine foliage as food for diprionid sawflies. Zeitschrift fur angewandte Entomologie 98: 33-43.

Paine, T. D., F. M. Stephen, and R. G. Cates. 1985. Induced defenses against Dendroctonus frontalis and associate fungi: variation in loblolly pine resistance. In: Proceedings, Integrated pest management research symposium (S. J. Branham and R. C. Thatcher, Eds.); 1985 April 15-18; Asheville, NC. New Orleans, LA: USDA, Forest Service, Southern Forest Experiment Station, Gen. Tech. Rep. SO-56; 169-176.

Raupp, M. J. and R. F. Denno. 1984. The suitability of damaged willow leaves as food for the leaf beetle, Plagioder versicolora. Ecol. Entomol. 9: 443-448.

Rhoades, D. F. 1983. Response of alder and willow to attack by tent caterpillars and webworms: evidence for pheromonal sensitivity of willows. In: Plant resistance to insects. American Chemical Society Series 208; 55-68.

Risch, S. J. 1985. Effects of induced chemical changes on interpretation of feeding preference tests. Entomol. Exp. Appl. 39: 81-84.

Schultz, J. C. and I. T. Baldwin. 1982. Oak leaf quality declines in response to defoliation by gypsy moth larvae. Science 217: 149-151.

Tallamy, D. W. 1985. Squash beetle feeding behavior: an adaptation against induced cucurbit defenses. Ecology 66(5): 1574-1579.

Thielges, B. A. 1968. Altered polyphenol metabolism in the foliage of Pinus sylvestris associated with European sawfly attack. Can. J. Bot. 46: 724-725.

Tuomi, J., P. Niemelä, E. Haukioja, S. Siren, and S. Neuvonen. 1984. Nutrient stress: an explanation for plant anti-herbivore responses to defoliation. Oecologia 61: 208-210.

Valentine, H. T., W. E. Wallner, and P. M. Wargo. 1983. Nutritional changes in host foliage during and after defoliation, and their relation to the weight of gypsy moth pupae. Oecologia 57: 298-302.

Wagner, M. R. 1986. Influence of moisture stress and induced resistance in ponderosa pine, Pinus ponderosa, on the pine sawfly, Neodiprion fulviceps. For. Ecol. and Mang. 15: 43-53.

Wagner, M. R. and P. D. Evans. 1985. Defoliation increases nutritional quality and allelochemics of pine seedlings. Oecologia 67: 235-237.

Wallner, W. E. and G. S. Walton. 1979. Host defoliation: a possible determinant of gypsy moth population quality. Ann. Entomol. Soc. Am. 72(1): 62-67.

Walker-Simmons, M. and C. A. Ryan. 1984. Proteinase inhibitor synthesis in tomatoe leaves. Plant. Physiol. 76: 787-790.

Williams, K. S. and J. H. Myers. 1984. Previous attack of red alder may improve food quality for fall webworm larvae. Oecologia 63: 166-170.

Wratten, S. D., P. Goddard, and P. J. Edwards. 1981. British trees and insects: the role of palatability. Am. Nat. 118: 916-919.

Wratten, S. D., P. J. Edwards, and I. Dunn. 1984. Wound induced changes in the palatability of Betula pubescens and B. pendula. Oecologia 61: 372-375.

9

Changes in Levels of Foliar Minerals and Phenolics in Trembling Aspen, *Populus tremuloides*, in Response to Artificial Defoliation

William J. Mattson and Sean R. Palmer

Plants may be able to regulate the amount of herbivory they sustain if they can somehow provide negative feedback to herbivores that increases in proportion to the amount of their herbivore injury. Depending on the strength of this feedback and its timing relative to the herbivore's population processes, it could keep herbivory to nearly negligible levels, or on the other hand, it could allow wide variations (cycles) in herbivory. Hence, learning how plants react to injury and defoliation is essential to test the regulation hypothesis. Because plants offer both nutrients and potentially dangerous allelochemicals to insects, investigations of plant responses must at least consider changes in both of these broad classes of substances.

Several studies have clearly shown that one common reaction by plants to defoliation is an increase in the class of foliar allelochemicals known as phenolics (Thielges 1968, Kosuge 1969, Niemelä et al. 1979, Schultz and Baldwin 1982, Waters and Stafford 1984, Wratten et al. 1984, Wagner and Evans 1985, Nef in this volume, Wagner in this volume). Other studies have shown a variety of changes in plant nutrient levels following defoliation. Water content may increase (Svejcar and Christiansen 1987) as may nitrogen (Landsberg and Wylie 1983, Piene and Percy 1984, Ericsson et al. 1985, Wagner and Evans 1985, Mika 1986, Wagner in this volume), calcium (Valentine et al. 1983), and potassium (Nef in this volume). On the other hand, several studies have reported decreases in plant nitrogen (McClure 1980, Baltensweiler 1984, Tuomi et al. 1984, Myers and Williams 1987), various minerals (Mo, Cu, Zn, Ca) (Nef in this volume), and sugars and starch (Webb and Karchesy 1977, Ericsson et al. 1980, Valentine et al. 1983).

This study was designed to evaluate the nutrient (N and minerals) and phenolic (total) responses of trembling aspen, Populus tremuloides, induced by two different kinds of manual defoliation and to investigate whether induction is localized or systematic.

We selected trembling aspen, Populus tremuloides, because it is one of the most widely distributed tree species in North America, occurring from Newfoundland to Alaska and from northern Mexico to the subarctic. Moreover, it forms the base for food chains involving dozens of species of birds and mammals, hundreds of insects (some are outbreak defoliators), and untold numbers of microorganisms. It is an early successional species which grows under a wide variety of site conditions. Because it reproduces prolifically by root suckering (as well as by seed), trembling aspen frequently grows in dense, mono-species clones, i.e., clusters of stems (ramets) of identical genotype.

METHODS

We established this study in two even-aged stands of trembling aspen (resulting from harvesting); one near Cloquet, MN and the other near Cass lake, MN. The Cloquet stand was 9-years old and the Cass lake stand was 2-years old (hereafter designated C-9 and CL-2). The soil at Cloquet was Omega loamy sand over gravely sand with a site index for aspen of 55 while that at Cass Lake was Warba very fine sandy loam over clay loam with a site index of 80.

Within each stand, we classified all clones as being early, middle, or late flushing (based on whether they flushed among the first, middle, or last third of all clones in that stand (Table 1)), and, except in the single branch induction experiments, equal numbers of each type were used in all samples and treatments. Determining whether or not individual ramets were conclonal was based primarily on the time of spring leaf flush, but also on leaf shape, size, and color, and overall ramet appearance (Barnes 1969).

Table 1. Mean flushing dates for early, middle, and late flushing clones at Cloquet (C-9) and Cass Lake (CL-2).

Stand	Early	Middle	Late
C-9	17 May	22 May	25 May
CL-2	11 May	14 May	17 May

Artificial Defoliation Procedures

Whole Leaf Versus Half-Leaf Removal. At CL-2, we measured the effects of two types of 50 percent defoliation on entire ramets: 1) completely cutting off every other leaf at the petiole base and 2) cutting all leaves in half. Two ramets were selected from opposite ends of each of twelve clones. Between 17 and 21 June, every other whole leaf of the two selected ramets of six of these clones was cut off at the leaf-petiole junction using fingernails. At the same time, the left half (as viewed looking at the upper surface with the tip pointed away) of all leaves of the two selected ramets from the remaining six clones was cut off along the midrib using stainless steel scissors. We saved excised leaves or leaf portions from the midcrown of the defoliated ramets for chemical analysis. Three weeks later, the remaining midcrown leaves or leaf portions of the defoliated ramets were sampled, along with midcrown leaves of the nearest conclonal ramets which were to serve as one line of internal controls. The distance between the defoliated and adjacent control ramet was measured to determine if any defoliation effects on control ramets were linked with the distance to the treated ramet.

Defoliation Affecting Half Versus All Leaf Clusters. At C-9, we measured the effects of two types of 25 percent defoliation on a single midcrown branch: 1) cutting in half 50 percent of the leaves in every other leaf cluster, and 2) cutting in half 25 percent of the leaves in all leaf clusters. One branch was selected at random from the midcrown of each of 2 ramets of 12 clones. Ramets were selected as previously described for 50 percent defoliation of whole ramets. Between 28 June and 5 July, each defoliation treatment was applied to six of these clones. Leaf portions removed at the time of defoliation were saved for chemical analyses. Approximately 2 weeks later, the remaining half leaves and uncut leaves of the defoliated branches were sampled. At this time, samples were also taken from the corresponding branches of the nearest conclonal ramets to serve as internal controls.

Establishing Independent Controls for the Defoliation Study. To back-up our internal controls within the defoliation induction experiments at each site, we had two extrinsic controls. In one, we monitored the foliar chemistry of each of two ramets from six clones (two early, two middle, two late) on four dates (late May, mid-June, early July, early August). Although the same clones were sampled throughout the summer, individual ramets were never sampled more than once. In the second, we sampled six new clones (as above) on each date. We did this because we felt it was necessary to learn whether merely sampling the same clones repeatedly throughout the season had any effect on the future leaf chemistry of other conclonal ramets because members of the same clone are frequently interconnected by roots. Hence at each date we collected foliage from ramets of unsampled clones for comparison with those clones that had been sampled during sampling periods 2, 3, and 4.

Foliar Analyses

Foliage samples were collected in plastic petri dishes, and then immediately placed on ice in a cooler until returning to the laboratory, at which time they were frozen at -20 ^{o}C. The samples were later freeze-dried and ground in a Wiley mill to pass through a 60 mesh screen. We stored them in sealed jars at room temperature in the dark until analyzed.

Total phenolics were measured using the Folin-Denis method with a tannic acid standard (Rosenblatt and Peluso 1941). Twenty ml of 76 percent ethanol/water (v/v) was added to 100 mg aspen leaf powder in a 125 ml Erlenmeyer flask and shaken (50 cycles/min) for 24 hours under continuous light. The suspension was then centrifuged (11,000 g, 10 min) and the supernatant analyzed for phenolics. Nitrogen was analyzed using the standard micro-Kjeldahl technique. Phosphorus, potassium, calcium, magnesium, aluminum, iron, manganese, sodium, zinc, copper, and boron were measured using inductively coupled plasma emission spectroscopy. All quantities are expressed as mg/g or ppm freeze-dried weight.

RESULTS AND DISCUSSION

General Considerations

There was a general trend for foliar phenolics to increase during the early part of the growing season but then to become more or less constant after mid-to-late June (Fig. 1). Several others have reported similar trends in deciduous trees (Hillis and Swain 1959, Feeny and Bostock 1968, Haukioja *et al*. 1978). This pattern runs counter to the well-known phenological trend for foliar N, which always peaks at the beginning of the growing season.

For this and perhaps other reasons (competitive biosynthetic pathways, see Phillips and Henshaw 1977), there was an obvious, although not precise, negative relationship between foliar phenolic (PH) and nitrogen levels (N): $\ln PH = 6.85 - 0.75 \ln N$, $r^2 = 0.34$ (Fig. 2). This has also been noted by Haukioja et al. (1985).

At C-9, left leaf halves had small, but significantly higher concentrations of N, Mg, Al, Fe, Mn, and B than right halves (Table 2). All other elements and phenolics were similar between leaf halves. At CL-2, only N and B were significantly different between halves, both again being higher in the left side. We corrected all results concerning the effects of cutting off half of a leaf for these differences.

The foliar chemistry of conclonal ramets adjacent to defoliated ramets did not differ from the control ramets in control clones (those that suffered no defoliation). Therefore, these ramets were acceptable as internal controls in our defoliation study.

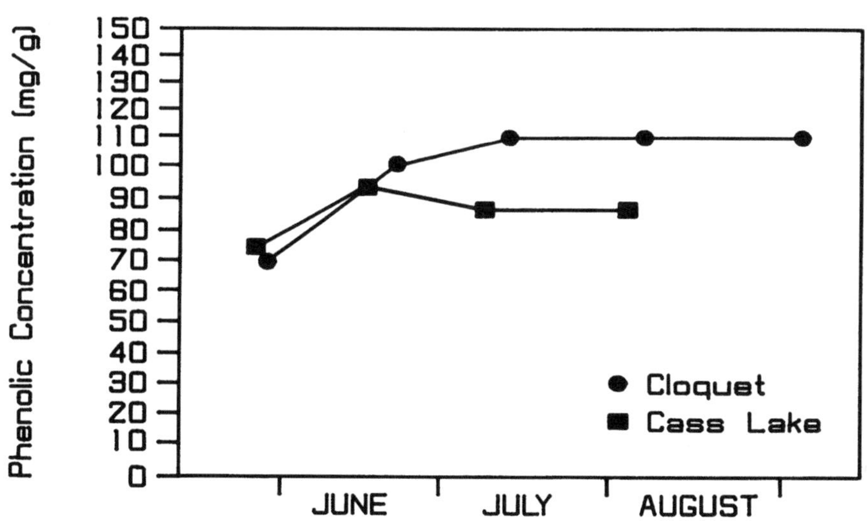

Figure 1. Seasonal change in foliar phenolic concentrations (mg/g dry weight) at Cass Lake and Cloquet. Each point is the mean of six clones, two ramets per clone.

Effects of Foliage Sampling on Foliar Chemistry of Control Clones

At C-9, there were a few apparent instances where sampling a ramet apparently had a significant effect ($p \leq .05$) on the chemistry of other ramets of the same clone at a later date. For example, during sampling period 2, unsampled ramets of clones which had been sampled during period 1 had higher K (13,622 ppm versus 11,118 ppm) and lower Zn (214 ppm versus 302 ppm) than equivalent ramets from unsampled clones. Phenolics and all other elements were unaffected. During sampling period 3, N was higher in unsampled ramets of sampled clones than in equivalent raments of unsampled clones (29.3 mg/g vs. 25.8 mg/g, $p < 0.01$). Previous foliage removal had no effect on phenolics nor on any of the other elements at this time. There were no other effects of sampling on the foliar chemistry of either the sampled ramet or other ramets of the same clone at C-9.

In CL-2 during the sampling period 4, there was a significant interaction between sampling effect and flushing-time affecting Mn concentration. Unsampled ramets of early and late clones had lower Mn

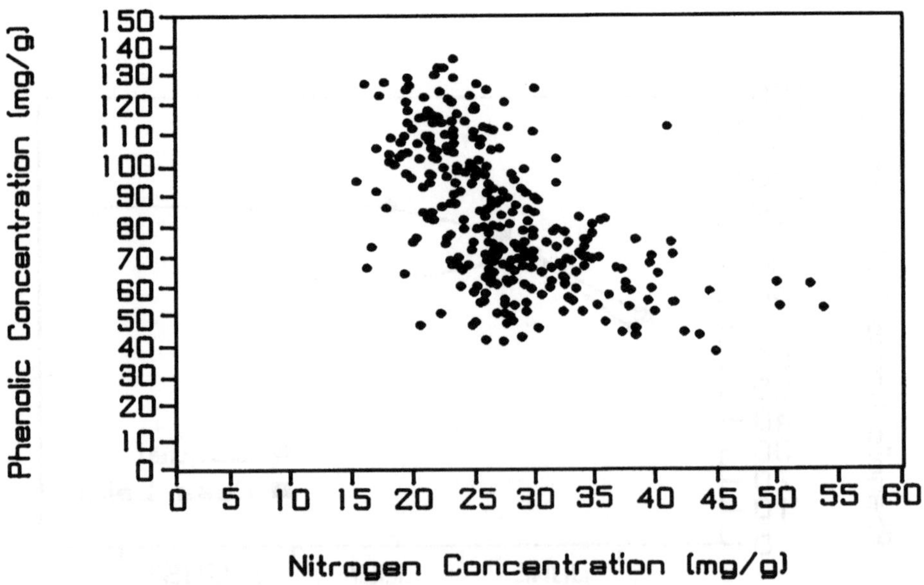

Figure 2. Relationship between foliar phenolic and nitrogen concentrations (mg/g dry weight), pooled over all plants over the growing season. Each point is a single ramet, ($n = 372$).

Table 2. Mineral elements showing significant differences ($p \leq .05$) between left[a] and right halves of aspen leaves (n = 10 ramets at C-9, 11 ramets at CL-2, 200 to 300 leaves per ramet).

Element[b]	Cloquet (C-9)		Cass Lake (CL-2)	
	Left	Right	Left	Right
N	28.8	28.0	26.4	25.5
Mg	2702.0	2673.0		
Al	19.1	18.2		
Fe	65.3	63.7		
Mn	227.4	224.3		
B	33.9	33.1	35.6	34.9

[a]As viewed from the upper surface of the leaf with the tip pointed away.
[b]N in mg/g, all other elements in ppm, dry weight.

than corresponding ramets of unsampled clones. On the other hand, unsampled ramets of sampled middle clones had higher Mn than ramets of unsampled middle clones. There were no other significant effects of sampling on the foliar chemistry of the same clone at a later date. We believe that all of the forementioned effects were small and could be strictly due to chance owing to the large number of contrasts made.

<u>Whole Versus Half Leaf Removal on Whole Ramets</u>

When every other whole leaf of a ramet was removed, two major changes occurred: N increased by about 10 percent and Na decreased by about 10 percent in the remaining whole leaves (Table 3). Levels of phenolics and all other elements were unaffected by this type of defoliation. In no case was the difference in leaf chemistry between the defoliated and adjacent control ramets correlated in any way with the amount of distance between them.

In the other 50 percent defoliation experiment, where each leaf of a ramet was cut in half, two major changes occurred: concentrations of phenolics and Cu increased by about 18 percent and 9 percent, respectively, in the remaining half-leaves (Table 3). Mn concentration was affected by a defoliation by flushing time interaction in which defoliation increased Mn in early and late clones but decreased its concentration in middle clones. The concentrations of all other elements remained unchanged.

Table 3. Differences in foliar chemistry between control and artificial defoliation treatments (n = 12).

	50% Defoliation of Whole Ramets						25% Defoliation of Single Branches											
	Half of all leaves removed			All leaves cut in half			Half of all clusters treated						All clusters treated					
	Remaining whole leaves			Remaining half leaves			Remaining half leaves			Remaining whole leaves			Remaining half leaves			Remaining whole leaves		
	Cntrl	Trtmt		Cntrl	Trtmt		Cntrl	Trtmt		Cntrl	Trtmt		Cntrl	Trtmt		Cntrl	Trtmt	
Phenols[a]	87.4	90.7	+[b]	89.0	106.1	+ **	89.7	101.9	+ **	89.7	90.6	+	79.0	95.3	+ **	79.0	89.0	+ *
N	25.4	27.8	+ **[c]	26.1	25.9	-	25.9	26.0	+	25.9	25.7	-	28.5	27.3	-	28.5	27.4	-
P	2144	2204	+	2218	2146	-	1921	1840	-	1921	1915	-	2070	1955	- *	2070	1991	-
K	10033	9714	-	11532	11102	-	11331	11031	-	11331	10991	-	11530	11456	-	11530	11131	-
Ca	15709	15893	+	16008	15860	-	10959	11067	+	10959	11875	+	9976	9052	-	9976	9370	-
Mg	2635	2744	+	2687	2691	+	2356	2506	+	2356	2545	+ *	2597	2520	-	2597	2505	-
Al	10.6	9.6	-	9.8	11.6	+	28.3	32.5	+	28.3	28.8	+	27.0	34.0	+ **	27.0	26.9	-
Fe	61.4	62.8	+	53.9	52.5	-	66.3	62.9	- **	66.3	64.4	-	68.1	67.0	-	68.1	62.6	-
Mn	107	109	+	101	105	+	282	311	+	282	327	+ *	239	212	-	239	203	- *
Na	10.7	9.0	- *	17.6	17.9	+	10.1	12.1	+	10.1	11.6	+	10.4	17.9	+	10.4	1.07	+
Zn	372	411	+	356	400	+	336	343	+	336	359	+	307	279	-	307	281	-
Cu	7.87	8.43	+	7.68	8.28	+ *	7.25	8.12	+	7.25	7.64	+	8.22	9.32	+	8.22	8.71	+
B	40.1	4.23	+	34.6	36.7	+	40.0	36.0	- **	40.0	40.4	+	36.6	32.6	-	36.6	34.4	-

[a]Phenolics and N in mg/g, all other elements in ppm, dry weight.
[b]Sign (+ or -) indicates direction of change (increases or decrease, respectively).
[c]* Difference significant at ≤ 0.05; [c]** difference significant at ≤ 0.01.

There was, on the average, no significant difference in K concentration between defoliated (all leaves cut in half) and adjacent ramets of the same clone, but the difference in K (K_{diff}) between defoliated and adjacent ramets was significantly ($p < 0.01$) correlated with the distance (D) between them: $K_{diff} = -389.3 + 1981.2$ D, $r^2 = 0.62$ (Fig. 3). When the adjacent control ramets were very close to the defoliated ramets, there was no difference in their K concentrations, but as the distance between them increased, control ramets tended to have increasingly more K than the defoliated ramets. This may have occurred because K^+, one of the most mobile mineral ions in plants, was leached out of the wounded foliage of the defoliated ramets. The defoliated ramets may then have acted as K^+ sinks for nearly conclonal control ramets. As the distance between the defoliated and control ramets increased, the amount of K^+ transported from the latter to the former decreased, and therefore the difference in K

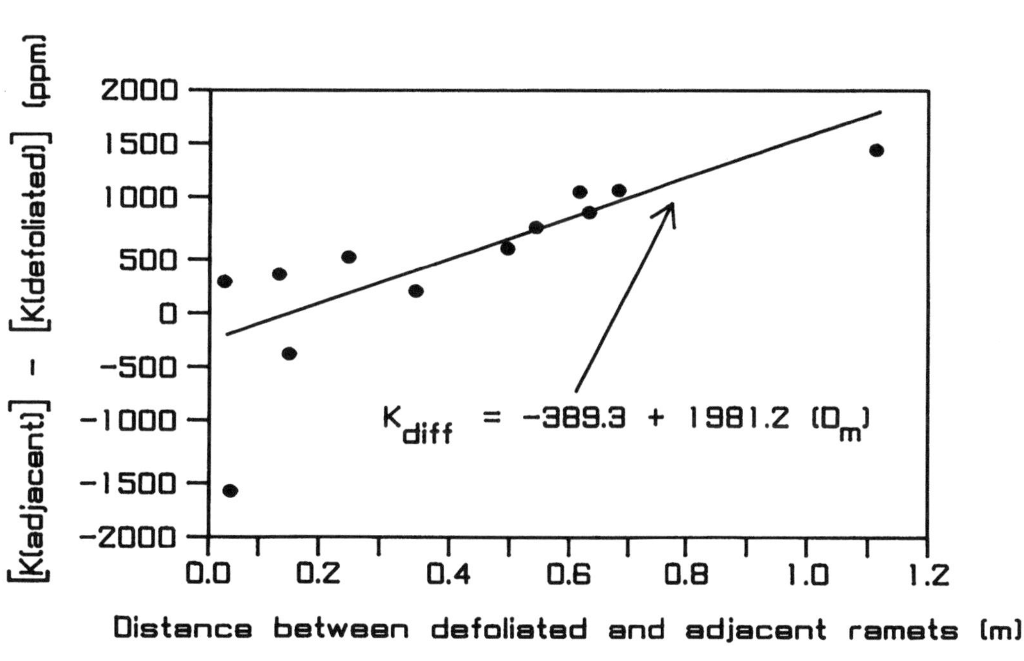

Figure 3. Difference in foliar potassium (K) concentrations (ppm dry weight) between the defoliated and the adjacent "control" ramets at Cass Lake in relation to distance (m) between them. Each point represents one defoliated and adjacent ramet pair.

between them increased. Neither phenolics nor any other element exhibited this kind of correlation with distance.

Defoliation Affecting Half or All Leaf Clusters on Single Branches

When 50 percent of the leaves from half of the leaf clusters of a single branch were cut in half, the remaining half leaves increased in phenolics (33 percent) and decreased in Fe (5 percent) and B (10 percent) (Table 3). Uncut leaves increased in Mg (2 percent) and Mn (20 percent). There were no other significant changes in the leaf chemistry. In the other case, where 25 percent of the leaves from all leaf clusters were affected, the remaining half leaves increased in phenolics (20 percent) and Al (24 percent) and decreased in P (7 percent) (Table 3). Uncut leaves also increased in phenolics (12 percent) but decreased in Mn (20 percent). There were significant defoliation-by-clone interactions affecting concentrations of N and Ca ($p < 0.01$) in remaining half leaves and Ca and Fe in uncut leaves, possibly indicating that all clones do not respond similarly to defoliation. No other statistically significant changes occurred.

Phenolics increased significantly in whole leaves only when all leaf cluster were damaged. Damaging only half of all clusters did not elicit significant changes in the phenolics of uncut leaves (Table 3). This indicates that the phenolic response to defoliation was localized at the level of leaf clusters. The increase in phenolics in whole leaves of partially defoliated clusters may have resulted from transport of phenolics or phenolic "elicitors" from the remaining half leaves to uncut leaves.

Responses to Defoliation in General

Cutting a leaf in half always increased the concentrations of phenolics, Al, and Cu in the remaining half and decreased its concentration of Fe and P. Although these changes were not always significant, in at least one case for each substance it was, and the direction of change was always consistent. This suggests that the measured responses were real, and that our sample size ($n = 12$ ramets) was marginal for detecting them. Na always increased and K always decreased in remaining half leaves, but in no case were these changes significant. All other elements exhibited inconsistent, insignificant responses except for B, which decreased significantly in remaining half leaves at Cloquet, but increased non-significantly in them at Cass Lake. When every other whole leaf on an entire ramet was completely excised at the petiole, the remaining whole leaves did not change in phenolic concentration. This suggests that damaged leaves must remain attached to the plant in order to elicit a wound reaction in the remaining whole leaves. Likewise, the single branch defoliation experiment suggested that there must be a damaged leaf within a leaf cluster to elicit a wound response by whole leaves belonging to that cluster.

The increase in foliar phenolics in response to defoliation was negatively correlated with the concentration of phenolics in the adjacent conclonal control ramet (Fig. 4). In other words, the change in phenolics (delta PH) induced by defoliation was related nonlinearly to the phenolic concentrations (PH_f) that the treated ramet would have achieved in the absence of defoliation: delta PH = -44.8 + 1.80 PH_f -0.01 PH_f^2, $R^2 = 0.27$. The higher the expected phenolic concentration in the absence of defoliation, the smaller the increase in phenolics

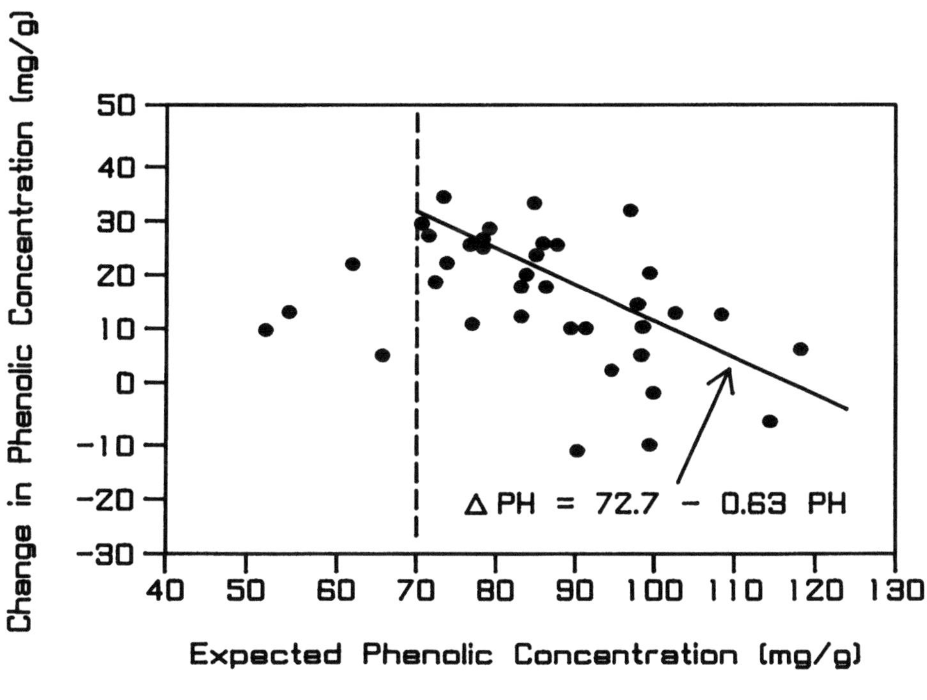

Figure 4. Absolute changes in foliar phenolic concentrations induced by defoliation in relation to the ramet's expected phenolic concentration attained in the absence of defoliation. Each point is a single ramet.

that resulted from defoliation, at least for expected levels between 70 mg/g and 120 mg/g (Fig. 4). The opposite appears to be the case for ramets having expected phenolic concentrations of less than 70 mg/g. At this lower end of the scale, ramets having the highest expected concentrations increased the most when defoliated. However, data on these low phenolic clones are sparse. These data clearly agree with those of Nef (in this volume) working with Populus clones: the induced foliar phenolic response per tree was negatively correlated with its normal constitutive level of foliar phenolics.

Trembling aspen and other trees in the genus Populus may have evolved a variety of responses to deal with herbivory. Some clones may maintain a normally high level of phenolics at all times and increase this level only slightly when defoliated (Nef in this volume). Others may have a generally low level but increase this level dramatically when wounded. For example, based on a regression (excluding data in Fig. 4 for clones with $PH_f < 70$ mg/m, delta PH = 72.7 - 0.63 PH_f, $r^2 = 0.36$)), a clone which would normally have attained 70 mg/g phenolics in absence of defoliation will attain 98 mg/g phenolics if it is defoliated, whereas a clone which normally attains a level of 110 mg/g in absence of defoliation will increase to only 113 mg/g. Perhaps clones which contain less than 70 mg/g phenolics lack the capacity to produce significant increases in phenolics when defoliated.

REFERENCES

Baltensweiler, W. 1984. The role of environment and reproduction in the population dynamics of the larch budmoth, Zeiraphera diniana Gn. (Lepidoptera: Tortricidae). In: Advances in invertebrate reproduction (W. Engels et al., Eds.). Elsevier Science Publishers B.V.; 3: 291-302.

Barnes, B. V. 1969. Natural variation and delineation of clones of Populus tremuloides and P. grandidentata in northern lower Michigan. Silvae Genetica 18: 130-142.

Ericsson, A., J. Hellkvist, K. Hillerdad-Hagerstomer, S. Larsson, E. Mattson-Djos, and O. Tenow. 1980. Consumption and pine-growth--Hypotheses on effects on growth processes by needle-eating insects. In: Structure and function of northern coniferous forests--an ecosystem study (T. Persson, Ed.). Ecol. Bull. 32; 537-545.

Ericsson, A., C. Hellqvist, B. Långström, S. Larsson, and O. Tenow. 1985. Effects of simulated and induced shoot pruning by Tomicus piniperda as related to carbohydrate and nitrogen dynamics in Scots pine. J. Appl. Ecol. 22: 105-124.

Feeny, P. and H. Bostock. 1968. Seasonal changes in the tannin content of oak leaves. Phytochem. 7: 871-880.

Haukioja, E., P. Niemelä, L. Iso-Iivari, H. Ojala, and E. Aro. 1978. Birch leaves as a resource for herbivores. I. Variation in the suitability of leaves. Kevo. Subarctic Research Station Rep. 14; 5-12.

Haukioja, E., P. Niemelä, and S. Siren. 1985. Foliage phenols, and nitrogen in relation to growth, insect damage, and ability to recover after defoliation, in the mountain birch Betula pubescens spp tortuosa. Oecologia 65: 214-222.
Hillis, W. E. and T. Swain. 1959. The phenolic constituents of Prunus domestica. II. The analysis of tissues of the Victoria plum tree. J. Sci. Food Agric. 10: 135-144.
Kosuge, T. 1969. The role of phenolics in host response to infection. Annu. Rev. Phytopath. 7: 195-222.
Landsberg, T. and F. R. Wylie. 1983. Water stress, leaf nutrients and defoliation: a model of dieback in rural eucalypts. Aust. J. Ecol. 8: 27-41.
McClure, M. S. 1980. Foliar nitrogen: a basis for host suitability for elongate scale, Fiorinia externa (Homoptera: Diaspididae). Ecology 6: 72-79.
Mika, A. 1986. Physiological responses of fruit trees to pruning. Hort. Rev. 8: 337-378.
Myers, T. H. and K. S. Williams. 1987. Lack of short or long term inducible defenses in the red alder-western tent caterpillar system. Oikos 48: 73-78.
Niemelä, P., E. Aro, and E. Haukioja. 1979. Birch leaves as a resource for herbivores. Damage-induced increase in leaf phenols with trypsin-inhibiting effects. Kevo. Subarctic Research Station Rep. 15: 37-40.
Phillips, R. and G. G. Henshaw. 1977. The regulation of synthesis of phenolics in stationary phase cell cultures of Acer pseudoplatanus L. J. Exper. Bot. 28: 785-794.
Piene, H. and K. Percy. 1984. Changes in needle morphology, anatomy, and mineral content during the recovery of protected balsam fir trees initially defoliated by the spruce budworm. Can. J. For. 14: 238-245.
Schultz, J. C. and I. T. Baldwin. 1982. Oak quality declines in response to defoliation by gypsy moth larvae. Science 217: 149-150.
Svejcar, T. and S. Christiansen. 1987. Grazing effects on water relations of Caucasian bluestem. J. Range Manage. 40: 15-18.
Thielges, B. A. 1968. Altered polyphenol metabolism in the foliage of Pinus sylvestris associated with European pine sawfly attack. Can. J. Bot. 46: 724-725.
Tuomi, J., P. Niemelä, E. Haukioja, S. Siren, and S. Neuvonen. 1984. Nutrient stress: an explanation for plant anti-herbivore responses to defoliation. Oecologia 64: 208-210.
Valentine, H. T., W. E. Wallner, and P. M. Wargo. 1983. Nutritional changes in host foliage during and after defoliation, and their relation to the weight of gypsy moth pupae. Oecologia 57: 298-302.
Wagner, M. R. and P. D. Evans. 1985. Defoliation increases nutritional quality and allelochemicals of pine seedlings. Oecologia 67: 235-237.
Waters, T. and H. A. Stafford. 1984. Variability in accumulation of proanthocyanidins (condensed tanins) in needles of Douglas-fir, Pseudotsuga menzeiesii, following long term budworm defoliation. J. Chem. Ecol. 10: 1469-1476.
Webb, W. L. and J. J. Karchesy. 1977. Starch content of Douglas fir defoliated by the tussock moth. Can. J. For. 7: 186-188.
Wratten, S. D., P. J. Edwards, and J. Dunn. 1984. Wound-induced changes in the palatability of Betula pubescens and B. pendula. Oecologia 64: 372-375.

10

The Role of Resin Acids in the Relationship Between Scots Pine and the Sawfly, *Diprion pini* (Hymenoptera: Diprionidae). I.—Resin Acids in the Needles

L. Buratti, J. P. Allais, and M. Barbier

Throughout the northern hemisphere, there are many sawflies of the family Diprionidae which defoliate conifers and sometimes cause significant damage during their outbreaks. For example, in North America, the pine sawflies: *Neodiprion swainei*, *Neodiprion rugifrons*, *Neodiprion dubiosus* and *Neodiprion lecontei* are important pests on jack pine, *Pinus banksiana*. In Europe, *Neodiprion sertifer*, *Microdiprion pallipes*, and *Diprion pini* cause widespread damage to Scots pine, *Pinus sylvestris*. In France, Scots pine is usually preferred by *D. pini*, but when Scots pine is unavailable, this insect also feeds on the black pines, *Pinus nigra* ssp. *laricio* and *austriaca*, or on introduced species such as *Pinus radiata* and *Pinus contorta*.

In the spring, the first *Diprion* sawfly instars always feed on 1-year-old foliage (mature foliage), and they do not willfully consume juvenile, current-year needles (May to June). This is also true for the following sawfly/pine couples: *N. rugifrons*, *N. swainei*, *N. dubiosus*/*P. banksiana* (Becker and Benjamin 1964, All and Benjamin 1975a); and *N. sertifer*/*P. sylvestris* (Larsson and Tenow 1980).

When sawfly larvae are reared on juvenile foliage only, they develop slower and weigh less than larvae reared on mature foliage. These facts are observed with the following sawfly/pine couples: *N. swainei*, *N. rugifrons*/*P. banksiana* (All and Benjamin 1975a); *N. sertifer*/*P. sylvestris* (Niemelä *et al*. 1984); and *D. pini*/*P. sylvestris* (Geri *et al*. 1985).

The larch sawfly, *Pristiphora erichsonii*, prefers tufted over single needles (Harman and Brown 1970) because of differences in their chemistry--primarily ether extractable compound(s) (Wagner *et al*. 1979). In the case of *N. rugifrons* and *N. swainei*, All and Benjamin (1975b) reported antifeedant activity in both polar and nonpolar extracts of jack pine needles. Ohigashi *et al*. (1981) identified several diterpene acids (Fig. 1) as antifeedants for the larch sawfly and

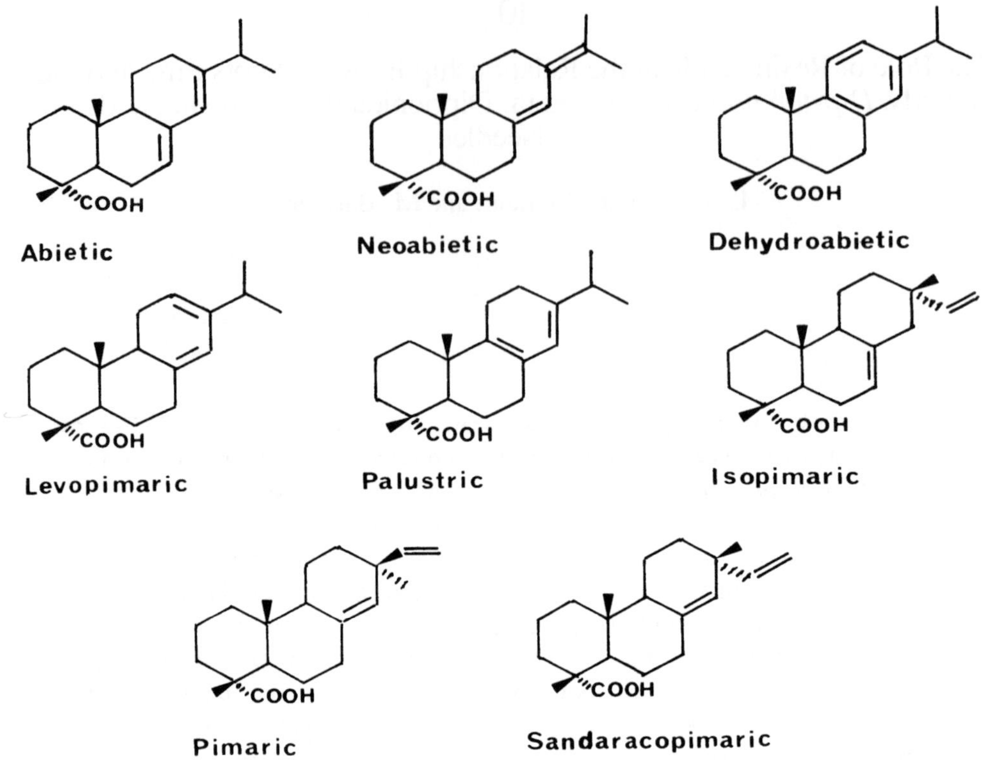

Figure 1. Abietane and pimarane diterpene acids.

Wagner and Benjamin (1981) implicated abietic acid as a growth inhibitor chemical for the same insect.

Schuh and Benjamin (1984a, 1984b) demonstrated that the chemicals by which *N. dubiosus*, *N. lecontei*, and *N. rugifrons* larvae chemically differentiate foliage are based on the foliar resin acids. Palustric acid is the most efficient feeding deterrent against the three species, whereas levopimaric acid is an antifeedant for *N. dubiosus*, and dehydroabietic and neoabietic acids are antifeedants for *N. rugifrons*. In the case of *P. erichsonii*, Wagner *et al.* (1983) showed that abietic, neoabietic, dehydroabietic, and isopimaric acids significantly reduced consumption rates, feeding efficiency, and growth rate of this insect. On the other hand, sandaracopimaric acid reduced growth and efficiency only but did not influence consumption rates.

Ikeda et al. (1977a, 1977b) claimed that they identified the two major antifeedants governing feeding behavior of N. rugifrons and N. swainei on jack pine--dehydroabietic acid and 13-keto 8(14)podocarpen 18-oic acid (Fig. 2). Ketopodocarpenoic acid was the most effective; it was responsible for approximatively 64 percent of the total feeding inhibition.

This component is present at high levels in juvenile foliage, but it decreases during the growing season. Niemelä et al. (1982) found the same negative correlation between the feeding period of N. sertifer and the levels of 13-keto 8(14)podocarpen 18-oic acid in P. sylvestris foliage.

The aim of this study was to find whether similar biochemicals prevent D. pini larvae from feeding on juvenile Scots pine needles. We also asked if 13-keto 8(14)podocarpen 18-oic acid could explain why this insect does not regularly develop on other pine species.

To test the long lasting inducible defense hypothesis (Haukioja and Hakala 1975, Haukioja 1980, Gref and Ericsson 1984), we measured changes in 13-keto 8(14)podocarpene 18-oic acid levels in P. sylvestris juvenile needles 1 year after defoliation.

MATERIAL AND METHODS

Biological Material

Scots pine needles were collected from a 10-year-old pine plantation near Orleans, France, at different dates in 1984. We also collected needles from 3- and 20-year-old pines. Further, mature

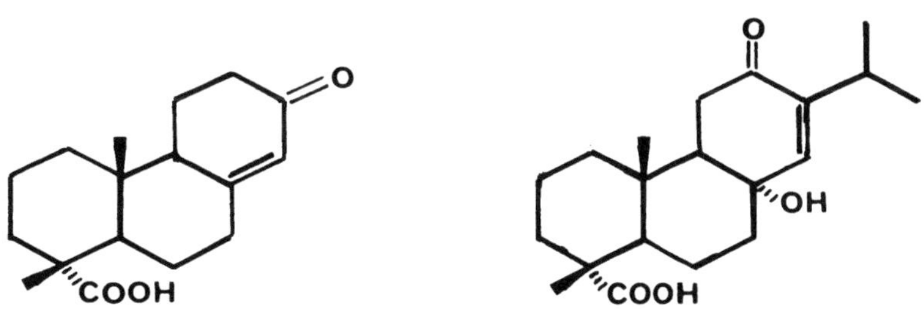

13-Keto 8(14)podocarpen 18-oic Acid

8-Hydroxy 12-keto 13(14) abieten 18-oic Acid

Figure 2. Ketopodocarpenoic acid and hydroxyketoabietenoic acid.

foliage (1-year-old) was collected from several other pine species: *P. contorta*, *P. pinaster*, *P. radiata*, *P. nigra* spp. *laricio*. They were all at least 10-years old. We measured the impact of artificial and natural defoliation on new foliage quality in 1984 (on July 19 and September 10, respectively).

Collected needles were frozen at -20 °C until analysis. We ground 50 g (fresh weight) of each needle type using a Waring blender and then extracted them with methanol dichloromethane 1/1 (v/v). The extracts were filtered through a glass fritted filter and then dried in a Buchi rotavapor at 20 °C. Needle DW was obtained by summing the dry weights of crude extract, filter residual, and the extracted needles.

Lipid Fractionation

The crude extract was fractioned into an acid lipid fraction (ALF) and a neutral lipid fraction (NLF) as indicated in Fig. 3. However, with the methanol/dichloromethane extraction we also had many other products such as polyphenols, carbohydrates, and amino acids. Therefore, the total lipid fraction (TLF) is only given by summing ALF with NLF.

ALF Analysis

ALF, containing diterpene resin acids, was chromatographied by reversed-phase H.P.L.C. (Perkin Elmer series 2A pumps with LC 75 UV-Visible detector) on Partisil-10 CCS/C8 M9 Whatman column (50 x 0.9 cm) and detected at 241 nm. The elution solvent was the mixture methanol/bidistilled water/isopropanol/orthophosphoric acid (350:150: 50:0.1 v/v). The flow rate was 3 ml/mn. We obtained a resin acid peak at 53 mn. H.P.L.C. allowed us to separate three major fractions (Fig. 4): first a polar acid fraction (PAF), then a resin acid fraction (one peak, RAF) composed of tricyclic diterpene resin acids (abietic, dehydroabietic, neoabietic, palustric, levopimaric, pimaric, isopimaric, and sandaracopimaric acids), and finally a polar weak acid fraction (WAF) obtained with a second eluent mixture: methanol/dichloromethane 1/1 (v/v).

13-Keto 8(14)Podocarpen 18-Oic Acid Synthesis

Following the experimental method of Pelletier *et al*. (1970), we methylated 100 mg of neoabietic acid (Helix Biotech, Ltd., Vancouver,

Canada) with diazomethane in 5 ml anhydrous ether. After complete evaporation, an ozonolysis reaction was carried with the methyl ester at -70 ^{o}C in 5 ml anhydrous ethyl acetate. The ozonide is opened by addition of 0.4 ml methyl sulfide. The resulting mixture was stirred at room temperature for 3 hours. Removal of solvent yields a yellow oil giving 45 mg enone ester after a preparative thin layer chromatography on silicic acid. This enone ester has all the physical data of the methyl 13-keto 8(14)podocarpene 18-oate. The enone ester is saponified with KOH 4N to yield an acid which we call neoabietone.

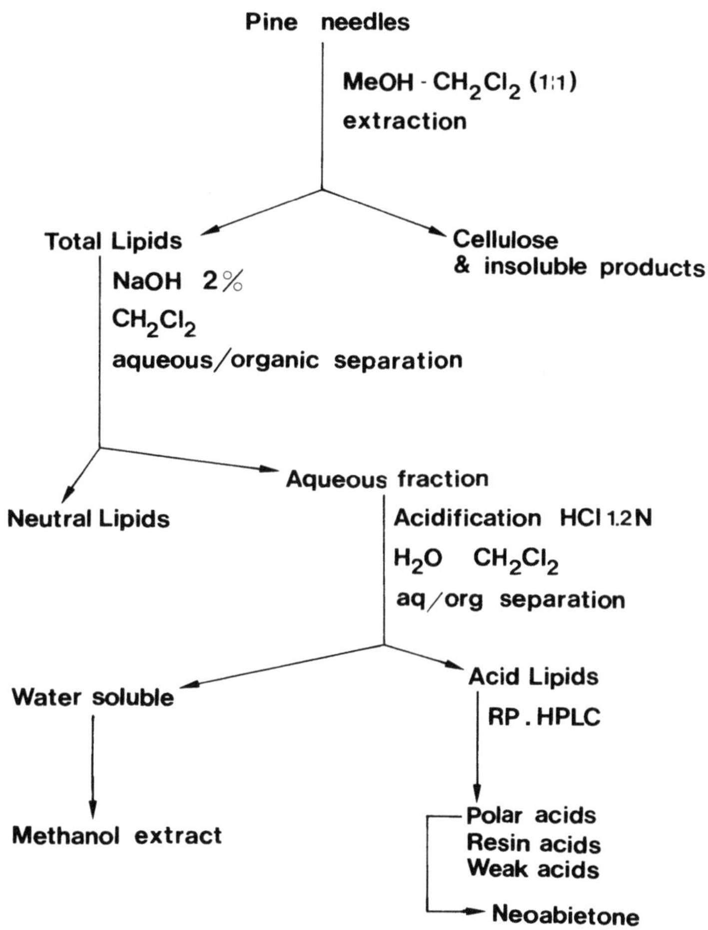

Figure 3. Fractionation of Scots pine lipids.

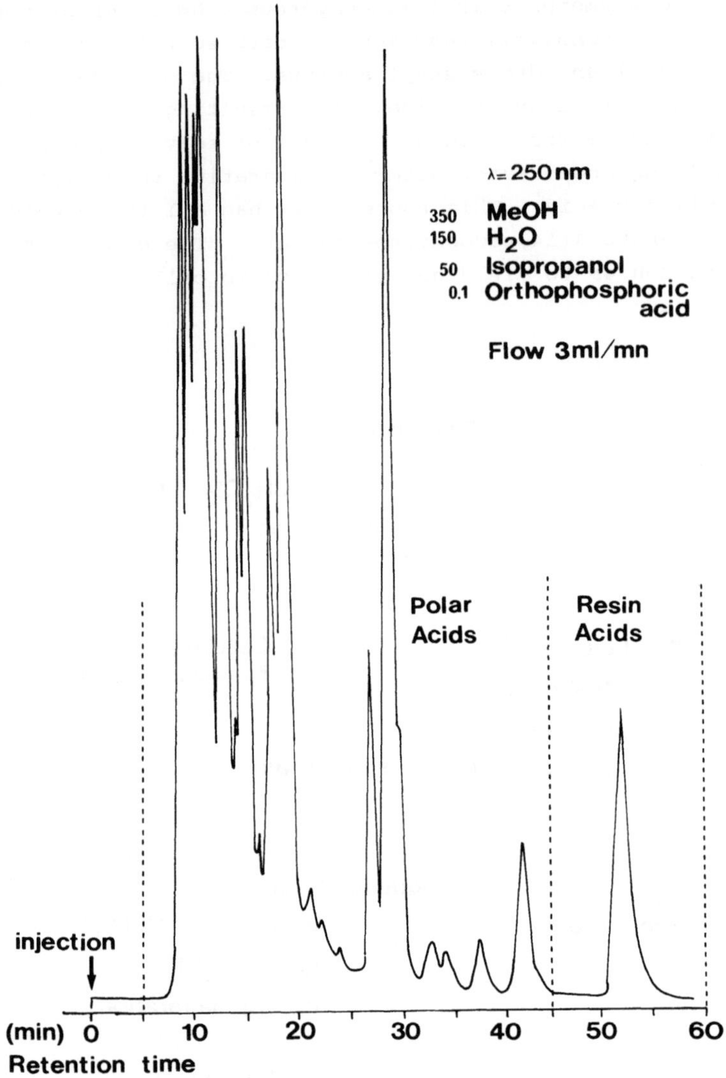

Figure 4. Reversed phase H.P.L.C. of ALF (for conditions, see text).

Purification, Isolation, and Dosage of Neoabietone

ALF or PAF were chromatographied by reversed-phase H.P.L.C. on ODS-2/C18 Whatman column (50 x 0.9 cm). The elution solvent was the mixture: methanol/bidistilled water/isopropanol/acetic acid (350:150: 50:0.1; v/v). The products were detected by UV absorption at 241 nm.

The flow rate was 2 ml/mn. The retention time of the neoabietone and close products is 27 mn.

This binary mixture was chromatographied again by reversed-phase H.P.L.C. on ODS(5 micron)/C18 Altex ultrasphere column (25 x 0.46 cm). The elution solvent is the mixture methanol/bidistilled water/isopropanol/acetic acid (350:250:50:0.1; v/v). The flow rate was 1 ml/mn. The neoabietone retention time was 9.5 mn and that of similar products was 12.25 mn.

The neoabietone dosage is carried with a comparative peak height between a known synthetic neoabietone solution and the natural product present in ALF or PAF.

CHANGING LIPIDS OF *P. SYLVESTRIS* DURING SHOOT DEVELOPMENT

TLF and ALF Seasonal Change

Figure 5 shows that Scots pine juvenile needles contain low levels of lipids in the early growing season when they emerge from

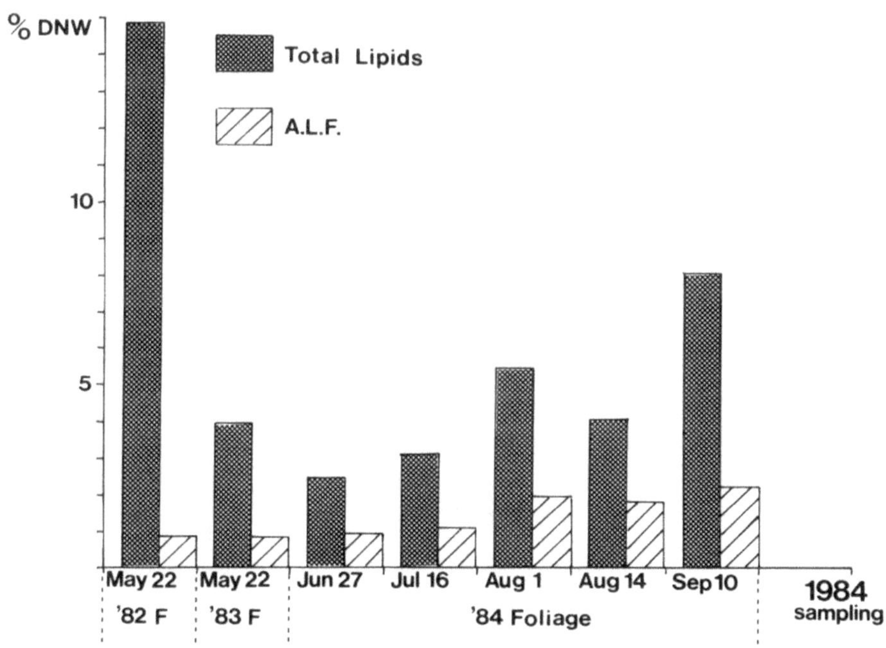

Figure 5. Total lipids and acid lipid fraction (ALF) in Scots pine needles (in percent of needle DW) during the 1984 growing season.

their fascicle sheaths. For example, on June 27, the juvenile needles contained only 2.5 percent lipids DW compared with 7 percent in late summer. Mature 1-year-old needles had 3.8 percent lipids and 2-year-old needles contained 15 percent during the same period.

Both total lipids and ALF increased linearly during the growing season. Moreover, the increasing ALF level seemed to be correlated with the annual plant cycle rather than with the age of the needles because the ALF level was almost the same for the juvenile foliage and for the 1- or 2-year-old needles (namely 0.77 to 0.87 percent of needle DW in June). In September, ALF was more than doubled. The polar acid fraction (PAF) level increased along with ALF. PAF represents 90 percent of ALF in spring and 70 percent of ALF in late summer (Fig. 6).

RESIN ACIDS OVER THE GROWING SEASON

One can see that the resin acid fraction (RAF) always stays low. In late spring, the RAF level was 0.015 percent of needle DW, and in late summer it was 0.06 percent of needle DW (Fig. 6).

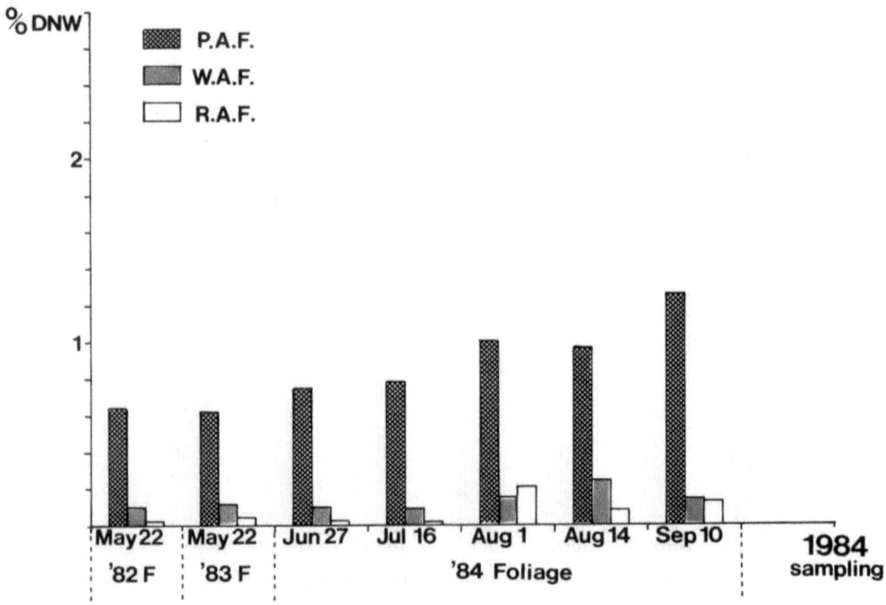

Figure 6. Polar, weak, and resin acid fractions (PAF, WAF, RAF) evolution in Scots pine needles (in percent of needle DW).

13-Keto 8(14)Podocarpen-18-Oic Acid (Neoabietone): Identification and Evolution

The ALF separation by H.P.L.C. gives a natural product that has the same retention time and the same physico-chemical data as the synthetic product (Table 1).

This natural product represents 0.015 percent to 0.063 percent of needle DW and 1 percent to 3 percent of ALF. The neoabietone level increases with the growing season--it is low in May and June and becomes higher in August and September (Fig. 7).

Hydroxy-12-Keto 13(14)Abieten-18-oic Acid Identification (Fig. 2.)

When we have isolated neoabietone, we get a retention time close to the product that we have identified as 8-hydroxy-12-keto 13(14)abieten-18-oic acid.

The U.V. absorption (in MeOH) at 224.5 nm ($\xi \approx 15000$) and 289.2 nm suggests the presence of an alpha-, beta-unsaturated ketone.

The broad I.R. absorption band at 3500-3300 cm^{-1} indicates the presence of a carboxylic acid group (COOH), whereas the absorption band at 3600 cm^{-1} with the product methylated by diazomethane indicates the presence of an hydroxyl group (OH). The absorption band

Table 1. Comparative physico-chemical data between synthetic and natural neoabietone.

	Synthetic product	Natural product
λ U.V. max(EtOH)	241.2 nm	241.1 nm
δ 1H.NMR. (CDC13)	0.863 ppm 1.220 ppm 5.920 ppm	0.852 ppm (3H, s, C4-Me) 1.218 ppm (3H, s, C10-Me) 5.891 ppm (1H, s, C14-H)
Mass m/e	276 261 232 231 230 167 139 123 121 110	276 261 232 231 230 167 139 123 110

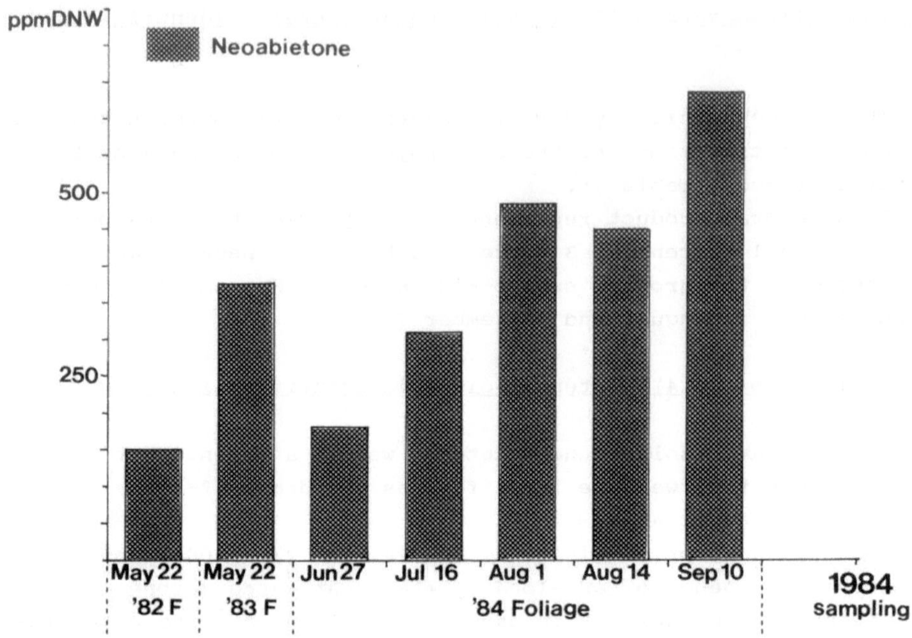

Figure 7. Neoabietone evolution in Scots pine needles (in ppm of needle DW).

at 1700 cm^{-1} and 1675 cm^{-1} is characteristic of a keto group (C=O) and of a carboxymethyl group (COOMe) for the methylated product.

The mass spectrum of the acid gives a molecular ion at m/e 334(M) and major fragment peaks at m/e: 316(M-18), 301(M-18-15), 288(M-46), 273(M-46-15), 255(M-46-15-18), 227, 213. The mass spectrum of the methyl ester gives a molecular ion at m/e 348(M) which indicates that we have only one carboxylic acid group.

Major fragment peaks are m/e: 330(M-18), 319, 316, 305, 288 (elimination of the C4 carboxymethyl group with one hydrogene), 270, 271, 149, 121.

The proton N.M.R. (in CDC13, 400 Mhz) spectrum of the methyl ester exhibits signals at: 0.661 ppm (3H,s,C10-Me), 1.035 ppm (3H,d) and 1.073 ppm (3H,d) for the isopropyl, 1.142 ppm (3H,s,C4-Me), 3.683 ppm (3H,s,COOMe), 6.383 ppm (1H,s,C14-proton). This NMR spectrum is in agreement with the literature's values for the 8 alpha-Hydroxy-12-keto 13(14)abietenoate, respectively (ppm): 0.65, 1.01, 1.04, 1.13, 3.68 (Herz et al. 1965, Herz and Schmid 1969).

However, we cannot compare this product with an authentic sample.

So, we suggest this foregoing structure for this product, because it can easily proceed by oxidation of the levopimaric acid (Moore and Lawrence 1959).

It seems that as for neoabietone in spring, this hydroxyketo-abietenoic acid has a low foliar level in the early growing season in both the juvenile and the mature needles.

EFFECTS OF PREVIOUS DAMAGE ON SCOTS PINE FOLIAGE LIPIDS

Artificial or natural defoliation in the previous year causes an increase in foliar lipids the next year (Table 2). The TLF is increasing, but the ALF stays at the same level during all the sampling period. We cannot make any conclusion about the neoabietone levels. So, if defoliation can induce a reaction inimical to diprionids outbreaks, it will not likely be in the ALF but rather in the NLF.

As we can see in Table 3, all the analyzed pines have neoabietone, but its level is highly variable from one species to another.

Table 2. Effects of previous damage on lipid content and dry weight of Scots pine foliage. S.D. = sampling dates; Prev. def. = previous defoliation. Artif. = artificial.

S.D.	Prev. def.	Dry[a] weight	Lipids[b]	Acid[b] lipids	Neoabietone[c]
		Grams	% DW	% DW	ppm
June 27	None	35.636	2.50	0.85	164
Jul 16	None	34.670	3.25	1.07	306
Jul 19	Artif.	21.873	6.65	0.93	298
Aug 1	None	22.253	5.35	1.87	489
Aug 14	None	29.286	4.00	1.65	455
Sep 10	None	24.030	7.10	2.05	634
Sep 10	Natural	25.400	12.10	1.20	71

[a]Dry weight of 50 g fresh needles (in grams).
[b]In percent of dry weight.
[c]In ppm of dry weight.

Table 3. Lipids and neoabietone levels in various pine species.

Species	Dry[a] weight	Lipids[b]	Acid[b] lipids	Neoabietone[c]
	Grams	% DW	% DW	ppm
P. sylvestris	38.3	3.9	0.78	354
P. contorta	32.25	16.9	1.03	4
P. pinaster	19.86	10.1	0.94	161
P. nigra	20.11	10.9	1.25	181
P. radiata	32.30	4.5	0.46	15

[a]Dry weight of 50 g fresh needles (in grams).
[b]In percent of Dry weight.
[c]In ppm of Dry weight.

DISCUSSION

On the Regulation of the Diprionid Population Dynamic by Diterpenes Resin Acids

The resin acid levels we found in the Scots pine needles amounted to 0.02 percent to 0.06 percent of needle DW compared with earlier reports of 3 percent to 4 percent of DW in the needles (Tobolski and Zinkel 1982) and 2 percent to 3 percent DW in the bark (Gref and Ericsson 1984) of Scots pine. However, it is difficult to compare our results with those of other authors because due to our experimental process, we have only abietane and primarane serials in RAF, whereas with the D.E.A.E. cellulose chromatography done by Tobolski and Zinkel (1982), other diterpene acids such as pinifolic acid, 4-epi-imbricataloic acid, and manoyl oxide acid are also isolated. Gref and Ericsson (1984) did not mention these products, but we believe that they occur in the acidic fraction if the Zinkel and Rowe (1964) separation process is used. So, if we isolate abietane and pimarane resin acids in the Tobolski and Zinkel (1982) data, they represent only 0.6 percent to 1.9 percent of needle DW.

For the first ones, the resin acids decrease from June to September (Tobolski and Zinkel 1982), and for the others the resin acids slightly increase (Gref and Ericsson 1984). Also, dehydroabietic and strobic acids increase (Bridgen and Hanover 1980) from May 15 to June 15, whereas the other resin acids slightly decrease.

Therefore, the RAF slightly increases during the growing season in correlation with a differential shoot elongation.

The lowest RAF level in spring for the 1- or 2-year-old foliage or the juvenile foliage (0.02 percent of NDW) must be compared with 0.06 percent of needle DW in late summer. It seems, therefore, that the total resin acid fraction fluctuates slightly from June to September.

We question whether the resin acids could act as repellents for the sawfly larvae because of their low level in the needles and their indefinite change during the growing season. Hence, we do not believe that resin acids are the main deterrents. Moreover, the quantities of pure resin acids added to sawfly diets during the rearing and feeding behavior experiments (Wagner and Benjamin 1981, 1983; Schuh and Benjamin 1984a, 1984b) were very high (0.5 to 10.0 mg/ml of solvent) relative to the resin acid level in needles.

In addition, we must remember that resin acids (except for dehydroabietic acid) are versatile compounds that are easily oxidizable. It's entirely possible that a nonactive resin acid becomes biologically active by oxidation during the experimentation. If we analyze the RAF impact on the diprionid development, we must emphasize the fact that all the experiments have occurred over long periods with resin acid supplemented needles. Therefore, we question whether the resin acids or their degradation products are the repellents.

On the Presence of 13-Keto 8(14)Podocarpen 18-Oic Acid (Neoabietone) and 8-Hydroxy 12-Keto 13(14) Abietene-18-Oic Acid in the Needles

When Ikeda *et al*. (1977a) found neoabietone in the pine needles, they correctly thought they had a product which governed the differential feeding behavior of *N*. *rugifrons* and *N*. *swainei* on *P*. *banksiana*, because neoabietone was antifeedant against the two diprionids and its rate was decreasing during the growing season. This decreasing neoabietone level allowed the larvae to feed only on mature or 1-year-old foliage.

Then, Niemelä *et al*. (1982) reported the same results for *N*. *sertifer* on *P*. *sylvestris*. They confirmed the presence of neoabietone and its decreasing level between June and September by measuring the U.V. absorption at 240 to 242 nm of products isolated with a thin layer chromatography. However, using this experimental process, the U.V. absorption at 240 to 242 nm could also be attributable to many other products besides neoabietone. Our results suggest that the conclusions of Ikeda *et al*. (1977a) do not apply to diprionids on *P*.

sylvestris. For example, our experiments show that Scots pine needles always contain neoabietone. This level fluctuates between 0.01 and 0.06 percent of needle DW which is close to those obtained by Ikeda et al. (1977a) with P. banksiana needles. But we find quite the opposite time-pattern: lowest levels are in spring in the juvenile foliage, with increasing levels thereafter. So, it is difficult to correlate the diprionid establishment on Scots pine needles with neoabietone levels.

Neoabietone is a constituent of the PAF, and PAF is more than 80 percent of the ALF increasing from spring to late September. In PAF, we also find the 8-alpha-hydroxy 12-keto 13(14)abieten 18-oic acid. Many oxygenated compounds can easily be derivated from resin acids: for instance, neoabietone from neoabietic acid and 8-alpha-hydroxy 12-keto 13(14)abieten 18-oic acid from levopimaric acid. It seems that an increase in oxygenated diterpenes is correlated with the resin acid metabolism which parallels shoot elongation.

On the Effects of Previous Damage on Scots Pine Foliage Lipids

Long lasting defenses induced by defoliation have been proposed to play a crucial role in the collapse of insect populations (Haukioja and Hakala 1975, Haukioja 1980). The Diprionidae give rise to sudden and spectacular outbreaks throughout Europe followed by a similarly rapid collapse. Therefore, it is interesting to ask if this pattern of population change could be correlated to a long-lasting resistance induced by defoliation.

Gref and Ericsson (1984) show that the total resin acid concentration increased after wounding Scots pine. The most significant increases occurred for dehydroabietic acid. But, the accumulation of these acids were only localized in tissues adjacent to the wounds, and there is no data to support a possible long-lasting resin acid production.

Niemelä et al. (1984) concluded that there is neither short-term nor long-term damage-induced defenses in the mature foliage of Scots pine against diprionid sawflies. They also proposed that deterrents, such as neoabietone in high concentrations, could save current year needles and thus the whole tree if the defoliators used only the older needles having low concentrations of deterrents.

Our results show that defoliation induces an increase in neutral lipids but no change in acid lipids. So, if defoliation can induce a defensive reaction of Scots pine, the responsible natural product must be in the NLF rather than in ALF.

On the Differential Feeding Behavior of D. Pini

In France, *D. pini* chiefly attacks and outbreaks on *P. sylvestris*. *P. nigra* ssp. *laricio* and *austriaca* are attacked and only partially defoliated at the end of outbreaks (Dusaussoy and Geri 1966, Geri and Goussard 1984). *P. contorta* and *P. radiata* can also be infested but to a lesser extent.

Our results (Table 3) show that it is not possible to correlate this feeding behavior to the variations in neoabietone levels among the different pines as has been suggested by many authors. *P. pinaster* is never infested by *D. pini* and contains a mean level of neoabietone (161 ppm of needle DW). *P. contorta* and *P. radiata* contain the lowest neoabietone levels, and *P. sylvestris*, the principal host of *D. pini*, contains the highest levels (354 ppm of needle DW).

Considering the ALF concentrations, no correlation is possible: all levels fluctuate between 0.78 and 1.25 percent of needle DW except *P. radiata* where ALF concentration is 0.46 percent.

GENERAL CONCLUSION

It is well established that the juvenile foliage is usually a deterrent for diprionid larvae. However, it is difficult at this time to correlate this biological fact with the existence of a known foliar compound in the lipid fraction.

REFERENCES

All, J. N. and D. M. Benjamin. 1975a. Deterrent(s) in jack pine, *Pinus banksiana*, influencing larval feeding behavior and survival of *Neodiprion swainei* and *N. rugifrons*. Ann. Entomol. Soc. Am. 68: 495-499.

All, J. N. and D. M. Benjamin. 1975b. Influence of needle maturity on larval feeding preference and survival of *Neodiprion swainei* and *N. rugifrons* on jack pine, *Pinus banksiana*. Ann. Entomol. Soc. Am. 68: 579-584.

Becker, G. C., Jr. and D. M. Benjamin. 1964. Biology of the swaine jack-pine sawfly in Wisconsin. Can. Entomol. 96: 589-599.

Bridgen, M. R. and J. W. Hanover. 1980. Indirect selection for pest resistance using terpenoid compounds. Resist. Dis. Pests, For. Trees, Proc. Int. Workshop Genet. Host-parasite interaction For. 3rd, 161-168.

Dusaussoy, G. and C. Geri. 1966. Etude d'une population de *Diprion pini* (Hym: symphytes) en foret de Fontainebleau. I. Données biologiques sur *Diprion pini* et sur les principaux parasites. Ann. Soc. Entomol. Fr. (N.S.) 2: 503-534.

Geri, C., J. P. Allais, F. Goussard, A. Liger, and A. Yart. 1985. Incidence de l'age du feuillage sur le développement de *Diprion pini* L. (Hymenoptera: Diprionidae). Conséquences sur l'évolution des populations. Acta Oecologica, Oecol. Applic. 6(4): 349-365.

Geri, C. and F. Goussard. 1984. Evolution d'une nouvelle gradation de lophyre du Pin (Diprion pini) dans le sud du bassin parisien. I. -Développement de la gradation jusqu'en 1982 et relation avec les facteurs du milieu. Ann. Sci. For. 41(4): 375-404.

Gref, R. and A. Ericsson. 1984. Wound-induced changes of resin acid concentrations in living bark of Scots pine seedlings. Can. J. For. Res. 15: 92-96.

Harman, D. M. and M. L. Brown. 1970. Feeding habits of the larch sawfly Pristiphora erichsonii (Hymenoptera: Tenthredinidae) on Japanese larch in Maryland. Chesapeake Sci. 11: 183-190.

Haukioja, E. 1980. On the role of plant defenses in the fluctuation of herbivore populations. Oikos 35: 202-213.

Haukioja, E. and T. Hakala. 1975. Herbivore cycles and periodic outbreaks. Formulation of a general hypothesis. Kevo. Subartic Research Station Rep. 12; 1-9.

Herz, W. and J. J. Schmid. 1969. Resin acids XVI. Some transformations of methyl 12-alpha-hydroxy 13-beta-abiet-8(9)ene 18-oate. J. Org. Chem. 34: 2775-2777.

Herz, W., H. J. Wahlborg, W. D. Lloyd, W. H. Schuller, and G. W. Hedrick. 1965. Resin acids IV. 12-hydroxyabietic acid and its reduction. J. Org. Chem. 30: 3190-3195.

Ikeda, T., F. Matsumura, and D. M. Benjamin. 1977a. Mechanism of feeding discrimination between matured and juvenile foliage by two species of pine sawflies. J. Chem. Ecol. 3: 677-694.

Ikeda, T., F. Matsumura, and D. M. Benjamin. 1977b. Chemical basis for feeding adaptation of pine sawflies Neodiprion rugifrons and N. swainei. Science 197: 497-499.

Larsson, S. and O. Tenow. 1980. Needle eating insects and grazing dynamics in a mature Scots pine forest in central Sweden. In: Structure and function of northern coniferous forests--an ecosystem study (T. Persson, Ed.). Ecol. Bull. 32; 269-306.

Moore, R. N. and R. V. Lawrence. 1959. Preparation of 6-hydroxydehydroabietic acid from the photoperoxide of levopimaric acid. J. Am. Chem. Soc. 81: 458-460.

Niemelä, P., R. Mannila, and P. Mantsälä. 1982. Deterrent in Scots pine Pinus sylvestris influencing feeding behavior of the larvae of Neodiprion sertifer (Hymenoptera: Diprionidae). Ann. Entomol. Fenn. 48: 57-59.

Niemelä, P., J. Tuomi, R. Mannila, and P. Ojala. 1984. The effect of previous damage on the quality of Scots pine foliage as food for Diprionid sawflies. Z. Angew. Entomol. 98: 33-43.

Ohigashi, H., M. R. Wagner, F. Matsumura, and D. M. Benjamin. 1981. Chemical basis for differential feeding behavior of the larch sawfly, Pristiphora erichsonii (Hartig). J. Chem. Ecol. 7: 599-614.

Pelletier, S. W., K. N. Iyer, and C. W. J. Chang. 1970. Oxidative degradation of resin acids. J. Org. Chem. 35: 3535-3538.

Schuh, B. A. and D. M. Benjamin. 1984a. Evaluation of commercial resin acids as feeding deterrents against Neodiprion dubiosus, N. lecontei, and N. rugifrons (Hymenoptera: Diprionidae). J. Econ. Entomol. 77: 802-805.

Schuh, B. A. and D. M. Benjamin. 1984b. The chemical feeding ecology of Neodiprion dubiosus Schedl., N. rugifrons Midd., and N. lecontei Fitch. on jack pine Pinus banksiana Lamb. J. Chem. Ecol. 10: 1071-1079.

Tobolski, J. J. and D. F. Zinkel. 1982. Variation in needle and cortex resin acids during shoot development in Pinus sylvestris, P. nigra, and P. strobus. For. Sci. 28: 785-796.

Wagner, M. R. and D. M. Benjamin. 1981. Allelochemics and nutritional indices for larch sawfly, Pristiphora erichsonii (Hartig): A specialist feeding on larix spp. J. Chem. Ecol. 7: 167-174.

Wagner, M. R., D. M. Benjamin, K. M. Clancy, and B. A. Schuh. 1983. Influence of diterpene resin acids on feeding and growth of larch sawfly *Pristiphora erichsonii* Hartig. J. Chem. Ecol. 9: 119-127.

Wagner, M. R., T. Ikeda, D. M. Benjamin, and F. Matsumura. 1979. Host derived chemicals: the basis for preferential feeding behavior of the larch sawfly, *Pristiphora erichsonii* (Hymenoptera: Tenthredinidae), on tamarack, *Larix laricina*. Can. Entomol. 111: 165-169.

Zinkel, D. F. and J. W. Rowe. 1964. A rapid method for the quantitative separation without alteration of ether-soluble acidic and neutral materials. Anal. Chem. 36: 1160-1161.

11

The Role of Resin Acids in the Relationship Between Scots Pine and the Sawfly, *Diprion Pini* (Hymenoptera: Diprionidae). II.—Correlations with the Biology of *Diprion pini*

C. Geri, L. Buratti, and J. P. Allais

In the southern Paris basin, Diprion pini larvae mainly attack Scots pine, Pinus sylvestris. They sometimes attack black pines, Pinus nigra ssp. laricio and austriaca, after outbreaks have developed on Scots pine. It does not attack maritime pine, P. pinaster, but can occasionally be observed on introduced species such as P. radiata and, especially, P. contorta.

In France, this insect is mostly bivoltine. In April, the first generation's eggs (spring cohort) are laid on 1-year-old foliage. The larval colonies feed on this foliage from late May until July. They consume little current-year foliage, only in the late growing season. The larvae then transform into eonymphs and weave cocoons from which adults emerge in late July to August. They lay eggs on current-year foliage, which gives rise to the second generation. These second generation larvae feed on current-year foliage from September to October or November. They overwinter in the cocoon stage.

However, some eonymphs of each generation may go into a prolonged diapause ranging from a few months to 3 years, emerging in either June or August (Geri and Goussard 1984). The June or summer cohort adults are scarce. The August emerging populations are easily confused with the usual second generation (autumn cohort). The diapause depends on external conditions (day length, temperature) and on complex physiological processes based on transmission of over-generation information (Geri 1986). The spring cohort is generally exposed to long daylight hours and evolves without diapause (Geri and Goussard 1984). But if they are late in developing for some reason, they are exposed to decreasing daylight, and they all undergo diapause. Moreover, the percentage of diapausing larvae increases when insects come from nondiapausing generations.

Outbreaks can occur quickly and are generally composed of low-diapausing and low-parasitized insects. One year later, usually in the autumn, the outbreak is at the highest level and causes spectacular defoliations. Then the starvation, parasitism, and rodent predation on cocoons become important; likewise, a great part of the sawfly population undergoes diapause (Geri and Goussard 1984, Geri 1986). During the next spring, the residual populations are usually decimated by parasitism and by other important mortality, perhaps occurring from poor nutrition. High populations may reappear 1 or 2 years later from the diapausing sawflies and sometimes cause reinfestations (Dusaussoy and Geri 1971, Geri 1986).

Contrary to expectation, there is a positive relationship between foliar levels of the resin acid neoabietone and diprion sawfly development (Buratti _et al_. in this volume). In fact, a high level of neoabietone is correlated with the period of maximal foliage consumption. However, this correlation does not imply that there is any benefit from consuming neoabietone. Herein we report on several experiments to define how diterpene resin acids and foliage quality influence the feeding behavior and several other performance characteristics (development rate, mortality, weight gain, sex-ratio, fecundity, and diapause). We carry out feeding bioassays on different kinds of foliage (1-year-old, juvenile, and previously defoliated pine foliage), and on 1-year-old foliage (mature foliage) coated with needle extracted fractions or diterpene resin acids.

EXPERIMENTAL

General Considerations

All bioassays were carried out with larvae of the last three instars collected in infested forests near Orleans or reared in a pine plantation. Following All and Benjamin (1975a, 1975b), the feeding behavior bioassays were executed at 20 °C in the laboratory. Larvae were deposited on both sides of a twig having two types of foliage--juvenile and mature. To physically separate the two kinds of needles, each twig was artificially defoliated at the mid-point. The control branches (only mature foliage) were treated in the same manner.

Other bioassays were carried out with diterpene resin acids, needle extracts, or solvent alone (ether) applied on 1-year-old foliage. Rearing experiments were carried out with different kinds of foliage either in an external shelter, in cages on isolated pines, or in a laboratory at 20 °C and 16h/8h photoperiod.

Some whole trees in a plantation were deprived of their old foliage to force consumption of juvenile foliage. In other cases, we gave fresh foliage to the larvae every 2 or 3 days. Every time we supplied foliage, we sprayed chemicals on the fresh needles.

We measured the following biological characteristics: mortality, time of development, cocoon weight, sex-ratio, percentage of diapausing eonymphs, adult emergence, and fecundity (ten female dissections). To minimize heterogeneity, in some cases we worked with larvae of the same colony.

Foliage Bioassays

Using different sources of sawfly larvae (4th to 6th instars), we carried out a feeding behavior bioassay with 1-year-old foliage (control) and with different age-classes of current-year foliage (June 14, June 18, July 12, July 26, August 20, 1983), replicated at least 6 times at every date.

In 1983, we carried out a rearing experiment on juvenile and mature foliage collected in Fontainebleau Forest on June 28 (1-year old) under shelter (2 x 150 (L5)). The cocoons were stocked at 20 ^{o}C, 16h/8h photoperiod.

In 1984, we carried out a rearing experiment on juvenile and mature foliage in a pine plantation. We used 6 colonies (70 to 95 larvae each) coming from insects collected in Orleans in 1983, 3 were reared on a control pine and 3 others (from the third instar) on old-foliage of artificially defoliated pines (June 20).

We executed another rearing experiment in 1984 on juvenile and mature foliage under laboratory conditions. We used 3 colonies (80 to 160 larvae, same origin, and all were reared at 20 ^{o}C, 16h photophase). Two colonies were divided into two groups of L3 (June 20), one reared on juvenile foliage, the other on mature foliage, and the third colony was reared totally on mature foliage.

In 1985, we carried out a rearing experiment on juvenile and mature foliage with and without previous defoliation. Four groups of 50 (L4) collected in Rambouillet Forest were reared in the laboratory on normal pine foliage, two groups on mature foliage, two others on juvenile foliage. Four other groups of 40 (L4) were set in the same manner on foliage of a pine previously defoliated in spring 1984.

Abietic Acid Bioassays

This diterpene resin acid or its metabolic derivatives may be biologically active. We tested it in 1984 on both spring and autumn cohorts. On June 21, 350 (L3) insects collected in Orleans Forest (1983) were divided into 7 experimental groups (50 larvae each): control, solvent-control (methanol); and abietic acid at 2.5 mg, 5 mg, 10 mg, 20 mg, and 40 mg by ml solvent.

On September 7, 400 insects (L3) collected from the second generation were divided into 8 experimental groups (50 larvae each): control, solvent-control (methanol), and abietic acid at 5 mg/ml and 40 mg/ml with two replicates.

Extracted Fractions and Neoabietone Bioassays

After foliage extraction, we tested the total lipid fraction (TLF), neutral lipid fraction (NLF), and acid lipid fraction (ALF). ALF was divided into polar acid fraction (PAF), resin acid fraction (RAF), and weak acid fraction (WAF). So far we have tested only PAF. In these experiments, we also tested synthetic neoabietone (Buratti 1985, Buratti et al. 1986).

RAF contains classical tricyclic diterpene resin acids (abietic, dehydroabietic, neoabietic, palustric, levopimaric, pimaric, isopimaric, and sandaracopimaric acids). PAF contains many oxydated diterpenes as neoabietone. PAF is the most important acid fraction in the needle extracts, and its level increases slowly until August.

Two feeding behavior bioassays were carried out: (1) The first one (spring cohort) on June 28 with 8 experimental groups of 20 (L3) (10 on each side) collected in the Rambouillet Forest: mature foliage (MF) as control, MF + solvent (ether), MF + 0.1 mg/ml and MF + 0.5 mg/ml methylated neoabietone (2 replications each). (2) The second one (autumn cohort), on October 3, with 13 experimental groups of 10 (L5) (5 on each side) collected in the Orleans Forest: mature foliage (MF) + solvent, MF + TLF, MF + NLF, MF + ALF (4 mg/ml and 40 mg/ml for each fraction, replicated twice for the last 3 groups). The foliage extracts were derived from June foliage (juvenile) and laid drop-by-drop on the needles. The twigs were 10 cm long with 10 needles on each side. Larval movement was measured at 1h, 2h, 3h, 4h, and 20h after release.

Two rearing experiments were carried out: (1) The first one (spring cohort) on June 25, with 16 experimental groups of 50 (L3), collected in the Rambouillet Forest: mature foliage (MF) as control, MF + solvent (ether), MF + June NLF (23 mg/10 ml), MF + June PAF (12 mg/10 ml), MF + September NLF (23 mg/10 ml), MF + September PAF (12 mg/10 ml), MF + methylated neoabietone (0.06 mg/10 ml), MF + methylated neoabietone (0.6 mg/10 ml), replicated twice. (2) The second

second one (autumn cohort) on September 20, with 2 colonies, each divided into 4 experimental groups of 30 (L4), collected in the Orleans Forest: mature foliage (MF) as control, MF + TLF (80 mg/10 ml), MF + NLF (64 mg/10 ml), MF + ALF (56 mg/10 ml). The fractions are extracted from current-year June foliage (juvenile).

During all of these experiments, foliage consumption was estimated by measuring larval frass weight or volume (Buratti 1985).

RESULTS

Foliage Bioassays

Feeding Behavior. In all the experiments using twigs with only mature foliage (juvenile foliage removed), the larvae settled in a uniform distribution on both sides (foliated and defoliated) of the twigs (Table 1). In the others, with both mature and juvenile foliage, the larvae steadily left the juvenile foliage and selected the mature foliage (Table 1). This reaction was most obvious on June 14 (1 month after budbreak), then gradually became less pronounced with time. The current-year foliage was no longer deterrent or repellent at the end of July.

Table 1. Mean percentage of larvae settling on (A) the juvenile foliage of twigs and on (B) the corresponding defoliated part of control twigs having only mature needles after 1h, 2h, 3h, 4h, of experiment (10 larvae PGR replication).

Dates	A					B				
	Twigs with juvenile and mature foliage					Twigs with only mature foliage				
	No. of rep.	1h	2h	3h	4h	No. of rep.	1h	2h	3h	4h
June 14	12	34	20	13	8	6	49	48	48	49
June 28	18	37	23	16	10	6	49	49	45	47
July 12	6	39	35	30	29	6	52	56	61	57
July 26	4	49	46	47	50	/	/	/	/	/
August 29	6	49	48	48	49	6	47	45	48	48

Rearing Experiment. From the 1983 experiment, we learned that the consumption of juvenile foliage caused (1) higher larval mortality (81 percent compared to 31 percent on mature foliage; (2) lower cocoon weight (♂♂ 55 ± 1 mg, ♀♀ 105 ± 3 mg versus 65 ± 4 mg and 133 ± 4 mg on mature foliage) and also lower cocoon size and diameter; (3) longer mean life time in the cocoon: 8.4 days (♂♂) and 10.6 days (♀♀) reported to 7.6 days and 9.8 days between the mean dates of cocoon spinning and adult emergence; (4) lower fecundity (74 ± 15 eggs versus 129 ± 12 eggs); and (5) slightly higher numbers of males.

For the 1984 experiments, we found important differences between laboratory and plantation experiments (Table 2). In the laboratory, larval development is faster at least for larvae feeding on mature foliage, and cocoons are larger. Males emerge 4 to 5 days before females. This asynchrony is not observed in the pine plantation. In spite of these differences, the effects of the diet are obvious. The mortality is higher on juvenile foliage and so is the ratio of males; cocoon weight and fecundity are reduced, and eonymph development time is increased.

Finally, there was a higher percentage of diapausing insects when reared on juvenile foliage under laboratory conditions (Table 2), but not for insects reared in the whole pine plantation.

Our 1985 experimental results (Table 3) confirm the effects of diet. Larval and eonymph mortality is much higher on juvenile foliage, cocoon weight is lower, and larval development time is longer ($p < .01$). These differences between juvenile and mature foliage are observed both with the control trees and with the previously defoliated trees. However, insects from these two treatments have different developmental rates. Larval development is faster on the defoliated pines. There are no differences in mortality, and nearly all the insects undergo diapause.

Abietic Acid Bioassays

1984 Spring Cohort. As was noted by Geri et al. 1985, there are no effects of abietic acid on mortality, cocoon weight, and percentage going into eonymph diapause. However, there was a difference in emergence time after diapause: most control group adults emerged during the first days of July 1985, whereas most of the solvent group emerged in August 1985, and the abietic acid groups emerged even later in September 1985 and June 1986.

1984 Autumn Cohort. Table 4 shows that abietic acid has little effect on mortality, cocoon weight, and fecundity. However, with the highest treatment level (40 mg/ml abietic acid), larval and eonymph

Table 2. Mean performance of larvae reared on juvenile and mature foliage in the field and laboratory. 1984 spring cohort.

Insect performance variables	Field-raised colonies				Laboratory-raised colonies				
	Mature foliage				Mature foliage			Juvenile foliage	
	Colony 1	Colony 2	Colony 3	Colony 4	Colony 1	Colony 2	Colony 3	Colony 4	Colony 5
Larval mortality (%)	9.9	24.0	7.1	58.8	10.5	2.6	8.4	50.0	51.6
Eonymphs[a] mortality (%)	0.0	5.4	1.3	49.4	0.0	1.3	46.7	14.3	67.7
Sex ratio[b] (males/ females x 100)	78	68	39	114	35	68	52	110	158
Time to 50% cocooning (days)	19.7	18.7	17.7	13.7	16.7	10.7	11.7	26.7	16.7
Development time (egg → cocoon) days	85.7	82.4	84.2	78.2	84.3	71.9	75.3	85.1	79.7
Development time (cocoon → adult) days	14.4	14.2	14.0	18.5	17.5	20.9	19.6	36.0	28.01
Male cocoon weight (mg)	55	48	55	39	73	72	67	50	56
Female cocoon weight (mg)	108	101	111	83	157	152	153	127	127
Emergence without diapause (%)[c]	69.0	92.4	74.4	89.1	43.7	35.6	46.5	16.7	10.0
Number of eggs/ female	81.5 ± 3.2		49.2 ± 12.4						

[a]1Estimated 1 year after cocoon spinning.
[b]Number of males/number of females x 100.
[c]In percent of cocoons with dead and parasitized indiduals removed.

Table 3. Mean performance of larvae reared on juvenile and mature foliage of control and defoliated trees. 1985 spring cohort.

Insect performance variables	Control trees				Defoliated trees			
	Mature foliage		Juvenile foliage		Mature foliage		Juvenile foliage	
	Colony 1	Colony 2	Colony 1	Colony 2	Colony 1	Colony 2	Colony 1	Colony 2
Larval mortality (%)	16	28	28	18	15	15	17.5	17.5
Eonymphs mortality (%)	0	2.8	11.1	12.2	0	0	15.2	12.1
Sex ratio (males/ females x 100)	40	9	50	37	22	42	27	6
Time to 50% cocooning (days)	16.7	17.7	19.7	17.7	12.7	14.7	16.7	17.7
Development time (4th → cocoon) days	19.9	22.2	24.6	20.8	17.4	18.8	20.9	21.2
Male cocoon weight (mg)	67	73	63	58	63	58	53	50
Female cocoon weight (mg)	142	136	125	116	138	130	114	115
Emergence without diapause (%)	0	0	0	0	0	3.5	0	0

Table 4. Mean performance of larvae reared on different foliar treatments with abietic acid. 1984 autumn cohort.

Insect performance variables	Foliage treatments			
	Control	Solvent	Abietic 5 mg/ml	Acid 40 mg/ml
Larval mortality (%)	15.6	8.7	30.0	10.7
Eonymphs mortality (%)	6.6	2.4	3.2	0.0
Sex ratio (males/ females x 100)	19	9	34	17
Time to 50% cocooning (days)	26.9	24.9	26.9	29.9
Development time (3d → cocoon) days	18.6	17.6	18.3	22.5
Development time (cocoon → adult) days	22.9	21.8	22.2	24.4
Male cocoon weight (mg)	63	71	64	70
Female cocoon weight (mg)	128	136	126	127
Emergence without diapause (%)	62.0	74.0	67.0	42.0
Eonymphs remaining in diapause (%)	25.4	18.2	18.2	51.9
Number of eggs/ female	113.0	128.1	109.6	112.6

development times were longer and the diapause rate was higher ($p \leq .01$). The increasing percentage of diapause was especially true for females.

Foliage Extracted Fractions and Neoabietone Bioassays

Feeding Behavior. For the 1985 spring cohort, there were no differences in feeding behavior with respect to any treatments. On the other hand, for the 1985 autumn cohort, branches treated with different lipid fractions (TLF, NLF, ALF) all showed decreasing numbers of larvae on treated sides of twigs (Table 5). The most important effect was observed for NLF: its effect increases with the dose. This was not true for ALF. For all the fractions except NLF, after 20h, the larvae come back to the treated twig side when the control twig side is totally consumed. However, after 20h, the two sides of a twig are consumed on solvent treated twigs, while in the case of the needles treated with lipid fractions, there were few bites for the apparently less active fractions (TLF and 40 mg ALF).

Table 5. Mean percentage of larvae standing on the treated side of the twigs after 1h, 2h, 3h, 4h and 20h of experiment (2 replications of 10 larvae).

	mg	1h	2h	3h	4h	20h
Total lipid fraction	4 40	35 20	20 40	30 30	20 5	70 10
Neutral lipid fraction	4 40	25 10	20 0	10 5	10 0	5 5
Acid lipid fraction	4 40	20 40	15 25	5 15	0 15	45 35
Solvent		30	/	/	/	20

Rearing Experiment. For the 1985 spring cohort, there were few differences between the different experimental groups: the mortality was only slightly higher for 0.6 mg neoabietone and for June extracted fractions. Cocoon formation was slightly later for some PAF groups. Heavier cocoons were noticed for June PAF groups.

For the 1985 autumn cohort, there were differences between the colonies: (1) Colony one insects were mostly affected by June ALF--i.e., higher mortality, lower developmental rates, lower needle consumption, and lower weights. On the other hand, NLF groups had the least mortality and the fastest development. The TLF groups gave intermediary results, close to those obtained with the control. (2) Colony two insects had a high mortality in the control groups. All the other groups had a lower mortality, faster development, higher consumption rates, and heavier cocoons. The treated groups showed no

Table 6. Mean performance of larvae of two colonies reared on current-year foliage. June foliage treated with different. 1985 autumn cohort.

Insect performance variance	Colony 1				Colony 2			
	Lipid fraction				Lipid fraction			
	Control	Acid	Neutral	Total	Control	Acid	Neutral	Total
Larval mortality (%)	33	67	30	37	63	30	30	27
Eonymphs mortality (%)	10	0	4.8	5.3	9.1	9.5	0	0
Sex ratio (males/ females x 100)	14	25	44	38	40	30	20	22
Time to 50% cocooning (days)	13.1	21.1	7.1	12.1	19.1	11.1	9.1	12.1
Development time (4th → cocoon) days	22.7	21.8	16.8	19.9	21.7	21.4	22.3	22.5
Frass weight by larvae (mg)	671	445	612	548	421	683	692	662
Male cocoon weight (mg)	56	50	62	67	55	71	59	64
Female cocoon weight (mg)	143	110	120	131	115	128	150	137
Emergence without diapause (%)	0	0	16.7	0	25	0	37.5	16.7

significant differences among themselves for mortality or consumption. However, development was fastest and the female cocoon weight the highest with NLF and the lowest with ALF.

CONCLUSIONS

In spite of a great variation in experimental results, both feeding behavior and rearing bioassays carried out with mature and juvenile pine needles were relatively clear and consistent. Juvenile foliage is deterrent or repellent to D. pini larvae. This deterrence decreases during the growing season, and the foliage eventually becomes edible at the end of July. The autumn cohort can therefore choose between several age-classes of foliage, whereas the spring cohort feeds exclusively on mature, 1-year-old foliage.

The juvenile foliage negatively affects performance: increasing mortality, increasing development time, decreasing weight and fecundity, and probably increasing tendencies to go into diapause.

Prior defoliation does not lower needle quality. Insects reared on defoliated pines did not suffer higher mortality and even had faster development than those reared on mature foliage. This agrees with the results of Niemelä et al. (1984) on Neodiprion sertifer.

The experiments done with needle extracts give less obvious results. The few reactions observed with sprayed-on natural fractions cannot explain the deterrence of juvenile foliage. Other natural products are implicated. There were few effects obtained with neoabietone and current-year (June) PAF. Moreover, the increasing levels of neoabietone in Scots pine foliage during the growing season suggest that this natural product has no deterrent action on sawfly larvae. The high rate of PAF in the lipids correlates with the foliage antifeedance qualities, but PAF gave few significant effects in the rearing experiments. Obviously, such correlations do not prove a products activity. Lipid fractions extracted from juvenile foliage were a deterrent for at least one colony. In another test, we also observed deterrence for abietic acid. On the contrary, some extracted fractions had beneficial effects: faster development, lower mortality for the June NLF-treated autumn cohort, and increasing consumption for the September ALF-treated spring cohort.

To explain this observed variability, we propose the following: (1) Spraying candidate substances on foliage may cause them to interact with foliage natural products. These substances may also be oxidized by air contact in spite of frequent foliage changes.

(2) Population heterogeneity in the sawfly is difficult to control. We used insects collected in infested forests during an outbreak.

Results of the experiments carried out with the foliage are most important to our understanding of D. pini population dynamics. After very heavy defoliation in autumn as occurs during the peak of an outbreak, there is little available foliage the following spring. The newly emerging foliage because of its antifeedant and diapause increasing effects contributes to the population collapse. The net result is heightened mortality, slowed development, and increased diapause.

REFERENCES

All, J. N. and D. M. Benjamin. 1975a. Deterrent(s) in Jack pine, Pinus banksiana, influencing larval feeding behavior and survival of Neodiprion swainei and N. rugifrons. Ann. Entomol. Soc. Am. 68: 495-499.

All, J. N. and D. M. Benjamin. 1975b. A feeding preference bioassay for Neodiprion sawflies on jack pine, Pinus banksiana. Ann. Entomol. Soc. Am. 68: 553-556.

Buratti, L. 1985. Etude des fractions constitutives du feuillage de Pinus sylvestris L. en fonction de la saison et de leurs influences sur le comportement alimentaire de Diprion pini L. (Hymenoptera: Diprionidae). DEA Universite Paris XI, Orsay, 41 p.

Buratti, L., J. P. Allais, and M. Barbier. 1986. The resin acids involved in the reactions between Scots pine and the sawfly Diprion pini L. I- The content of diterpene resin acids in the needles. 1st International meeting of the IUFRO Working Party "Plant resistance mechanism to insects and pathogens". Aug. 26-29 Orleans France.

Dusaussoy, G. and C. Geri. 1971. Etude des populations residuelles de Diprion pini L. apres la gradation de 1963-1964. Ann. Sci. For. 28(3): 297-322.

Geri, C. 1986. Facteurs influençant la dynamique des populations de Diprion pini L. dans le bassin parisien. Proceedings 18th IUFRO World Congress. Sept. 7-21, Division 2, Ljubljana, Yugoslavia, (2): 695-705.

Geri, C., J. P. Allais, F. Goussard, A. Liger, and A. Yart. 1985. Incidence de l'age du feuillage sur le développement de Diprion pini L. (Hymenoptera: Diprionidae). Conséquences sur l'évolution des populations. Acta Oecologica, Oecol. Applic. 6(4): 349-365.

Geri, C. and F. Goussard. 1984. Evolution d'une nouvelle gradation du lophyre du pin (Diprion pini L.) dans le sud du bassin parisien. I.-Développement de la gradation jusqu'en 1982 et relation avec les facteurs du milieu. Ann. Sci. For. 41(4): 375-404.

Niemelä, P., J. Tuomi, R. Mannila, and P. Ojala. 1984. The effect of previous damage on the quality of Scots pine foliage as food for Diprionid sawflies. Z. Angew. Entomol. 98: 33-43.

12

Variations in Nutrient Levels as a Defense: Indentifying Key Nutritional Traits of Host Plants of the Western Spruce Budworm

Karen M. Clancy, Michael R. Wagner, and Richard W. Tinus

VARIABILITY OF HOST PLANTS AND PLANT/HERBIVORE INTERACTIONS

Recent investigations on plant/herbivore interactions have emphasized that host plants are heterogeneous substrates for herbivores (Edmunds and Alstad 1978, 1981; Whitham 1978, 1983; Maxwell and Jennings 1980; Thompson 1982; Crawley 1983; Denno and McClure 1983; Futuyma 1983; Price 1984). There is reason to believe that this variation can significantly affect herbivore populations (Denno and McClure 1983). For example, Mattson et al. (1982) reasoned that the performance of insects depends on how well their properties (e.g., nutritional and physical requirements, tolerances for and detoxication of plant allelochemicals) match those of the host plant and how well the whole ecosystem (competitor consumers, natural enemies, the physical environment) fits the herbivore's requirements for survival, growth, and reproduction. Each individual plant has a unique set or collection of ever-changing traits that have behavioral and physiological ramifications for a potential consumer (Mattson and Scriber 1987).

For each plant trait (or collection of traits), there may be an optimal range or combination that maximizes the herbivore's performance (Mattson and Scriber 1987). If one or more traits are outside the herbivore's optimal range, the plant may be relatively more resistant to the herbivore than plants which have all traits that are within the consumer's optimal range (Mattson et al. 1982). Thus, an inadequate or suboptimal match between the herbivore's requirements and the attributes of the host plant is a potential mechanism for plant resistance to herbivore attack.

IDENTIFYING CANDIDATE KEY NUTRITIONAL TRAITS OF PLANTS

Which host plant nutrients are likely to be most important in making a host better or worse for an herbivore? Mattson and Scriber (1987) suggested that the key food traits are those that are fundamental to the chemistry of life and are highly variable between different foods.

Ontogenetic or seasonal variations in the levels of vital nutrients provide one line of evidence for selecting specific nutrients to be tested as potential key traits. The effects of such variation have been shown to be important in the performance of the eastern and western spruce budworms (*Choristoneura fumiferana* and *Choristoneura occidentalis*, respectively), both of which feed on the expanding new needles of their conifer hosts. However, when new foliage is entirely consumed, larvae will also feed on older needles (McGugan 1954, Carolin and Honing 1972, Furniss and Carolin 1977, Blais 1979, Knight and Heikkenen 1980, Fellin and Dewey 1982, Talerico 1983). Consuming older needles results in reduced fecundity, retarded development, and increased mortality rates (Blais 1952, 1953; Miller 1957; Heron 1964; Talerico 1983; Thomas 1983). Likewise, if larvae are forced to feed on mature rather than young current-year foliage, they also have reduced growth, survival, and pupal weight (Heron 1964, Mattson *et al*. 1983), or they may not survive at all (Blake and Wagner 1986). Thus, substantial seasonal changes in concentrations of a foliar nutrient in current year needles, or large differences between new (current year) and older (≥ 1-year-old) needles, indicate candidate key nutrients.

Another line of evidence for identifying key nutrients comes from variations in levels of nutrients between different individual trees, populations, or host plant species.

NUTRITIONAL TRAITS OF HOST PLANTS OF SPRUCE BUDWORMS

Several foliar nutrients appear to be candidate key traits for western and eastern spruce budworms based on patterns of their seasonal and ontogenetic variation. This discussion is limited to N and several mineral elements (P, K, Ca, Zn, and Fe), but other nutrients such as water, sugars, and fatty acids may be important.

Seasonal Variation in Foliar Nutrients

Foliar levels of N, P, K, and Zn in budworm host trees decline substantially as the new needles mature, while Ca concentrations steadily increase (Table 1). Such maturational declines in foliar N, P, and K are typical, as is a seasonal increase in Ca. The micronutrients Zn and Fe often show a concave concentration curve over the growing season, which was not observed here (Table 1). There may be variations in the typical seasonal patterns because of species and soil interactions (Scriber and Slansky 1981, Mattson and Scriber 1987).

Table 1. Seasonal changes in the concentrations of N, P, K, Ca, Zn, and Fe in the current-year foliage from different budworm host species.

Foliar nutrient (units)	Host plant species	Budworm growth period		
		Early feeding	Late feeding	Post feeding
N (% dry mass)	Balsam fir[a]	2.5	1.25	0.88
	Balsam fir[b]	4.4	1.4	0.9
	Douglas-fir[c]	1.56	1.16	0.81
	Engelmann spruce[c]	2.36	1.64	1.06
	White fir[c]	1.70	1.31	0.81
P (mg/g dry mass)	Douglas-fir[c]	2.84	2.29	1.65
	Engelmann spruce[c]	4.03	2.92	2.11
	White fir[c]	3.16	2.48	1.67
K (mg/g dry mass)	Douglas-fir[c]	12.51	10.93	9.95
	Engelmann spruce[c]	13.76	11.91	10.85
	White fir[c]	13.00	12.39	11.20
Ca (mg/g dry mass)	Douglas-fir[c]	1.44	2.60	3.45
	Engelmann spruce[c]	0.95	2.05	3.24
	White fir[c]	1.06	2.53	4.76
Zn (ug/g dry mass)	Douglas-fir[c]	33.65	24.30	21.55
	Englemann spruce[c]	56.06	55.18	32.35
	White fir[c]	41.55	30.95	24.90
Fe (ug/g dry mass)	Douglas-fir[c]	46.95	63.25	44.95
	Engelmann spruce[c]	47.41	55.47	38.18
	White fir[c]	47.55	69.25	45.40

[a]Shaw _et al_. (1978)
[b]Shaw and Little (1972)
[c]Clancy _et al_. (unpublished)

Ontogenetic Variation in Foliar Nutrients

Ontogenetic changes in levels of foliar nutrients are also well-known for budworm host trees (Table 2). Levels of N, P, and K are consistently lower in older needles than in current year needles. Conversely, Ca and Fe concentrations are consistently higher in older needles. The patterns for Zn concentrations are highly variable between different host species. Zn levels declined in older needles of Douglas-fir, but increased in balsam fir and Engelmann spruce and showed little change in grand fir.

The general pattern for plants that retain foliage for more than one growing season is an extension of the seasonal trends for nutrient concentration changes (Mattson and Scriber 1987). This pattern was observed for budworm host species in regard to N, P, K, and Ca but was not consistently observed for Fe and Zn (Table 2).

Variations in Foliar Nutrients Among Trees

The range in concentrations of N, P, K, Ca, Zn, and Fe reported for foliage from various budworm host trees is substantial (Table 3). Spruce budworms obviously encounter and cope with a wide range in foliar nutrient levels between individual trees, populations, and host species. Variability between trees is probably matched or exceeded by seasonal and ontogenetic changes that occur within individual trees.

IMPLICATIONS OF FOLIAR NUTRIENT VARIABILITY FOR SPRUCE BUDWORM

Several investigators have suggested that the early season feeding is an adaptation to utilize the most nitrogen-rich plant parts, namely flushes of new growth (Baker 1972, McNeill and Southwood 1978, Schwertzer 1979). However, concomitant seasonal declines in P, K, or Zn or increases in Ca also may influence preference for early season, new foliage (Table 1). Mattson et al. (1983) pointed out that excessively high levels of one mineral element can interfere with the absorption and utilization of other elements. Therefore, the proper balance of nutrients relative to one another may be the most critical factor influencing timing of feeding (Mattson and Scriber 1987). It is likely that the timing of spruce budworm feeding is such an adaptation--to utilize foliage with the most optimal balance of many different nutrients.

The singular importance of N in determining spruce budworm performance is difficult to assess in the field because plants that

Table 2. Ontogenetic changes in the concentrations of N, P, K, Ca, Zn, and Fe in the current year (new) and older age classes of foliage from different budworm host species.

Foliar nutrient (units)	Host plant species	Foliage age class (no. years old)					
		New	1	2	3	4	5
N (% dry mass)	Balsam fir[a]	1.42	1.30	1.26	--	--	--
	Balsam fir[b]	1.46	0.97	0.87	0.86	0.83	0.76
	Red spruce[c]	1.12	0.99	0.87	--	--	--
P (mg/g dry mass)	Balsam fir[a]	1.36	1.01	0.97	--	--	--
	Balsam fir[b]	2.70	1.48	1.28	1.20	1.08	1.05
	Douglas-fir (high)[c]	2.18	1.46	--	--	--	--
	Douglas-fir (medium)[c]	1.90	1.45	--	--	--	--
	Douglas-fir (low)[c]	1.75	1.52	--	--	--	--
	Red spruce[a]	1.29	1.08	0.98	--	--	--
K (mg/g dry mass)	Balsam fir[a]	6.37	5.78	5.33	--	--	--
	Balsam fir[b]	10.59	5.62	4.51	4.48	3.79	4.14
	Douglas-fir (high)[c]	8.29	5.77	--	--	--	--
	Douglas-fir (medium)[c]	8.12	5.26	--	--	--	--
	Douglas-fir (low)[c]	7.48	5.65	--	--	--	--
	Douglas-fir[d]	7.30	4.11	--	--	--	--
	Engelmann spruce[d]	17.0	5.8	--	--	--	--
	Grand fir[d]	11.4	5.0	--	--	--	--
	Red spruce[a]	9.06	5.89	4.63	--	--	--
Ca (mg/g dry mass)	Balsam fir[a]	10.32	17.75	14.67	--	--	--
	Balsam fir[b]	5.21	6.12	10.23	11.50	12.59	16.23
	Douglas-fir (high)[c]	3.12	6.50	--	--	--	--
	Douglas-fir (medium)[c]	3.93	8.32	--	--	--	--
	Douglas-fir (low)[c]	4.01	7.12	--	--	--	--
	Douglas-fir[d]	5.02	9.70	--	--	--	--
	Engelmann spruce[d]	2.10	12.71	--	--	--	--
	Grand fir[d]	6.10	10.15	--	--	--	--
	Red spruce[a]	4.18	6.05	6.11	--	--	--
Zn (ug/g dry mass)	Balsam fir[b]	38.3	37.6	50.9	52.4	56.2	71.0
	Douglas-fir[d]	13.2	4.9	--	--	--	--
	Englemann spruce[d]	42.9	69.4	--	--	--	--
	Grand fir[d]	26.4	24.2	--	--	--	--
Fe (ug/g dry mass)	Balsam fir[b]	35.2	58.9	83.4	102.5	124.9	145.3
	Douglas-fir[d]	58.6	99.8	--	--	--	--
	Engelmann spruce[d]	28.6	202.5	--	--	--	--
	Grand fir[d]	12.1	34.0	--	--	--	--

[a]Schmitt et al. (1983)
[b]Mattson and Scriber (1987)
[c]Kemp and Moody (1984). High, medium, and low designate stands that had different frequencies of outbreak populations of the western spruce budworm.
[d]McLean et al. (1983)

Table 3. Ranges in the concentrations of N, P, K, Ca, Zn, and Fe in the current year (new) and older age classes of foliage from different budworm host species.

Foliar nutrient (units)	Host plant species	Foliage age class	
		New	1-or-more years old
N (% dry mass)	Balsam fir[a-g]	0.88 - 4.4	0.76 - 1.30
	Black spruce[d]	0.70 - 1.0	---
	Douglas-fir[h-j]	0.70 - 3.5	---
	Engelmann spruce[h]	0.91 - 2.84	---
	White fir[h]	0.71 - 2.13	---
P (mg/g dry mass)	Balsam fir[c-g]	1.36 - 2.70	0.97 - 1.48
	Black spruce[d]	1.35 - 2.24	---
	Douglas-fir[h,k]	1.41 - 3.31	0.96 - 2.18
	Engelmann spruce[h]	1.81 - 4.45	---
	White fir[h]	1.35 - 3.80	---
K (mg/g dry mass)	Balsam fir[c-g]	5.3 - 12.74	3.79 - 5.78
	Black spruce[d]	7.47 - 7.60	---
	Douglas-fir[h,k,l]	1.02 - 19.8	0.50 - 9.53
	Engelmann spruce[h,l]	8.2 - 17.0	5.80
	White fir[h]	9.4 - 14.7	---
Ca (mg/g dry mass)	Balsam fir[c-g]	3.6 - 10.32	6.12 - 17.75
	Black spruce[d]	1.10 - 1.79	---
	Douglas-fir[h,k,l]	0.70 - 8.04	2.49 - 12.28
	Engelmann spruce[h,l]	0.70 - 4.55	12.71
	White fir[h]	0.65 - 7.72	---
Zn (ug/g dry mass)	Balsam fir[c,d,f]	34 - 54	37.6 - 71.0
	Douglas-fir[h,l]	12 - 52	4.9
	Engelmann spruce[h,l]	22 - 74	69.4
	White fir[h]	20 - 55	---
Fe (ug/g dry mass)	Balsam fir[c,d,f]	31 - 35.2	58.9 - 145.3
	Black spruce[d]	15.5 - 19.2	---
	Douglas-fir[h,l]	22 - 89	99.8
	Engelmann spruce[h,l]	23 - 103	202.5
	White fir[h]	22 - 89	---

[a]Shaw *et al*. (1978)
[b]Shaw and Little (1972)
[c]Mattson *et al*. (1983)
[d]Mattson and Koller (1983)
[e]Schmitt *et al*. (1983)
[f]Mattson and Scriber (1987)
[g]Piene (1980)
[h]Clancy *et al*. (unpublished)
[i]Wagner and Blake (1983)
[j]Cates *et al*. (1983)
[k]Kemp and Moody (1984)
[l]McLean *et al*. (1983)

have higher levels of N also tend to have higher levels of many other nutrients (water and minerals such as P, K, Zn, and Mg) and lower levels of fiber and various allelochemicals (Mattson 1980, Mattson and Koller 1983, Mattson and Scriber 1987, Clancy et al. unpublished). Thus, strong inter-correlations among many nutritional characteristics of plant foliage make it difficult to determine herbivore response to one specific nutrient. Many studies have shown positive correlations between spruce budworm performance and foliar N levels (Greenbank 1963, Kimmins 1971, Shaw and Little 1972, Shaw et al. 1978, McMurray 1980, Cates et al. 1983, Mattson et al. 1983, Mattson and Koller 1983, Montgomery 1983, Schmidt and Fellin 1983, Schmitt et al. 1983, Wagner and Blake 1983, Brewer et al. 1985), but the apparent positive responses to N may also reflect responses to other nutrients that are tightly linked to plant N.

Several studies have suggested that variations in host mineral elements may affect spruce budworm performance. Kemp and Moody (1984) found that Douglas-fir trees with higher foliar concentrations of Na, P, and K and lower concentrations of Ca were more frequently defoliated by western spruce budworms than trees with lower Na, P, and K and higher Ca (see Table 2). Eastern spruce budworm performance was correlated with foliar concentrations of several minerals (Mattson et al. 1983, Mattson and Koller 1983). Also, both eastern and western spruce budworms have higher body concentrations of many minerals than occur in foliage (Mattson et al. 1983, McLean et al. 1983). Mattson and Scriber (1987) listed probable optimal dietary levels of several mineral elements for the eastern spruce budworm and folivores in general. They suggested that levels of K and P may be particularly important to insect folivores, whereas levels of Ca and Na are not, because requirements for them are low.

Although there is variability in foliar N and mineral concentrations in budworm host plants, the significance of this variation cannot be appreciated until the budworm's dietary needs for these nutrients, both as single factors and in combinations, are better understood. The necessary facts are not yet available for spruce budworms (nor for any other insect folivores), particularly regarding mineral elements (Mattson and Scriber 1987).

THE BUDWORM'S NUTRITIONAL NICHE: DETERMINING HOW VARIATIONS IN KEY TRAITS AFFECT INSECT PERFORMANCE

Many questions remain to be answered before the role of nutritional factors as potential resistance mechanisms can be evaluated. For example, inadequate information is available on which specific nutrients or allelochemicals are important for insect herbivores and what are the upper, lower, and optimal levels of these traits that herbivores can tolerate (Mattson _et al_. 1982). Furthermore, it is necessary to determine how different traits, such as nutrients and allelochemicals, interact to influence herbivore success (Mattson and Scriber 1987). These questions can be answered only with detailed laboratory and field experiments.

The western spruce budworm and its host species in the southwestern United States (spruces, true firs, and Douglas-fir) provide a model system for investigating some of these questions. The "nutritional niche" of the budworm can be defined through a series of interrelated laboratory and field experiments. Insects can be reared for several successive generations on artificial diets that have prescribed levels of nutrients and allelochemicals. This will allow documentation of how different levels of a particular nutrient or allelochemical (or both) telescope their influence on budworm growth, weight, fecundity, and survival through several consecutive generations. Once key nutrients or defensive chemicals have been identified and levels required (or tolerated) for adequate survival and reproduction have been quantified, the laboratory results can be validated in the field by rearing budworms on trees that have a wide range in concentration of the significant traits. Quantifying the budworm's nutritional niche this way would allow comparison of the herbivore's requirements (or tolerances) for key traits of plants to levels that occur in the foliage of the host plants. This information could help explain why some species of host plants, populations of plants, or individual plants are more resistant/susceptible than others to the budworm.

ACKNOWLEDGEMENTS

We thank C. D. Johnson and T. G. Whitham for commenting on the manuscript. Work was supported by the Rocky Mountain Forest and Range Experiment Station contract 28-K3-309 to Michael R. Wagner.

REFERENCES

Baker, W. L. 1972. Eastern forest insects. USDA, Forest Service, Misc. Pub. No. 1175, 642 p.

Blais, J. R. 1952. The relationship of the spruce budworm (_Choristoneura fumiferana_ Clem.) to the flowering condition of balsam fir (_Abies balsamea_). Can. J. Zool. 30: 1-29.

Blais, J. R. 1953. Effects of the destruction of the current year's foliage of balsam fir on the fecundity and habits of flight of the spruce budworm. Can. Entomol. 85: 466-468.

Blais, J. R. 1979. Rate of defoliation in relation to spruce budworm attack and timing of spray application. Can. J. For. Res. 9: 354-361.

Blake, E. A. and M. R. Wagner. 1986. Foliage age as a factor in food utilization by the western spruce budworm, Choristoneura occidentalis. Great Basin Nat. 46: 169-172.

Brewer, J. W., J. L. Capinera, R. E. Deshon, and M. L. Walmsley. 1985. Influence of foliar nitrogen levels on survival, development, and reproduction of western spruce budworm, Choristoneura occidentalis (Lepidoptera: Tortricidae). Can. Entomol. 117: 23-32.

Carolin, V. M. and F. W. Honing. 1972. Western spruce budworm. USDA, Forest Service, Pest Leaflet 53, 8 p.

Cates, R. G., R. Redak, and C. B. Henderson. 1983. Natural product defensive chemistry of Douglas-fir, western spruce budworm success, and forest management practices. Z. Angew. Entomol. 96: 173-182.

Crawley, M. J. 1983. Herbivory: The dynamics of animal-plant interactions. Berkeley: Univ. of California Press, 420 p.

Denno, R. F. and M. S. McClure (Eds.). 1983. Variable plants and herbivores in natural and managed systems. New York: Academic Press, 717 p.

Edmunds, G. F. and D. N. Alstad. 1978. Coevolution in insect herbivores and conifers. Science 199: 941-945.

Edmunds, G. F. and D. N. Alstad. 1981. Responses of black pineleaf scales to host plant variability. In: Insect life history patterns: habitat and geographic variation (R. F. Denno and H. Dingle, Eds.). New York: Springer-Verlag; 29-38.

Fellin, D. G. and J. E. Dewey. 1982. Western spruce budworm. USDA, Forest Service, Forest Insect & Disease Leaflet 53, 10 p.

Furniss, R. L. and V. M. Carolin. 1977. Western forest insects. USDA, Forest Service, Misc. Pub. No. 1339, 654 p.

Futuyma, D. J. 1983. Evolutionary interactions among herbivorous insects and plants. In: Coevolution (D. J. Futuyma and M. Slatkin, Eds.). Sunderland, MA: Sinauer; 207-231.

Greenbank, D. O. 1963. Staminate flowers and the spruce budworm. In: The dynamics of epidemic spruce budworm populations (R. F. Morris, Ed.). Mem. Entomol. Soc. Can. No. 31; 202-218.

Heron, R. J. 1964. The role of chemotactic stimuli in the feeding behavior of spruce budworm on white spruce. Can. J. Zool. 43: 247-269.

Kemp, W. P. and U. L. Moody. 1984. Relationships between regional soils and foliage characteristics and western spruce budworm (Lepidoptera: Tortricidae) outbreak frequency. Environ. Entomol. 13: 1291-1297.

Kimmins, J. P. 1971. Variations in the foliar amino acid composition of flowering and non-flowering balsam fir (Abies balsamea (L.) (Mill)) and white spruce (Picea glauca (Moench) Voss) in relation to outbreaks of the spruce budworm (Choristoneura fumiferana (Clem.)). Can. J. Zool. 49: 1005-1011.

Knight, F. and H. J. Heikkenen. 1980. Principles of forest entomology. New York: McGraw-Hill, 461 p.

Mattson, W. J. 1980. Herbivory in relation to plant nitrogen content. Annu. Rev. Ecol. Syst. 11: 119-61.

Mattson, W. J. and C. N. Koller. 1983. Spruce budworm performance in relation to matching selected chemical traits of its hosts. In: The role of insect-plant relationships in the population dynamics of forest pests (A. S. Isaev, Ed.). International Union of Forestry Research Organizations/USSR Academy of Sciences; 138-148.

Mattson, W. J., N. Lorimer, and R. A. Leary. 1982. Role of plant variability (trait vector dynamics and diversity) in plant/herbivore interactions. In: Resistance to diseases and pests in forest trees (H. M. Heybroek, B. R. Stephan, and K. von Weissenberg, Eds.). Wageningen, Netherlands: Pudoc; 295-303.

Mattson, W. J. and J. M. Scriber. 1987. Nutritional ecology of insect folivores of woody plants: water, nitrogen, fiber, and mineral considerations. In: Nutritional ecology of insects, mites, and spiders (F. Slansky and J. Rodriguez, Eds.). New York: John Wiley and Sons; 105-146.

Mattson, W. J., S. S. Slocum, and C. N. Koller. 1983. Spruce budworm (Choristonuera fumiferana) performance in relation to foliar chemistry of its host plants. In: Proceedings, forest defoliator-host interactions: a comparison between gypsy moth and spruce budworms. USDA, Forest Service, Gen. Tech. Rep. NE-85; 55-65.

Maxwell, F. G. and P. R. Jennings. 1980. Breeding plants resistant to insects. New York: Wiley, 683 p.

McGugan, B. M. 1954. Needle-mining habits and larval instars of the spruce budworm. Can. Entomol. 86: 439-454.

McLean, J. A., P. Laks, and T. L. Shore. 1983. Comparisons of elemental profiles of the western spruce budworm reared on three host foliages and artificial medium. In: Proceedings, forest defoliator-host interactions: a comparison between gypsy moth and spruce budworms. USDA, Forest Service, Gen. Tech. Rep. NE-85; 33-40.

McMurray, T. I. 1980. Effects of drought stress induced changes in host foliage quality on the growth of two forest insect pests. Albuquerque: Univ. of New Mexico; M.S. Thesis, 56 p.

McNeill, S. and T. R. E. Southwood. 1978. The role of nitrogen in the development of insect/plant relationships. In: Biochemical aspects of plant and animal coevolution (J. B. Harborne, Ed.). New York: Academic Press; 78-98.

Miller, C. A. 1957. A technique for estimating the fecundity of natural populations of the spruce budworm. Can. J. Zool. 35: 1-13.

Montgomery, M. E. 1983. Biomass and nitrogen budgets during larval development of Lymantria dispar and Choristonuera fumiferana: allometric relationships. In: Proceedings, forest defoliator-host interactions: a comparison between gypsy moth and spruce budworms. USDA, Forest Service, Gen. Tech. Rep. NE-85; 133-140.

Piene, H. 1980. Effects of insect defoliation on growth and foliar nutrients of young balsam fir. For. Sci. 26: 665-673.

Price, P. W. 1984. Insect ecology. 2d ed. New York: John Wiley and Sons, 607 p.

Schmidt, W. C. and D. G. Fellin. 1983. Effect of fertilization on western spruce budworm feeding in young western larch stands. In: Proceedings, forest defoliator-host interactions: a comparison between gypsy moth and spruce budworms. USDA, Forest Service, Gen. Tech. Rep. NE-85; 87-95.

Schmitt, M. D. C., M. M. Czapowskyj, D. C. Allen, E. H. White, and M. E. Montgomery. 1983. Spruce budworm fecundity and foliar chemistry: influence of site. In: Proceedings, forest defoliator-host interactions: a comparison between gypsy moth and spruce budworms. USDA, Forest Service, Gen. Tech. Rep. NE-85; 97-103.

Schwertzer, D. F. 1979. Effects of foliage age on body weight and survival in larvae of the tribe Lithophanini (Lepidoptera: Noctuidae). Oikos 32: 403-8.
Scriber, J. M. and F. Slansky. 1981. The nutritional ecology of immature insects. Annu. Rev. Entomol. 26: 183-211.
Shaw, G. G. and C. H. A. Little. 1972. Effect of high urea fertilization on balsam fir trees on spruce budworm development. In: Insect and mite nutrition (J. G. Rodriguez, Ed.). Amsterdam: North-Holland; 589-597.
Shaw, G. G., C. H. A. Little, and D. J. Durzan. 1978. Effect of fertilization of balsam fir trees on spruce budworm nutrition and development. Can. J. For. Res. 8: 364-374.
Talerico, R. L. 1983. Summary of life history and hosts of the spruce budworms. In: Proceedings, forest defoliator-host interactions: a comparison between gypsy moth and spruce budworms. USDA, Forest Service, Gen. Tech. Rep. NE-85; 1-4.
Thomas, A. W. 1983. Foliage consumption by 6th-instar spruce budworm larvae, Choristoneura fumiferana (Clem.), feeding on balsam fir and white spruce. In: Proceedings, forest defoliator-host interactions: a comparison between gypsy moth and spruce budworms. USDA, Forest Service, Gen. Tech. Rep. NE-85; 47-48.
Thompson, J. N. 1982. Interaction and coevolution. New York: John Wiley and Sons, 179 p.
Wagner, M. R. and E. A. Blake. 1983. Western spruce budworm consumption--effects of host species and foliage chemistry. In: Proceedings, forest defoliator-host interactions: a comparison between gypsy moth and spruce budworms. USDA, Forest Service, Gen. Tech. Rep. NE-85; 49-54.
Whitham, T. G. 1978. Habitat selection by Pemphigus aphids in response to resource limitation and competition. Ecology 59: 1164-1176.
Whitham, T. G. 1983. Host manipulation of parasites: within-plant variation as a defense against rapidly evolving pests. In: Variable plants and herbivores in natural and managed systems (R. F. Denno and M. S. McClure, Eds.). New York: Academic Press; 15-41.

13

Phenological Resistance of Oaks to the Green Oak Leafroller, *Tortrix viridana* (Lepidoptera: Tortricidae)

P. Du Merle

Tortrix viridana is a major pest of the oaks in the west-palearctic region. It has a 1-year life cycle. Moths are present in late spring and early summer. Eggs are laid in pairs on the bark of twigs where they hatch the following spring. The first-instar (L1) larvae enter the flushing buds to initiate feeding. Large larvae finish feeding upon the expanded foliage.

Except in the case of starvation, the host range of T. viridana is limited to the genus Quercus. Numerous oak species, indigenous or introduced, are infested (see Fankhänel 1961, Du Merle 1983). The insect can proliferate both on deciduous oaks (such as the pedunculate oak, Q. robur, the sessile oak, Q. petraea, or the pubescent oak, Q. pubescens) and on evergreen oaks (such as the holly oak, Q. ilex, or the cork oak, Q. suber).

As shown by Gasow (1925) and Schütte (1957), in the case of the pedunculate and sessile oaks, and by Du Merle and Mazet (1983), in the case of the pubescent and holly oaks, the L1 can succeed in infesting the buds only when buds have reached a specific phenological stage: intermediate between the "brown" stage, or bud completely covered in its protective scales, and the "lengthening of the young shoot" stage (see description of the flushing stages of oak buds in Du Merle and Mazet 1983). A good synchronism between egg hatching and bud flushing in spring is therefore an indispensable condition for insect success.

The bud-flushing time varies among the oaks. Nevertheless, T. viridana succeeds in proliferating on species having very different phenologies by adjusting its development. For instance, we have shown that: (1) Buds flush, on the average, 1 to 3 weeks later in holly oak than in pubescent oak. (2) In the same way, the eggs from green oak leafrollers that grew up on the former hatch about 10 to 15 days later than eggs from those that grew up on the latter. (3) This difference is genetically determined (Du Merle 1983).

These results, and others (Altenkirch 1966; Rubtsova 1977, 1981) show that within the species, T. viridana, there coexist genetically distinct populations, differing in the mean date of egg hatching, each adapted to a certain phenological type of oak. These populations are sometimes sympatric, and hybridization between them may occur when moth flights are overlapping, which happens for the sympatric populations adapted to the pubescent and to the holly oak, respectively (Du Merle 1983).

For several years, I have studied the phenological coincidence between the egg hatching of T. viridana and the bud flushing of these two oaks in southeastern France. The following observations were made on the Petit Lubéron Mountain and on Mt. Ventoux in the region of Vaucluse.

PHENOLOGICAL RELATIONS BETWEEN A POPULATION OF TORTRIX VIRIDANA AND A STAND OF QUERCUS ILEX

Methods

The study was carried out on the high plateau of the Petit Lubéron at an elevation of 700 m in holly oak coppices about 40-years old. In 1983, the stands were very heavily attacked by the pest. The current foliage of many oaks was completely destroyed, but these trees were mixed with others less severely defoliated; some oaks were undamaged even when adjacent to severely defoliated trees.

I selected 60 oaks distributed on about 1.5 ha in a plot apparently very homogeneous with respect to environmental conditions. Twenty trees had only slight or no defoliation (< 10 percent of the current foliage destroyed) and 40 had heavy defoliation (> 50 percent of the current foliage destroyed). In 1984 and 1985, I estimated the values of the following variables for each oak: (1) The date on which the BR-50 phenological stage was reached--this stage is defined as follows: 50 percent of the terminal and subterminal buds still are in the "brown" stage and are unsuitable for the L1; the others are more advanced and, therefore, have become suitable for them; (2) The corresponding date for the AL-50 phenological stage, defined as follows: 50 percent of the same buds have reached the "lengthening of the young shoot" stage and are no longer suitable for the L1; the others have not yet reached this stage and, therefore, are still suitable for them (this date was also estimated in 1986); and (3) The defoliation level (DEF) of the current foliage (also estimated in 1983 and in 1986).

I estimated both dates (BR-50 and AL-50) by assessing twice weekly the relative frequencies of each of the phenological bud stages. I also determined the hatching of the T. viridana eggs by examining twice per week those occurring on holly oak twigs near the plot.

Results

For the 60 oaks, the average DEF was 65 percent in 1983, 51 percent in 1984, and 10 percent in 1985. These values agreed with the impression obtained from a general survey of the plot. In each of 4 years (1982 to 1985), I observed oaks defoliated from 0 to 100 percent.

There was considerable variation among the 60 oaks for each of the bud-flushing dates (Fig. 1); BR-50 and the AL-50 stages were strongly correlated in 1984 and in 1985 ($r = 0.89$ and 0.93, respectively). In both years, egg hatching began after the earliest developing oaks had already reached the BR-50 stage and ended before the latest developing oaks had reached this stage. The phenological coincidence between the pest and the plant was good for the "early" oaks, because they reached the AL-50 stage after egg hatching had ceased. In contrast, it was very bad for the "later" oaks but not necessarily disastrous because a rather considerable time (up to several weeks) may elapse between the date on which the earliest buds of a tree pass the "brown" stage and the date on which the tree reaches the BR-50 stage.

Figure 2 confirms these deductions, the later the oaks reached the BR-50 stage, the less defoliation they suffered. Almost all of the latest developing oaks escaped significant insect defoliation.

In both years, T. viridana populations proved to be phenologically unadapted to a part of the host population, namely the latest developing trees. Observations in other holly oak stands suggested that this situation was common. Therefore, it is highly probable that the 40 oaks heavily defoliated in 1983 were among the early-bud-flushing trees, whereas the 20 slightly or nondefoliated oaks were among the late-bud-flushing ones.

Figure 3 compares, for each of the 60 oaks, the dates on which the BR-50 stage was reached in 1984 and in 1985. While some oaks, like "A" or "B", developed relatively early in both years, many others varied widely in this respect: for example, the oak "C", among the earliest developing trees in 1984, was one of the latest in 1985 whereas the oak "D", among the latest developing trees in 1984, was one of the earliest in 1985. Moreover, the correlation coefficient calculated for the 60 1984/1985 pairs is very low: r = 0.31. The same calculations for the AL-50 stage gave a similar result: r = 0.39.

So the developmental order of different oak trees varies considerably from year to year. What causes these variations is still unknown. The extent of the damage suffered by the trees during the previous years might partially explain it. This is suggested by some of the results. For example, the very great majority of those oaks which were the latest developing in 1984 (8 of the 11 having reached the BR-50 stage after May 22, see Fig. 3) had been very heavily defoliated in 1983. The correlation between the dates on which the BR-50 stage was reached in 1984 and in 1985 was rather high for the 20 oaks slightly or nondefoliated in 1983 but very low for the 40 heavily defoliated ones (r = 0.65 and r = 0.15, respectively).

Figure 4 compares the defoliation level per tree in 1983 and in 1984. In this case too, the ranking of the oaks varied considerably from year to year. While some of them were defoliated similarly in both years (very lightly or very heavily), others, undamaged in 1983, were heavily defoliated in 1984 and yet others, completely defoliated in 1983, suffered no damage in 1984. This was true in both 1984 and

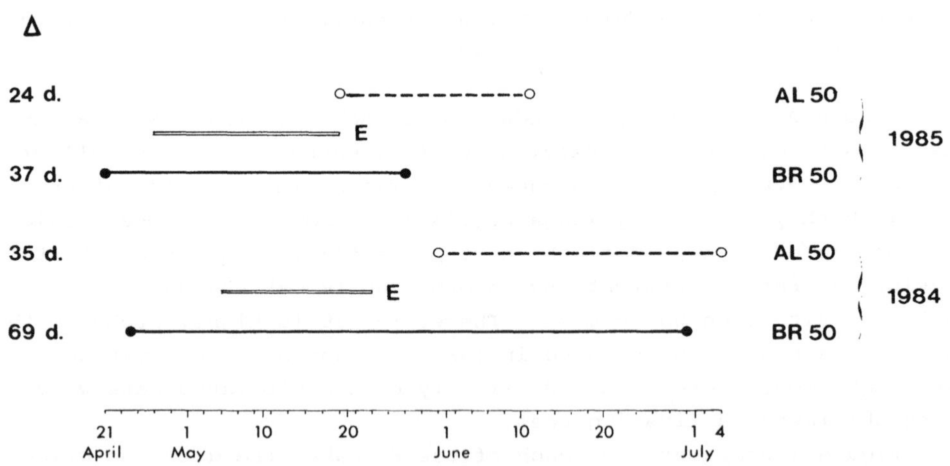

Figure 1. Variation between trees and between years of the bud-flushing date for the 60 holly oaks of the Petit Lubéron Mountain: the positions of the earliest and of the latest oaks are indicated for each of the BR-50 and AL-50 stages, delta being this time interval in days. E = hatching period of <u>T. viridana</u>.

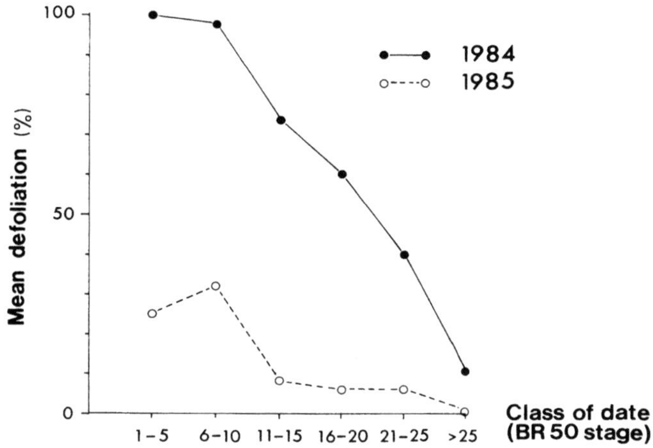

	1-5	6-10	11-15	16-20	21-25	>25	
1984	4	6	7	12	13	18*	n
1985	6	8	11	15	4	16**	

* For 14 of them DEF = 0 to 5%
** For 15 of them DEF = 0 to 5%

Figure 2. Defoliation of the holly oaks of the Petit Luberon Mountain in relation to the date on which they reached the BR-50 stage; dates are expressed by their number (1... 25... = April 24th to May 18th in 1984, and April 21st to May 14th in 1985) and trees are distributed into date classes; n = number of oaks per class.

1985. Moreover, the DEF correlation coefficient between years 1983/1984 and 1984/1985 for the 60 trees was very low (r = 0.31, r = 0.47).

Examination of the past foliage and of the branching pattern has likewise shown that, while some of the 20 oaks nondefoliated in 1983 were undamaged in previous years, others very presumably were severely defoliated in 1982.

Whereas both completely defoliated and undamaged oaks were seen in the plot every year between 1982 and 1985, the situation was completely different in 1986. On the entire high plateau of the Petit Lubéron, the average defoliation of the holly oaks was nearly 100 percent. All of the oaks except one in the 60 sample trees were entirely defoliated. Larval populations were so heavy that a considerable proportion died from starvation.

This widespread, complete defoliation does not contradict the observations made in previous years. On the plot, the variability in the bud-flushing date was again high in 1986 (for the AL-50 stage, a 24-day interval occurred between the earliest developing and the latest developing tree, as in 1985). The fact that all the trees (except one) were completely defoliated obviously resulted from a passive dispersal of larvae in search for food. After having dropped on silken threads, larvae were carried by the wind from the early developing trees to the neighboring late developing ones.

These results suggest the following conclusions: (1) In the stand considered, the population of the pest is phenologically adapted only to the early or relatively early developing segment of the host

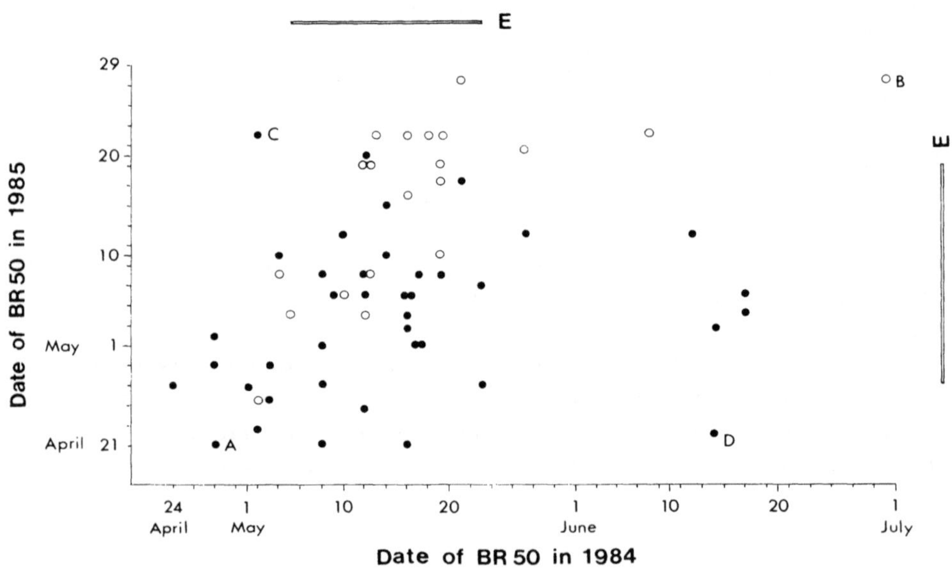

Figure 3. Comparison, for the 60 holly oaks of the Petit Lubéron Mountain, of the dates on which the BR-50 stage was reached in 1984 and in 1985. White circles represent the 20 oaks only slightly or nondefoliated in 1983; solid circles, the 40 oaks heavily defoliated. E = hatching period of <u>T</u>. <u>viridana</u>. A, B, C, D are particular oaks, see the text.

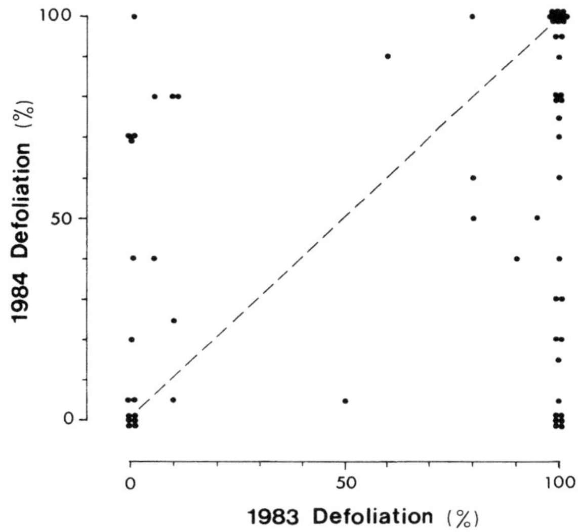

Figure 4. Comparison of the 1983 and 1984 defoliations for the 60 holly oaks of the Petit Lubéron mountain. The dashed line represents the equal defoliation in both years.

population. Except during extreme outbreaks, the latest developing oaks suffer little or no damage. They may be said to be "phenologically resistant." (2) The phenological order of the oaks, and therefore their degree of resistance, may vary considerably, sometimes completely, according to the year. During small scale outbreaks, some oaks are entirely defoliated one year but are undamaged the next, and vice versa. In this case, the phenological resistance observed one year is only a very fleeting characteristic. Nevertheless, a few rare oaks perhaps express it permanently. The result is a very strong year-to-year variation in the distribution of defoliation among trees.

The year-to-year variation in the phenological rank of the holly oaks results, perhaps in part, from the retarding effect of defoliation on the subsequent development of the buds. This may result in a reduction of *T. viridana* populations on some trees.

It would be of interest to know to what extent such results can be applied generally to all the holly oak stands and if similar processes are observed in deciduous oaks.

LACK OF ADAPTION OF A POPULATION OF TORTRIX VIRIDANA TO A HOST SPECIES

Like those of other tortricids, moths of the green oak leafroller can disperse over great distances, sometimes exceeding a hundred or so kilometers. This long-range dispersal is quite common and occasionally involves a considerable number of moths (Du Merle and Pinguet 1982; Du Merle 1985a, 1985b). Therefore, stands of one oak species can be invaded by females which are phenologically adapted to another oak species.

Starting from this observation, we have attempted to learn what happens when a population adapted to the holly oak invades pubescent oak stands.

Methods

Female moths were caught in the holly oak stand of the Petit Lubéron at an elevation of 700 m and then transported to various elevations of Mt. Ventoux, where they were placed into sleeve cages encasing 40 to 50 cm-long branch tips of pubescent oaks to lay their eggs. The sleeves were removed as soon as the adults died. The following spring, the branch tips were examined when their buds were no longer suitable for the L1 ("lengthening of the young shoot" stage). The healthy eggs and the larvae developing on the young shoots were counted. The success of *T. viridana* per stand is expressed by the mean of the ratios for each branch (the number of the larvae divided by the number of healthy eggs). It is an estimator of the phenological coincidence between the insect and the plant. This is, however, an underestimate because of the mortality of the L1 during their search for a suitable bud.

Results

The success of *T. viridana* was low to very low at the lower to medium elevations (400 and 740 m) but high or very high (up to 81 percent) at the higher elevations (1,080 up to 1,350 m) (Figure 5).

A population of *T. viridana* that is well-adapted to the holly oak in a given place is poorly adapted to pubescent oak there because of

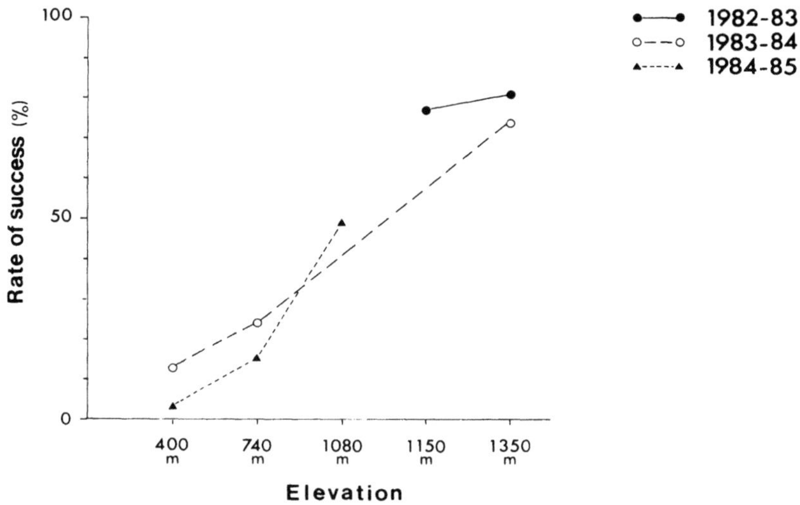

Figure 5. Success rate of a populations of T. viridana adapted to the holly oak at an elevation of 700 m and introduced into pubescent oak stands at various elevations of Mt. Ventoux.

the latter's much earlier bud flushing. This explains the low success rate at the lower elevations (close to where the females were caught).

On the other hand, the much greater success at the higher elevations is somewhat unexpected and shows that the phenological coincidence between the insect and pubescent oak is much higher. Pubescent oaks growing at high elevations would have retarded phenology compared to those growing at low to medium elevations, this difference being genetically determined.

Temperature may act on the development of the insect eggs and the host buds differentially such that the interval between the mean date of hatching of the former and the mean date of flushing of the latter vary considerably according to the type of climate. This hypothesis is probable since some results of Schütte (1957) argue for it. Therefore, the degree of adaptation/nonadaptation of a T. viridana population to a given host population, and consequently the degree of phenological resistance of the latter to the former, are very likely rather strongly dependent on the bioclimatic context.

PHENOLOGICAL ADAPTATION OF TORTRIX VIRIDANA TO ITS HOST IN MULTISPECIFIC OR MULTIVARIETAL OAK STANDS

The holly oak stands of the Petit Lubéron are intermingled in places with very few pubescent oaks. Whereas the former species has been heavily attacked by T. viridana since at least 1982, the latter has been undamaged or only slightly damaged. The contrast was particularly striking in 1986. However, the pubescent oaks were not free of T. viridana. On the contrary, at the beginning of the 1984 spring, for example, they supported a great number of healthy eggs (32 on the average per 30-cm-long branch tip), sufficient in theory to lead to a very severe defoliation. But subsequent samples have shown that these eggs hatched at the same time as those on the neighboring holly oaks. Thus, the eggs had nearly all been laid by the population ravaging the holly oaks and were, therefore, ill-adapted to the pubescent oak, which explains why the latter suffered only minor damage.

Judging from these observations only, it would be tempting to conclude that pubescent oak is phenologically resistant to T. viridana, which would be completely erroneous.

The situation was very different on Mt. Ventoux where the pest, in mixed stands of pubescent oak and holly oak, can proliferate on both species, owing to two populations of the insect respectively adapted to each host and coexisting at the same place (Du Merle 1983). In this case, neither of the two oaks is rare, even if one of them is sometimes markedly predominant.

These observations raise the problem of the adaptation of T. viridana to its hosts in the stands made up of several species or varieties of oaks differing in their phenology. When one of these species or varieties is very scarce in comparison with the others, which is the case for the pubescent oak on the Petit Lubéron, it is unlikely that a population of the pest genetically adapted to the rare species can remain. It would not be long before this population merges, following hybridizations, into those much superior in number, which are adapted to the predominant oaks. In such a situation, therefore, this species or variety will very presumably present a permanent phenological resistance to T. viridana. Its resistance will even be general if its relative abundance is everywhere very low, which can be the case, for example, for an exotic oak introduced in small numbers into stands of native oaks or for specially early- or late-bud-flushing genotypes of the latter.

However, it would be unwise to attempt to take advantage of such a fact by planting the species or variety in question on a large scale in the hopes of obtaining resistant stands. The primary cause of its "resistance" would be lost, so that, sooner or later, an adapted population of the pest would emerge--either derived from (1) those normally present in the region, by mutation or by selection from their earliest or latest part, or (2) those formed from immigrants from faraway stands of oaks phenologically similar to the local ones. In this respect, the following observation, reported by Moeller (1967), seems, as emphasized by this author, particularly instructive. In Germany, American red oak, Q. borealis, is phenologically earlier than the native oaks and appears resistant to T. viridana except in the few cases where it occupies relatively large areas.

CONCLUSIONS

All these observations suggest that the phenological resistance to T. viridana presented by some oaks is quite reliable but is dependent on the bioclimatic context, the abundance of these oaks in comparison with the others, the year, etc. On the other hand, considering its wide geographic distribution and the great diversity of its hosts, T. viridana certainly has genetically varied populations that differ very strongly, in the case of the most extreme ones, in their phenology. All things considered, it seems very doubtful that oaks can be found that will be absolutely resistant, i.e., uniformly resistant to all of T. viridana populations. Consequently, we can take advantage, for applied purposes, of the phenological variability observed among the oaks by creating or conserving phenologically heterogeneous stands where the bud-flushing date will vary in such a way among the trees that the average phenological coincidence between the pest and its different hosts will constantly be as low as possible.

REFERENCES

Altenkirch, W. 1966. Zur Vorkommen von Tortrix viridana L. in Portugal. Z. Angew. Zool. 53: 403-415.

Du Merle, P. 1983. Phénologies comparées du chêne pubescent, du chêne vert et de Tortrix viridana L. (Lép., Tortricidae). Mise en évidence chez l'insecte de deux populations sympatriques adaptées chacune à l'un des chênes. Acta Oecologica, Oecol. Applic. 4: 55-74.

Du Merle, P. 1985a. Piégeage sexuel de Tortrix viridana L. (Lép., Tortricidae) en montagne méditerranéenne. I. Epoque de vol et dispersion des adultes. Z. Angew. Entomol. 100: 146-163.

Du Merle, P. 1985b. Piégeage sexuel de Tortrix viridana L. (Lép., Tortricidae) en montagne méditerranéeenne. II. Relation entre le nombre des captures et le niveau de population. Rendement des pièges. Z. Angew. Entomol. 100: 272-289.
Du Merle, P. and R. Mazet. 1983. Stades phénologiques et infestation par Tortrix viridana L. (Lép., Tortricidae) des bourgeons du chêne pubescent et du chêne vert. Acta Oecologica, Oecol. Applic. 4: 47-53.
Du Merle, P. and A. Pinguet. 1982. Mise en évidence par piégeage lumineux de migrations d'adultes chez Tortrix viridana L. (Lép., Tortricidae). Agronomie 2: 81-89.
Fankhänel, H. 1961. Über die Massenvermehrung des grünen Eichenwicklers (Tortrix viridana L.) in der DDR in den Jahren 1957-1959 and über Massnahmen zur Überwachung des Schädlings. Archiv. f. Forstwesen 10: 512-530.
Gasow, H. 1925. Der grüne Eichenwickler (Tortrix viridana Linné) als Forstschädling. Arb. biol. Reichsanst. f. Land- u. Forstwirtsch. 12: 355-508.
Moeller, J. 1967. Untersuchungen über Eichenwicler (Tortrix viridana L.) an Roteiche (Quercus borealis). Forst- u. Holzwirt 22: 15-17.
Rubtsova, N. N. 1977. Reducing the injuriousness of the oak tortrix. Zashchita Rastenii 5: 44-45.
Rubtsova, N. N. 1981. Tortrix viridana L. in stands of late leafing oak. Lesovedenie 1: 83-88.
Schütte, F. 1957. Untersuchungen über die Populationsdynamik des Eichenwicklers (Tortrix viridana L.). Z. Angew. Entomol. 40: 1-36 and 285-331.

14

Wound Response of Living Bark of Scots Pine Seedlings and Its Influence on Feeding by the Weevil, *Hylobius abietis*

Anders Ericsson, Rolf Gref, Claes Hellqvist, and Bo Lågström

Defensive reactions by conifers against stem-boring insects, especially bark beetles, have been intensively studied in recent years (Hain et al. 1983, Matson and Hain 1985, Miller and Berryman 1985, Christiansen and Ericsson 1986). The reaction has often been described as a two-step process with primary resin flow as the first step and induced chemical changes in the resin composition as the second step (e.g., Miller and Berryman 1985). The chemical basis for defensive reactions is not well understood, but resin acids are thought to be part of the system protecting conifers from insect and pathogen attacks (Gref and Ericsson 1985).

Most studies on induced defense reactions have been performed with mature trees attacked by phloem-feeding insects, such as bark beetles, but seedlings probably react in a similar manner to attacks such as those of pine weevils. For example, Gref and Ericsson (1985) observed rapid increases in the content of resin acids in the stem bark of artificially wounded seedlings of Pinus sylvestris. This increase was especially pronounced for dehydroabietic acid.

This experiment simulated gnawing damage of Hylobius abietis (Coleoptera: Curculionidae), which is a pest of conifer reforestation over all the Palearctic region (Eidmann 1974, Långström 1982), to determine if the artificial wounding and the following wound response can induce increased resistance in the living bark of Scots pine seedlings to subsequent attacks by Hylobius abietis.

MATERIALS AND METHODS

Experiment 1

Scots pine seedlings were grown at Umea, Sweden, in 1983 according to routines described by Gref and Ericsson (1985). After winter storage in a cold store at about -2 °C, the seedlings were allowed to thaw at +20 °C in darkness for 3 days. On May 16, 1984, half of the seedlings were wounded as previously described by Gref and Ericsson (1985). Outer and inner bark was stripped (2 cm in length) on about 50 percent of the circumference of a stem section just above the cotyledons. On the day of wounding, all seedlings were planted in sand-filled trays measuring about 80 x 40 x 20 cm in length, width, and depth, respectively. Twenty seedlings were planted in each tray; 5 of the trays containing alternating controls and wounded seedlings; 5 contained controls only and 5 wounded ones only. All trays were kept outdoors and were protected by a transparent plastic roof.

On June 4, when the wounded stem section of most treated seedlings had almost completely healed over with callus tissue, each tray was covered with curtain netting supported on a steel frame, and 20 weevils were introduced into each cage. The weevils had been collected at a sawmill during the preceding week and then were stored at +10 °C with a continuous supply of food until 24 hours prior to the start of the experiment at which time they were starved at room temperature. One day after introduction of the weevils, all seedlings were checked for gnawing marks, and on June 7 the experiment was terminated. The seedlings were subsequently harvested and stored in a freezer for later measurement of the extent and distribution of gnawing patches.

In addition, control and wounded seedlings not used in the bioassay were analyzed for their contents of resin acids. Fifteen wounded and 15 control seedlings were harvested on the day weevils were introduced (June 4), and the appropriate stem sections of the seedlings were analyzed in groups of five.

Experiment 2

The second experiment was a replication of the first with the following modifications: only mixed trials were conducted with 10 trays containing 10 control and 10 wounded seedlings in each. The seedlings were taken from the cold storage on June 11, wounded, and planted on June 14. Weevils were released in the cages on July 2. The seedlings were examined on July 5 and the experiment was terminated on July 9. Seedlings were harvested as described above.

<u>Analyses</u>

In order to determine the intensity and location of gnawing activity, the stems of the wounded seedlings were divided into sections A, B, and C as in Fig. 1. In addition, these sections were divided longitudinally into a wounded side and a back side (Fig. 1). The control seedlings were also divided into similar sections to facilitate comparisons between the two treatments. We measured the area of the gnawed patches for each of the stem sections and reported it as a proportion of the total section area.

We used the methods of Gref and Ericsson (1985) for sample preparation, resin acid extraction and for qualitative and quantitative analyses of resin acids by gas chromatography.

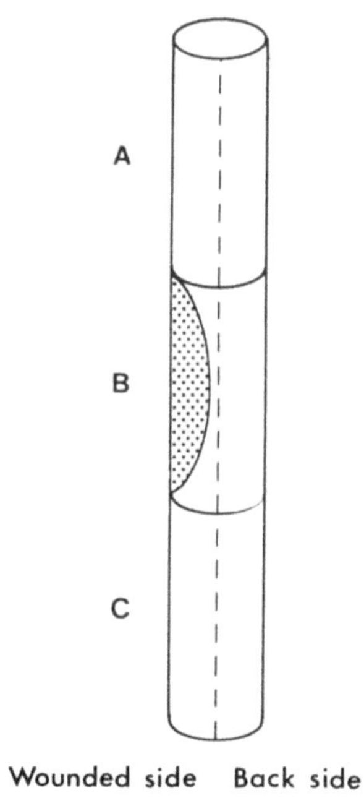

Figure 1. Stem sections of a wounded seedling. The wound section (B) started at the cotyledonal node and extended about 2 cm upwards. The section above the wound (A) contained the remaining stem internode, and the one below (C) was about 1 cm long.

RESULTS

In the five mixed trials in Experiment 1, the weevils fed voraciously on both control and wounded seedlings. Thus, only 12 of 98 seedlings were undamaged. On the first inspection, 1 day after the introduction of the weevils, many more wounded seedlings were attacked than controls, but this difference was less pronounced 2 days later when the experiment was terminated (Table 1). In addition, 85 percent of the seedlings in the cages containing only wounded seedlings had been gnawed upon compared with 70 percent in cages containing only control seedlings. In Experiment 2, the weevils fed less and were therefore allowed to feed for 7 days. The results corroborated the result of Experiment 1, i.e., wounded seedlings were preferred (Table 2).

There were marked differences between wounded and control seedlings in the locations of weevil feeding (Fig. 2). In the mixed trials of both experiments, less feeding occurred on the wounded stem sections compared with the corresponding stem sections of the control seedlings. This was also true for the control and wounded seedlings which were kept separately, although statistical testing in this case is questionable.

Table 1. Frequency distribution of weevil damage on wounded and control seedlings in five cages in Experiment 1. Twenty weevils were introduced in each cage on June 4, 1984; the seedlings were inspected on June 5 and harvested on June 7. Asterisks refer to significance levels ** = p<0.01.

Seedling treatment	June 5		June 7		No. of seedlings
	Gnawed	Not gnawed	Gnawed	Not gnawed	
Control	29	19	39	9	48[a]
Wounded	43	7	47	3	50
Total	72	26	86	12	98
	$X^2 = 6.96^{**}$		$X^2 = 2.61^{NS}$		

[a]Two control seedlings were accidentally damaged and had to be omitted.

Table 2. Frequency distribution of weevil damage on wounded and control seedlings in 10 cages in Experiment 2. Twenty weevils were released into each cage on July 2, 1984; the seedlings were inspected and harvested on July 9. Asterisks refer to significance levels ** = p<0.01.

Seedling treatment	Gnawed	Not gnawed	No. of seedlings
Control	42	58	100
Wounded	65	35	100
Total	107	93	200

$X^2 = 9.73^{**}$ (Corrected for continuity, df = 1)

A detailed analysis of the feeding pattern on the previously wounded seedlings (omitting those which were not gnawed upon), revealed a clear preference for the back side of the stems rather than the front side, which contained the wounded section (Table 3, Fig. 3). Furthermore, Table 3 shows that more feeding occurred on the front side above the wound than on the corresponding section of the back side. However, the intense gnawing on the stem section above the wound reflects the fact that this section included the rest of the stem internode and was hence larger than the other two sections.

The major resin acids present in the bark samples were isopimaric, levopimaric, palustric, dehydroabietic, abietic, and neobietic acids. In addition, pimaric and sandaracopimaric acids were detected in measurable quantities but were not included in the quantitative calculations (Table 4). Wounded stem sections contained significantly higher amounts of resin acids than controls. This difference was most pronounced for dehydroabietic and abietic acids.

DISCUSSION

The results indicate that the pine weevils preferred to attack the previously wounded seedlings compared to undamaged controls. It is well-known that host volatiles, mainly monoterpenes (Selander and Kalo 1979, Nordlander <u>et al</u>. 1986) but also ethanol (Tilles <u>et al</u>. 1986) attract pine weevils. Since many of the wounded seedlings had not completely healed the wound by the time of weevil introduction, they may have been more attractive than the undamaged control seedlings.

Despite intensive feeding on wounded seedlings, little gnawing occurred on the wounded stem section. Increased amounts of resin acids occurred in this stem section (cf. Gref and Ericsson 1985) and may be responsible for the low amounts of feeding. Crude pine oil and substances therein are also known to deter weevils from attacking trees (Alfaro et al. 1984, Eidmann and Nordenhem 1984), and Hansson

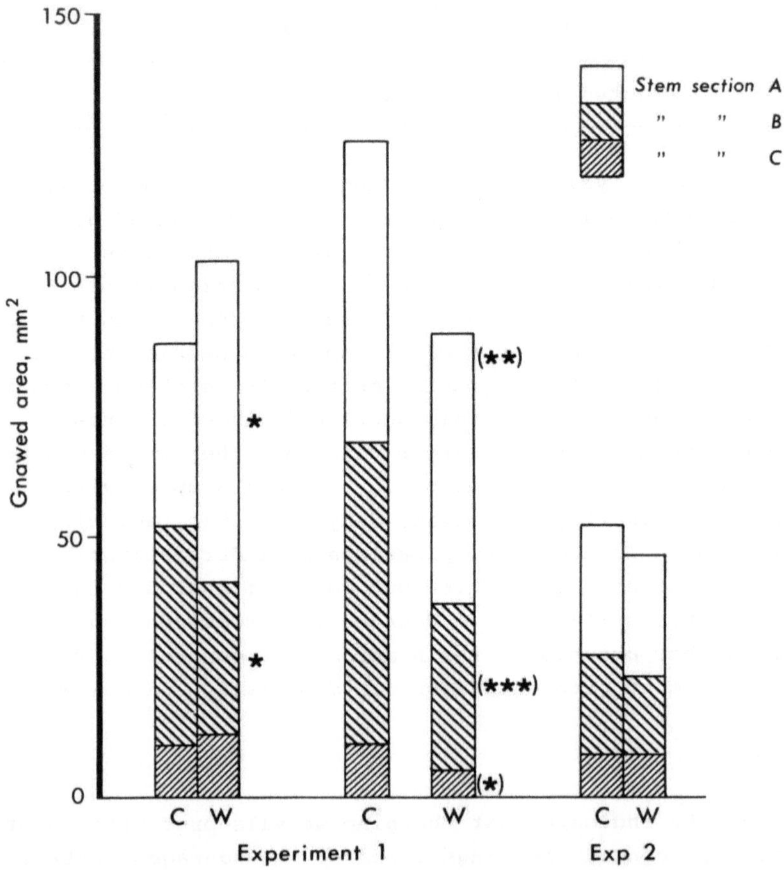

Figure 2. Average gnawed area on different stem sections of control (C) and wounded (W) seedlings in Experiment 1 for mixed (left) and separate trials (right), and in Experiment 2. All undamaged seedlings were omitted. Significance levels refer to t-tests: * $p < 0.05$, ** $p < 0.01$, *** $p < 0.001$.

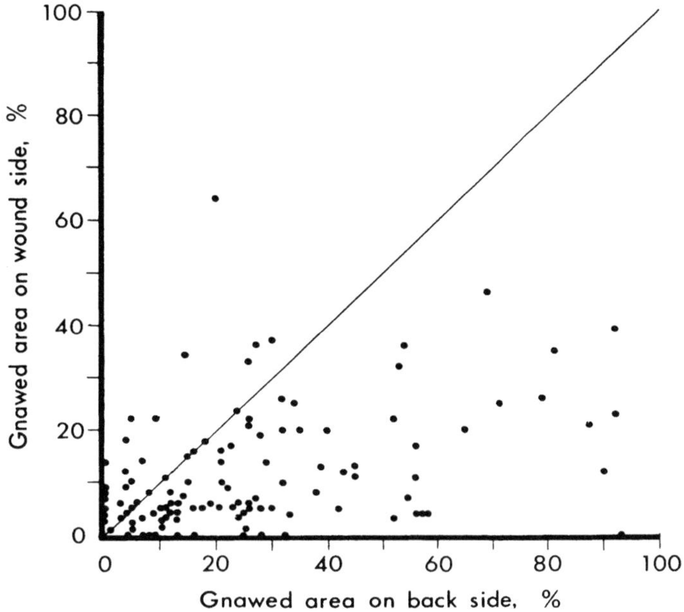

Figure 3. Gnawed area on the front side of the wound section as related to the corresponding back side for each damaged seedling. Experiments 1 and 2 pooled.

Table 3. Average gnawed areas (mm^2) on different stem sections of damaged seedlings in Experiments 1 and 2. (For legend to stem sections, see Fig. 1). Significance levels refer to t-tests: * $p<0.05$, ** $p<0.01$, *** $p<0.001$.

	Stem section	Wounded side	Back side	T-value
Experiment 1 (n = 132)	A	32.5	23.3	2.19*
	B	9.8	21.3	5.20***
	C	3.4	4.4	0.96
Experiment 2 (n = 65)	A	13.8	8.7	1.71*
	B	4.5	10.1	2.54**
	C	5.3	2.6	2.25*

Table 4. Resin acid contents (mean ± standard deviation, percent dry weight of living bark) in the lower stem (section B) of control and wounded seedlings, harvested on June 4 and July 2 in Experiments 1 and 2 respectively.

Resin acid	Experiment 1		Experiment 2	
	Control	Wounded	Control	Wounded
Isopimaric	0.27 ± 0.04	0.35 ± 0.02	0.29 ± 0.05	0.42 ± 0.09
Levopimaric + Palustric	0.34 ± 0.04	0.30 ± 0.04	0.43 ± 0.07	0.48 ± 0.17
Dehydroabietic	0.33 ± 0.03	0.77 ± 0.04	0.28 ± 0.05	1.27 ± 0.17
Abietic	0.43 ± 0.08	0.55 ± 0.04	0.41 ± 0.03	0.90 ± 0.06
Neoabietic	0.25 ± 0.03	0.23 ± 0.03	0.31 ± 0.03	0.31 ± 0.10
Total	1.62 ± 0.22	2.20 ± 0.12	1.72 ± 0.20	3.38 ± 0.50

et al. (1986) reported that certain resin acids present in the bark of P. contorta deterred feeding by voles (Microtus sp.).

The large amount of feeding by weevils above the wounded stem section may reflect an accumulation of carbohydrates and other nutrients in this area due to blocking of downward transport pathways (Noel 1970, Cerezke 1974, Christiansen and Ericsson 1986). There might also be a local depletion of allelochemicals above the wound tissue.

In conclusion, pine weevils preferred to attack wounded seedlings, but they avoided gnawing on the wounded stem section. This avoidance could be a result of the change in resin acid composition in the wound area. This change is restricted to the wounded stem section only. Further studies are needed to explain the chemical basis for defense reactions against insects which feed on stem phloem of seedlings.

ACKNOWLEDGEMENTS

We thank Kjell Olofsson for technical assistance and Goran Nordlander and David Tilles for reviewing the manuscript. This study was financially supported by the Swedish Council of Forestry and Agricultural Research.

REFERENCES

Alfaro, R. I., J. H. Borden, L. J. Harris, W. W. Nijholt, and L. H. McMullen. 1984. Pine oil, a feeding deterrent for the white pine weevil, Pissodes strobi (Coleoptera: Curculionidae). Can. Entomol. 116: 41-44.

Cerezke, H. F. 1974. Effects of partial girdling on growth in lodgepole pine with application to damage by the weevil Hylobius warreni Wood. Can J. For. Res. 4: 312-320.

Christiansen, E. and A. Ericsson. 1986. Starch reserves in Picae abies in relation to defense reaction against a bark beetle transmitted blue-stain fungus, Ceratocystis polonica. Can. J. For. Res. 16: 78-83.

Eidmann, H. H. 1974. Hylobius Schönh. In: Die Forstschädlinge Europas (W. Schwenke, Ed.). 2. Käfer. Hamburg and Berlin. 275-293.

Eidmann, H. H. and H. Nordenhem. 1984. Lovande försök med avskräckande medel mot snytbaggar och barkborrar. Skogen 9: 30-31.

Gref, R. and A. Ericsson. 1985. Wound-induced changes of resin acid concentrations in living bark of Scots pine seedlings. Can. J. For. Res. 15: 92-96.

Hain, F. P., W. D. Mawby, S. P. Cook, and F. H. Arthur. 1983. Host conifer reaction to stem invasion. Z. Angew. Entomol. 96: 247-256.

Hansson, L., R. Gref, L. Lundgren, and O. Theander. 1986. Susceptibility to vole attacks as due to bark phenols and terpenes in Pinus contorta provenances introduced into Sweden. J. Chem. Ecol. 12: 1569-1578.

Långström, B. 1982. Abundance and seasonal activity of adult Hylobius-weevils in reforestation areas during first years following final felling. Commun. Inst. For. Fenn. 106: 1-23.

Matson, P. A. and F. P. Hain. 1985. Host conifer defense strategies: a hypothesis. In: The role of the host in the population dynamics of forest insects (L. Safranyik, Ed.); Proceedings, IUFRO Conference; 1983 September 4-7; Banff, Alberta. Victoria, BC: Canadian Forestry Service and USDA, Forest Service; 33-42.

Miller, R. H. and A. A. Berryman. 1985. Energetics of conifer defense against bark beetles and associated fungi. In: The role of the host in the population dynamics of forest insects (L. Safranyik, Ed.); Proceedings, IUFRO Conference; 1983 September 4-7; Banff, Alberta. Victoria, BC: Canadian Forestry Service and USDA, Forest Service; 13-23.

Noel, A. R. A. 1970. The girdled tree. Bot. Rev. 36: 162-195.

Nordlander, G., H. H. Eidmann, U. Jacobsson, H. Nordenhem, and K. Sjödin. 1986. Orientation of the pine weevil Hylobius abiets (L.) to under-ground sources of host volatiles. Entomol. Exp. Appl. 41: 91-100.

Selander, J. and P. Kalo. 1979. Männyn taimen pihkan monoterpeenien vaikutuksista tuhonkestävyyteen tukkimiehentäitä, Hylobius abietis L. (Coleoptera, Curculionidae) vastaan. Summary: Evaluation of resistance of Scots pine seedlings against the large pine weevil, Hylobius abietis L. (Coleoptera, Curculionidae) in relation to their monoterpene composition. Silva Fenn. 13: 115-130.

Tilles, D. A., K. Sjödin, G. Nordlander, and H. H. Eidmann. 1986. Synergism between ethanol and conifer host volatiles as attractants for the pine weevil Hylobius abietis (L.) (Coleoptera: Curculionidae). J. Econ. Entomol. 79: 970-974.

III. Defenses Against Attached Imbedded Insects

15

Interactions Between the Leaf Miner, *Phyllocnistis suffusella,* and Poplars

L. Nef

Phyllocnistis suffusella is a microlepidoptera leaf miner which is very common in Belgium. It has two generations per year. Eggs are laid on young leaves in the growing stage, into which the caterpillar penetrates to make its mine. In an extensive study, it was found to be present in about 25 percent of the leaves examined (Nef 1987). Further information about the biology of Phyllocnistis suffusella may be found in Arru (1966) and in Nef and Janssens (1982).

The research objectives for this study were to define (1) those characteristics of the poplars which are quantitatively related to the insect population, (2) those tree characteristics which influence insect development, and (3) some influences of the insects on the host tree.

METHODS

Populeta and Poplars

Seven experimental poplar plantations, selected from the approximately 100 established by the Belgian Poplar Commission (de Jamblinne et al. 1973) were used in this study. I studied 14 poplar clones (see Table 1) belonging to three groups: Populus deltoids x nigra (DN), P. trichocarpa (T), and P. trichocarpa x deltoides (TD). The older clone, robusta, was used as a control.

To determine the rate of tree growth, I measured mean annual basal area growth for the last 5 years. Several other tree chacteristics were also measured but were not used in the analyses because they showed a very strong correlation with this mean annual growth (Nef 1985). The polyphenol (tannin) content in the leaves was determined by methods of Timmerman (1983) and Konanowicz (1984), after the method of Folin and Denis (1912). Bouyaiche (1987) has measured the

Table 1. Record of poplar clones used in this study: abbreviations and symbols.

Group	*P. deltoids* x nigra (DN)	*P. trichocarpa* (T)	*P. trichocarpa* x deltoids (TD)
Clones	Gaver (GA) Ghoy (GH) Gibecq (GI) Isières (IS) Ogy (OG) Primo (PR) Robusta (RO)	Columbia River (CR) Fritzy Pauley (FP) Trichobel (TR)	Beaupré (BE) Boelare (BO) Hummegem (HU) Raspalje (RA) Unal (UN)

foliar surfaces and the length of the mines in the populetum of Louvain-la-Neuve, and using emission spectrometry has also measured levels of mineral elements in both the attacked and the undamaged leaves.

RESULTS

Relationship Between Tree Characteristics and Populations of Phyllocnistis Suffusella

A highly significant positive correlation was observed between the number of larvae present in leaves, i.e., the relative sensitivity (R.S.) of the clones, and the polyphenol content of their leaves (Nef 1983, 1985). R.S. was also positively correlated with the foliar contents of K and of Mn in the undamaged leaves (Fig. 1). On the other hand, R.S. exhibited a strong ($p < .001$) negative correlation with the mean annual increment of the basal area (Fig. 2). Similar levels of correlation were found between the R.S. and the order of sprouting in the spring or the seasonal growth intensity (Nef 1985).

Influence of Some Tree Characteristics on the Insect

A study restricted to three clones belonging to each of the three main groups (DN, T, and TD) revealed very strong differences in the numbers and the weights of the pupae and the rates of pupal formation. As shown in Fig. 3 and 4, all of these variables were negatively correlated with the tannin contents of the leaves ($p < .001$). The ranking is DN > TD > T (from most to least favorable for the

Phyllocnistis suffusella). On the other hand, Bouyaiche (1987) has shown that the length of the galleries increases in the direction DN < TD < T. In other words, gallery lengths are positively correlated with polyphenol contents of their leaves (Fig. 5).

The value of the conclusion is enhanced by the fact that this relationship comes from two separate sets of measurements: the length of the mines was measured in Louvain-la-Neuve in 1985, the polyphenol contents by Timmerman in 1982. It is also noteworthy that the mean foliar surface per clone for the undamaged leaves is significantly correlated with its foliar polyphenol content, with the length of the mines, and with its mean annual increment of the basal area.

Influence of the Insect on the Host Tree

As shown by Konanowicz (1984), an attack provokes an important increase in tannin content. In leaves of three clones, each belonging

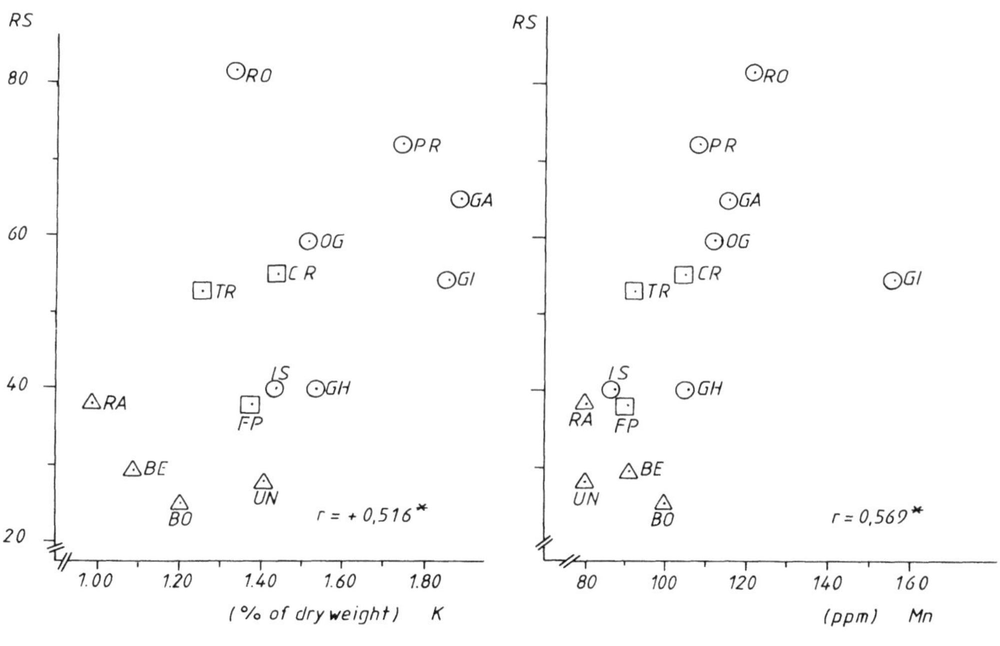

Figure 1. Relationship between the "relative sensitivity" (R.S.) and the K or Mn content in the undamaged leaves.

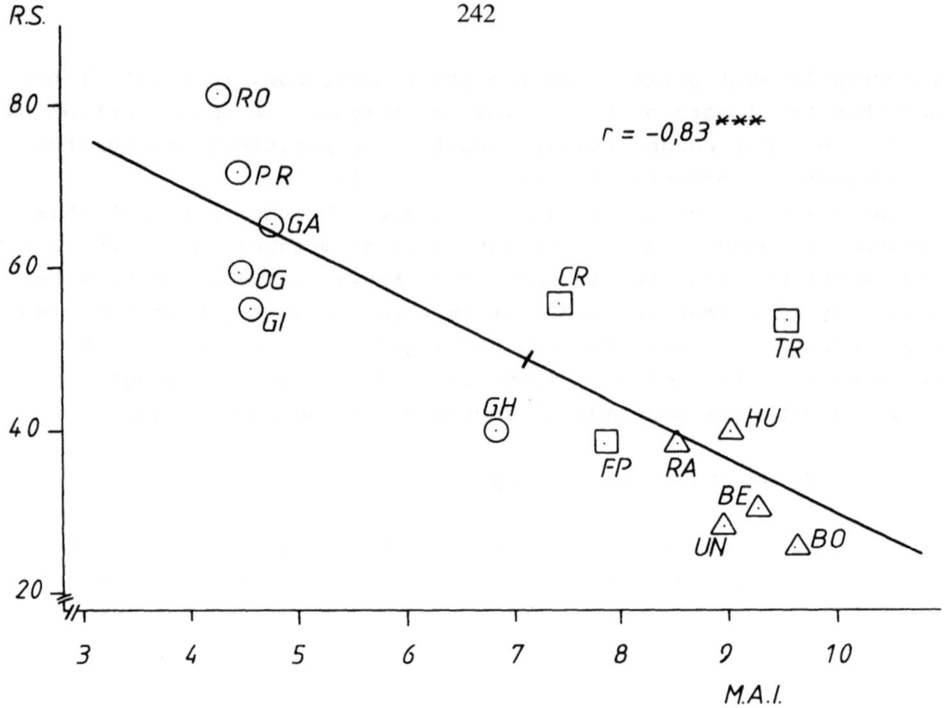

Figure 2. Relationship between the "relative sensitivity" (R.S.) and the mean annual increment (M.A.I.) of the basal area (in cm^2/year).

to a different group: Ghoy (DN), Columbia River (T) and Beaupré (TD), I compared the polyphenol content of the attacked half with that of the undamaged half of the same leaf. The increase, expressed as a percentage of the content in the undamaged half, shows a very high negative correlation with the mean polyphenol content (Timmerman 1983) in these clones (Fig. 6).

The eggs are laid on young, still growing leaves. The attack by the caterpillar causes a reduction in leaf growth. The resultant loss in foliar surface area shows a positive correlation with the polyphenol content of the leaves (Fig. 7) and with the mean surface of undamaged leaves (Fig. 8). These last two figures reveal also that this effect is linked to the clone's genetic group.

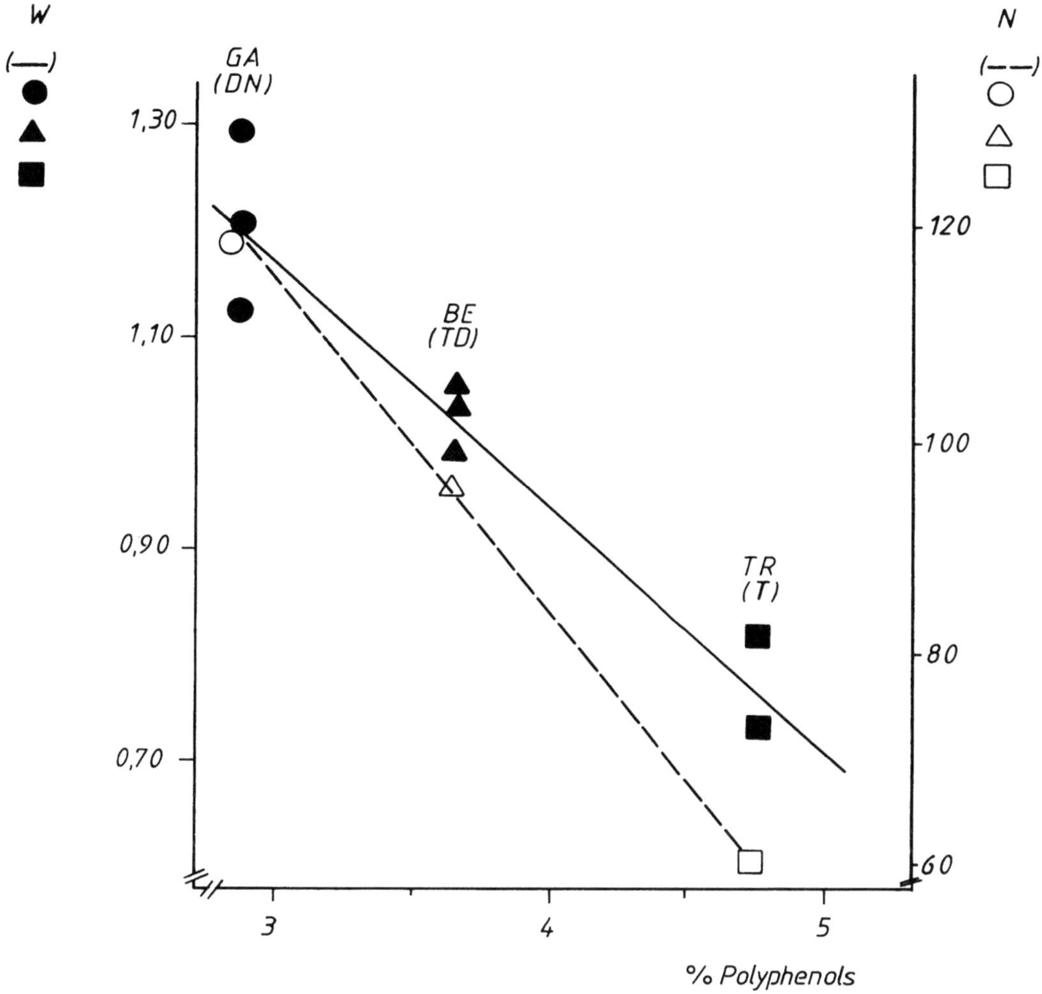

Figure 3. Relationship between the foliar polyphenol content (percent of fresh weight) and W, the weight of the chrysalides in mg, and N, the total number of chrysalides found in the samples (results for three clones).

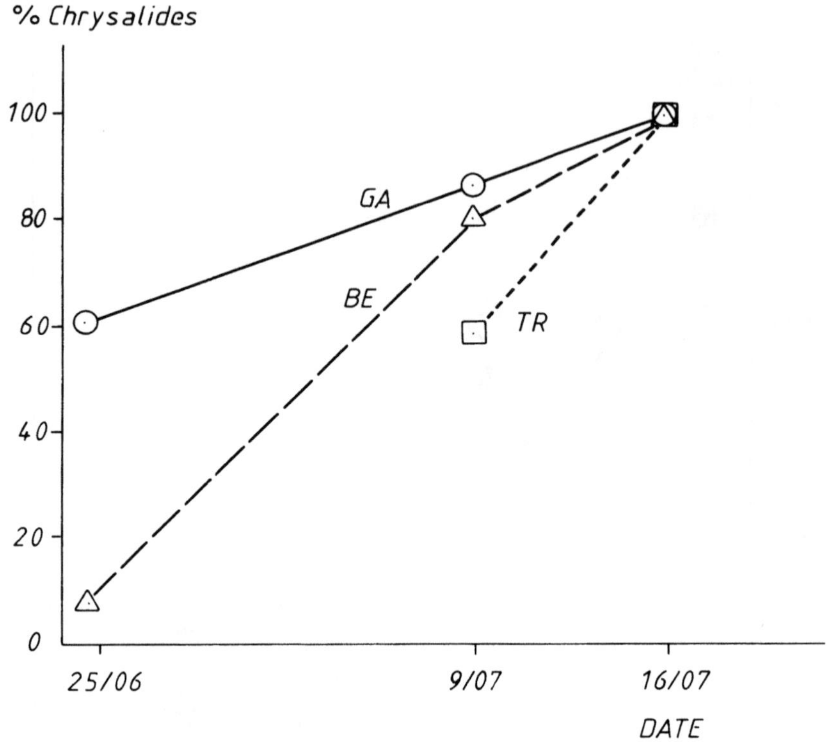

Figure 4. Percent chrysalides: chrysalides as a percentage of the total number of immature stadia found on different dates (results for three clones).

Other frequent observations are that the attacked part of a leaf grows less, which imparts an asymmetrical shape to the full grown leaf, a fact already illustrated by Arru (1966). The presence of a mine also modifies the mineral composition of the leaves. No significant changes were found for B, Na, Mg, Al, P, Cr, Mn, Fe, Ni, or Cd. But, on the contrary, there were significant decreases for Mo, Cu, Zn, Ca, and increases for K (Table 2).

DISCUSSION AND CONCLUSIONS

As indicated in a previous publication, the number of larvae present in the leaves of a tree, expressed by "relative sensitivity," is strongly correlated with the mean annual basal area increment of the tree, and with other characteristics of the tree's physiology (Nef 1985). The mean foliar surface is linked on the one hand with this expression of tree growth and on the other hand with its foliar polyphenol content.

When attacked, leaves react by somehow lowering their mineral content (Mo being the most affected) and by an increasing their K and polyphenols. The tannin content appears to be a decisive growth factor for the insect. The results can be explained, quite probably, by the hypotheses that polyphenols reduce rates of feeding and/or reduce the digestibility of the food by tanning the proteins or by

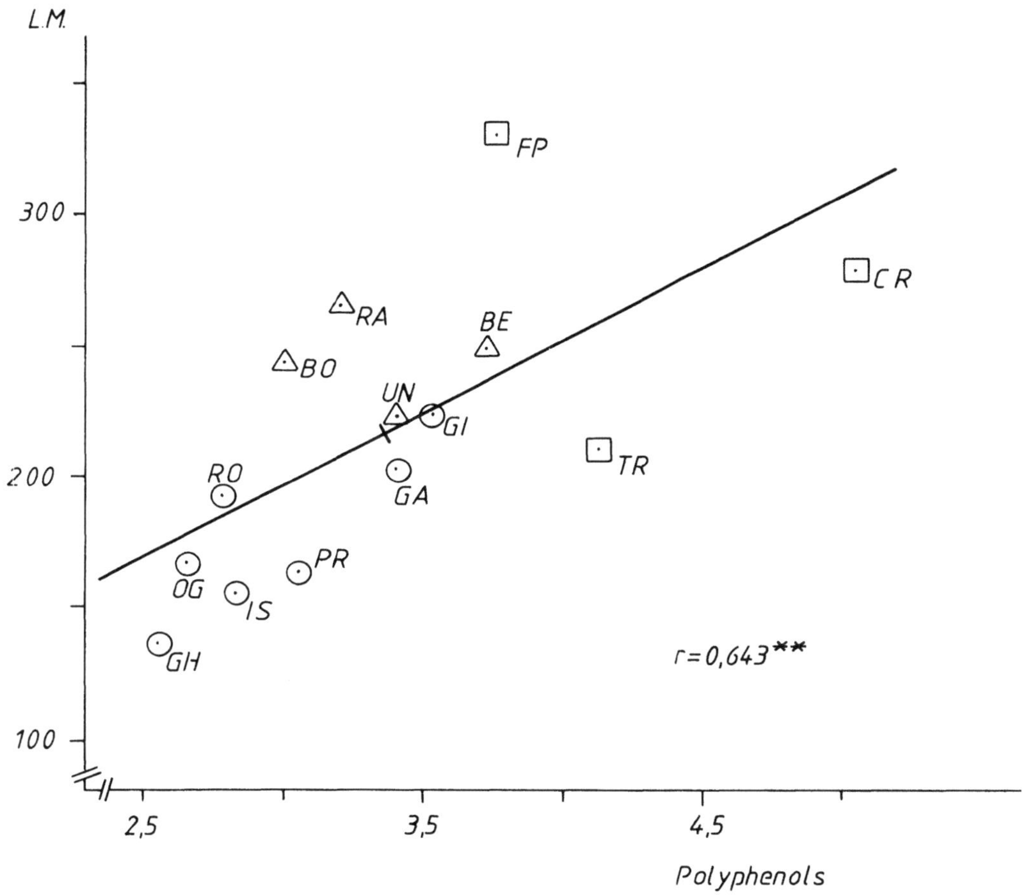

Figure 5. Relationship between the length of the larval mines in mm (L.M.) and the foliar polyphenol content (percent of fresh weight).

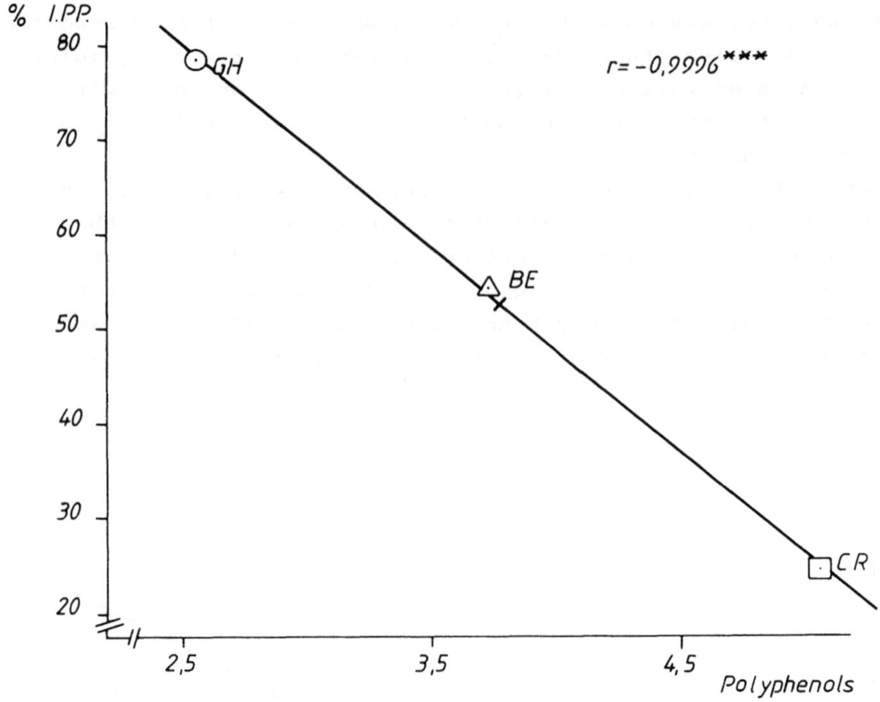

Figure 6. Relationship between the percentage of increase in foliar polyphenols (percent I.PP.), and the normal polyphenol content (percent of fresh weight) (results for three clones).

damaging the insect gut. The final result is that in leaves containing more tannins, the insects grow slower, must eat more to obtain sufficient nourishment (thus making longer mines), attain a lower weight, and suffer a higher mortality rate. All of these factors contribute to a decrease of the insect population density. These relationships are summarized and illustrated in Fig. 9.

The negative relationship between the quantity of phenols induced after attack and the amount prior to attack (Fig. 6) is based only on three observations; but the very high level of significance permits one to infer that trees with a low primary tannin content, thus with low "preventive defense mechanisms" react more heavily to an attack, the opposite reaction occurring in leaves rich in polyphenols. Data of Mattson and Palmer (in this volume) suggest the same relationship with natural clones of Populus tremuloides.

It is evident that factors other than polyphenols are important in this insect/host-tree relationship. However, in this study, polyphenols were the "causal" element most considered. In spite of this short-coming, the following hypothesis may be proposed: the clones with the highest primary polyphenol content are the fastest growing clones, have the biggest leaves, and are the least favorable to insect development (number, mine length, weight, and speed of growth). When attacked by insects, they form less induced or secondary polyphenols. On the whole, this appears to be an efficient "preventive (or primary) defense strategy," but a consequence is that an insect attack causes a greater loss of foliar surface (and probably of growth for the tree). On the contrary, trees with low levels of foliar polyphenols are more frequently attacked, but their growth suffers to a lesser degree.

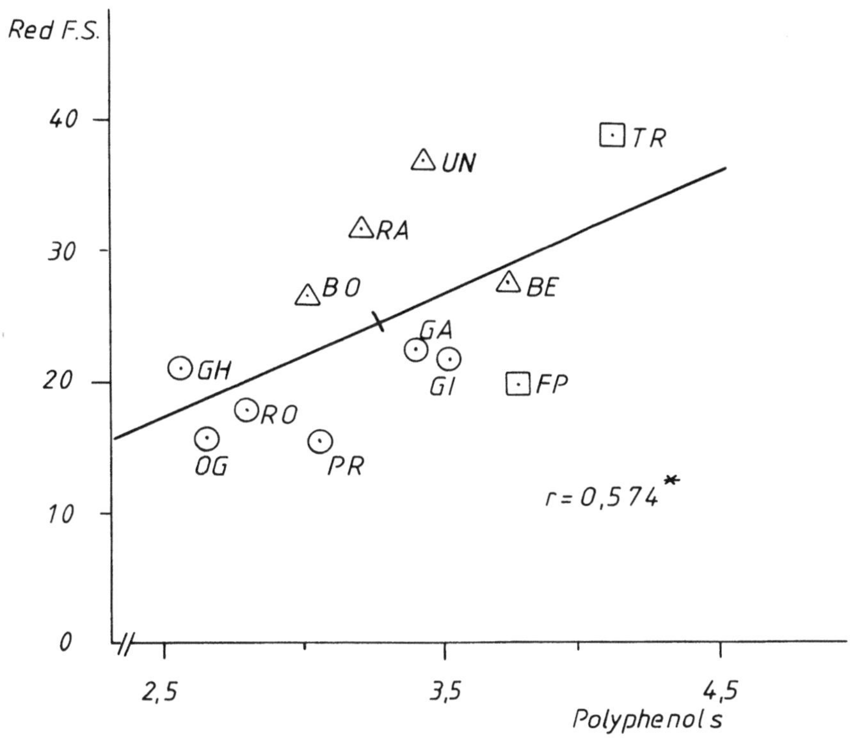

Figure 7. Relationship between the reduction of foliar surface (Red. F.S.) after insect attack (in cm^2) and the foliar polyphenol content (percent of fresh weight).

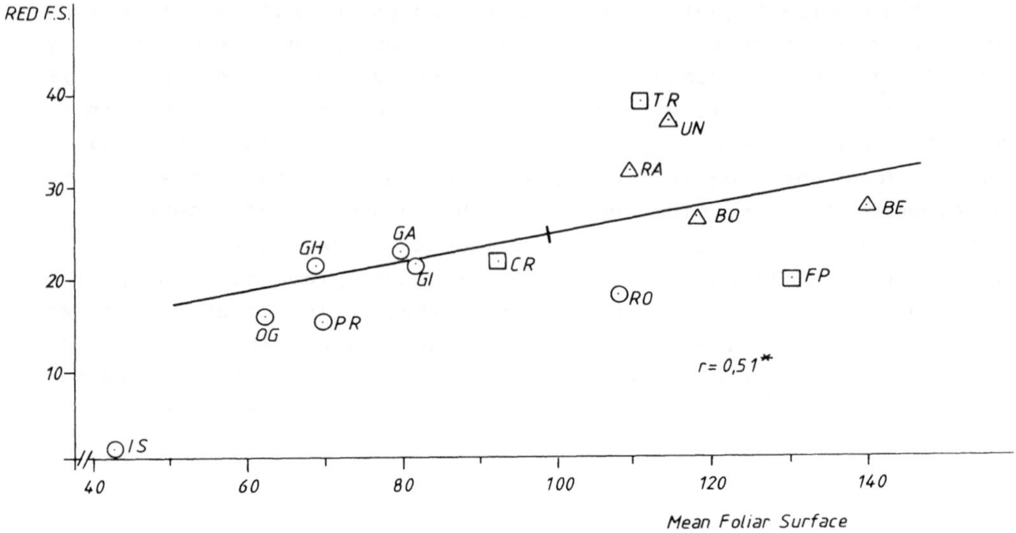

Figure 8. Relationship between the reduction of foliar surface (Red. F.S.) after insect attack (in cm^2) and the mean foliar surface of undamaged leaves (in cm^2).

Table 2. Levels of some mineral elements in attacked (Atk) and undamaged (Und) leaves. Mean values in ppm of dry weight for the group DN and for the pooled groups T and TD (after Bouyaiche 1987).

Clones	Attacked or control leaves	Levels of different foliar mineral elements (ppm)				
		Mo	Cu	Zn	Ca	K
DN	Atk Und	12 26	22 31	117 136	18,500 19,300	17,800 16,200
	p=	0.01	0.01	0.05	0.01	0.05
T/TD	Atk Und	14 28	27 33	104 118	20,900 20,400	15,500 12,600
	p=	0.01	0.05	n.s.	n.s.	0.05

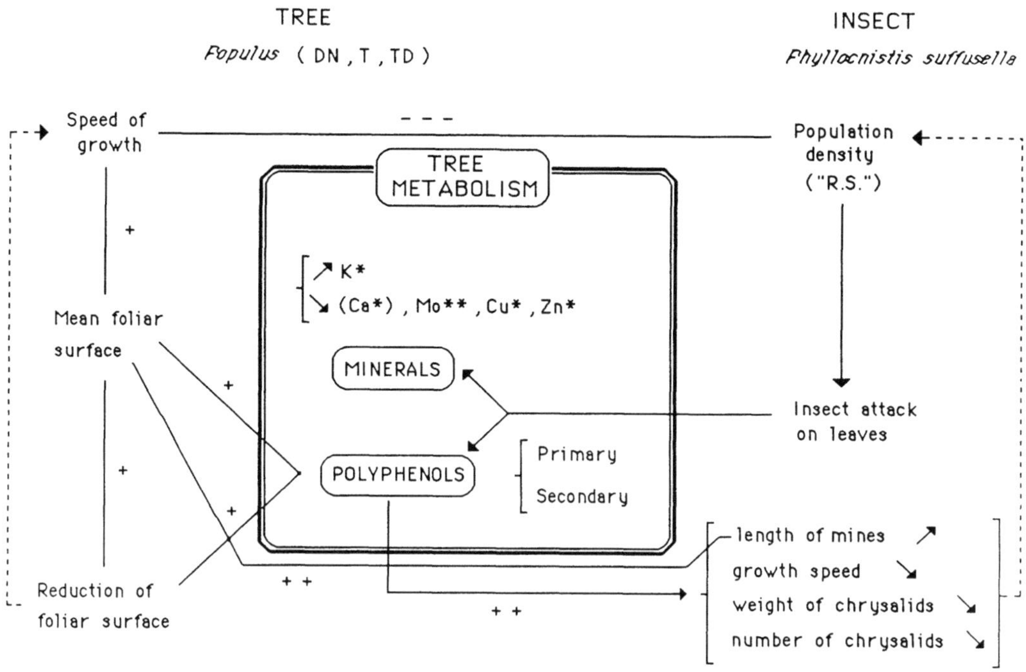

Figure 9. Summary and synthesis of the main relationships between insect performance and tree metabolism and growth.

When attacked, they form more secondary polyphenols. Therefore, they appear to have a rather "repressive (or secondary) defense strategy," which is probably better adapted to situations with a lower risk of damages. Those two extremes are summarized in Table 3.

In the recent considerations on defense mechanisms, it is hypothesized that a plant species disposing of a given capital of energy can "choose" over evolutionary time to invest in growth or in defense, the latter resulting in less growth. Our results do not necessarily support this hypothesis. Therefore, we suggest another view, namely that trees investing in an efficient constitutive defense suffer fewer attacks and thus less growth reduction than trees "neglecting" their defense mechanisms. In environments with great pressure from pests, this "preventive" strategy can result in better growth. This can be still more profitable to the tree if the energetic cost of the production of defense metabolites is low compared to the overall economy of the plant, as pointed out by Harborne (1982).

Table 3. Some characteristics of the two extreme types of defense strategies.

Plant characteristics	Strategy	
	Preventive or primary	Repressive or secondary
Foliar polyphenol content	Higher	Lower
Tree growth	Higher	Lower
Effect on insect development	Unfavorable	Favorable
Under identical conditions, the trees are attacked	Less frequently	More frequently
In case of attack,		
· the quantity of formed secondary polyphenols is:	Small	Large
· the reduction of leaf growth is:	More pronounced	Less pronounced
This strategy is better if the risk of attack is:	High	Low

Regarding the care of the tree breeder in selecting the "best" clones, it must be stressed that in some clones strong secondary (inducible) reactions are somehow linked to concomitant reductions in tree vigor; and in the case of repeated insect aggressions, trees can eventually die. This is a second reason to prefer clones with more pronounced preventive defense mechanisms.

REFERENCES

Arru, G. 1966. I piu importanti Insetti minatori delle foglie di Pioppo nell'Italia settentrionale. Boll. Zool. Agrar. Bachic. 2(8): 41-74.

Bouyaiche, M. 1987. (en préparation). Interactions chimiques et biologiques entre Phyllocnistis suffusella Z. et divers clones de peupliers. Mém. S.N.A.P., Louvain-la-Neuve.

De Jamblinne, A., R. Veldeman, and V. Steenackers. 1973. Le groupe de travail des champs d'essais de la Commission Nationale du Peuplier. Bull. Soc. roy. for. Belg. 80(3): 85-102.

Folin, O. and W. Denis. 1912. On phosphotungstic - phosphomolybdic compounds and color reagents. J. Biol. Chem. 12: 239-243.

Harborne, J. A. 1982. Introduction to Ecological Biochemistry. London and New York: Academic Press.

Konanowicz, E. 1984. Invloed van tijd en insektenaantasting op het polyphenolgehalte van populierenbladeren. Diepenbeek: K.I.H. Limburg.

Nef, L. 1983. Estimation non-paramétrique de la sensibilité des plantes envers les déprédateures phytophages. Biom. Praxim. 23: 73-82.

Nef, L. 1985. Relations entre certaines caractéristiques des peupliers et l'abondance d'insectes phytophages. Z. Angew. Entomol. 99: 160-170.

Nef, L. 1987. (In preparation). Etude quantitative de populations de Phyllonictis suffusella Z. (Lepid: Lithocolletidae) en Belgique.

Nef, L. and R. Janssens. 1982. Les Insectes nuisibles au Peuplier. Bokrijk, C.V.B.O.

Timmerman, Ph. 1983. Kwalitatieve en kwantitatieve dosering van polyphenolen in populierenbladeren. Diepenbeek: K.I.H. Limburg.

16

A Resistance Response of *Picea excelsa* to the Aphid, *Adelges abietis* (Homoptera: Aphidoidea)

Odette Rohfritsch

The adelgids of the superfamily Aphidoidea are all cortical parenchyma feeders on conifers. Their very long and slender mouthparts (stylets) penetrate intercellularly and leave multibranched salivary tracks in the plant tissues. Most have a pentamorphic life cycle, which takes two years to complete, and involves two different host plants (Gaumont 1957, Carter 1971). Galls are produced only on their primary host which is always a spruce, *Picea spp*. (Fig. 1, 2).

In the autumn, the fundatrix nymph (holocyclic forms) settles down on the current year's shoot near or on the bud, its mouthparts deeply inserted into the plant tissue, where they remain. During winter, the fundatrix grows very little; its feeding activity starts again in mid-March and seems closely synchronized with the flow of sap. By the time the buds have started to swell in April, the fundatrix is a mature female, which lays *in situ* a large cluster of eggs. The gallicolae nymphs hatching from these eggs find easy access to the tender young shoot in the bud that has already been modified into a cone-like gall (Fig. 3, 4) by the feeding activity of the fundatrix (Plumb 1953, Meyer 1957, Rohfritsch 1971). The gallicolae emerge from the gall as winged nymphs, and after ecdysis fly to the secondary host. That is the case for *Adelges laricis*, a very common holocyclic species. In anholocyclic species (with only two forms: the pseudo-fundatrix and the gallicolae) as is the case for *Adelges abietis*, the winged form does not migrate to a secondary host. Large numbers of galls often occur on individual trees.

Field observations strongly suggest that there are trees resistant to *A. abietis*, although regularly infested by the winged forms. Observations made in Germany on different clones of *P. excelsa* suggested a correlation between the time of bud flushing and the frequency of galls. The clones which flush late have very few galls (Bishoff *et al*. 1969). In Sweden, Eidmann and Ericsson (1978) worked with trees of different genetic origin, and they observed that galled trees had, on the average, better height increment than trees without galls. Tjia and Houston (1975) analyzed the total phenol content of resistant and susceptible Picea abies and found that total phenol content was higher in resistant trees. Thalenhorst (1972) observed that phenol and lignin may accumulate in the cortex of attacked shoots. However, this reaction may not be strictly correlated with the resistance phenomenon. Rohfritsch (1981) localized the resistance reaction

Figures 1-4. Figure 1. Mature gall of Adelges abietis on Picea excelsa. Distal portion of needles and distal part of shoot remain normal. Figure 2. Mature gall of Adelges laricis on Picea excelsa. Needles and shoot are totally modified. Larval cavities begin to open (arrows). The bar represents 1 mm. Figure 3. Young gall of Adelges abietis. Only the base of the needle and a few needles of the shoot are modified by pseudofundatrix. The gallicolae will find shelter between the modified needle bases (arrows). Bud scales have been removed. Figure 4. 4a. Young gall of Adelges laricis. The feeding of the fundatrix modifies the entire bud: it becomes swollen and achlorophyllous. The gallicolae developed from the eggs (Eg) will settle down between the modified needles. 4b. Normal bud of Picea excelsa. Compare with Fig. 4a.

of Picea excelsa to A. abietis in the cortical cells of the bud. At the end of winter when the aphid resumes its probing and feeding activity, the parenchyma cells are killed by plasmolysis at the place where host plant nurse cells of the pseudofundatrix normally differentiate. This resistance reaction is precisely localized in space and time at the initiation of development of the pseudofundatrix. The gallicolae of A. abietis can develop and mature on the resistant tree in a gall initiated by the fundatrix of A. laricis. No phenolic reaction and no lignin nor cell death appear around the feeding site of A. abietis gallicolae (Rohfritsch 1971).

This paper further analyzes the plant resistance reaction to A. abietis by means of cytological and ultrastructural observations at earlier stages of insect-plant interaction. By comparing the feeding behavior of both A. abietis and A. laricis on the resistant and susceptible trees, ethological factors are characterized and their possible role in resistance induction analyzed.

MATERIALS AND METHODS

The resistant and the susceptible trees grow near each other in the Strasbourg Botanical Garden. Infested shoots from both trees were collected from October throughout the winter during several years (1977 to 1981 and 1985). The shoots were dissected to examine the progression of the stylets and the probing and feeding activity of both aphids (A. abietis and A. laricis).

For stylet dissection, longitudinal slices (0.25 mm thick) of the bud are prepared on glass slides according to Gazet du Chatelier (1948). After 20 minutes, gentle taps on the cover slide allow squashing of the plant tissue, and the stylets and stylet tracks become apparent. By stronger tapping, one can totally isolate the stylets and tracks from the host plant tissue. For cytological observation and ultrastructural analysis, 0.5-1 mm thick slices are fixed following the classical method of fixation and embedding for electron microscope observation (Rohfritsch 1977).

RESULTS

Characteristics of the Resistant Spruce

The resistant tree can be considered as totally immune to A. abietis because during 25 years of observation it has never produced a single gall of A. abietis. Nevertheless, it is surrounded by several susceptible trees, and it is colonized each autumn by the winged form of the aphid.

Compared to nearby susceptible trees, the resistant one can be considered as slow growing with a low height increment. Its leaves are small and dark green. The time of bud flushing is late. It is, however, a good host for A. laricis.

Feeding Behavior of the Fundatrix Nymph and Gall Initiation

Autumn, The First Feeding Site. Both A. abietis and A. laricis attack buds of the same trees at the same moment, but they do not choose the same type of buds. They have evolved discriminating ethological traits which allow them to share the same ecological niche and yet avoid competition for space. For example, A. abietis attacks vigorous terminal buds of main branches which normally are on the periphery and the top of the tree and which burst first in the spring. On the other hand, A. laricis selects small lateral buds or terminal buds of small secondary branches, located inside the tree, which burst late.

A very specific pattern of stylet sheaths is secreted by each species in the cortical tissues of the stem and the bud (Fig. 5, 6, 7, 8). By following these stylet tracks, it is possible to follow the aphids' behavior and to know the exact location of the aphid/plant interaction (Fig. 5). A. abietis inserts its stylets into the 1-year shoot between the pulvini or leaf stalklets surrounding the bud. If there is a high population density, the aphids attack all along the 1-year shoot preferentially at a bud base and on the terminal part of the shoot.

It takes about 4 weeks (mid-October to mid-November) for the larvae of A. abietis to reach the final feeding site in a young bud. Only the larvae that reach that location before the winter have a chance to survive until spring (Thalenhorst 1972). During several weeks, the insect feeds and probes on the cortical tissue of the 1-year shoot where cells become modified and are transformed into "nurse cells" enriched in the nucleoplasm and cytoplasm with lipids and starch (NT_1, Fig. 5) (Rohfritsch 1981). To reach the bud, the stylets again join the vascular bundles of the stem and follow it upwards to the collenchyma plate and bud base. The aphid behaves similarly on both resistant and susceptible trees and likewise both kinds of host react similarly.

A. laricis finally settles down in November. It is precisely located on the bud, its stylets inserted always through the first bud scale. The stylets then go downwards toward the scale base and

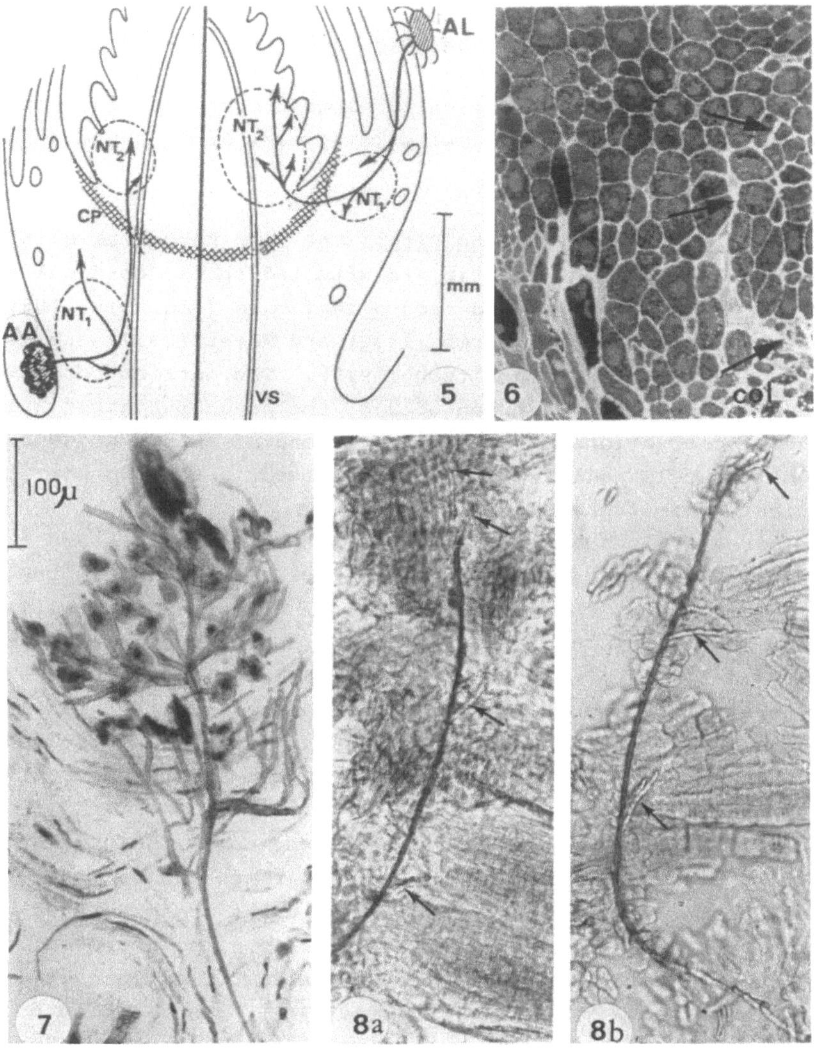

Figures 5-8. Figure 5. Diagram showing buds attacked by *Adelges abietis* (AA, on the left) and *Adelges laricis* (AL on the right). The selected buds are different in size and in quality. Primary (NT_1) and main nutritive tissues (NT_2) are also seen. Figure 6. Early nutritive tissue (NT_2) of the fundatrix of *Adelges laricis* observed in the cortex of the modified bud (mid-March). The cells are hypertrophied, have large nuclei, dense cytoplasm, and abundant lipid globules (Sudan black staining). Arrows point to the stylet tracks; Col.: collenchyma plate. Figure 7. Dissected stylets and salivary tracks left by *A. abietis* in the cortical tissue of the bud at the first and second leaf base. Figure 8. Dissected stylets and salivary tracks of *A. laricis*. 8a. This figure shows the less dissected stylets and their location in the leaf bases. 8b. This figure exhibits the more dissected stylets. Arrows denote the salivary tracks in the first, second, and third leaf base.

penetrate the plant tissue between the first and second bud scale. They pass through the base of the more centrally located scales, through the base of the most basal young leaf toward the cortical cells of the bud (Fig. 5). The cells along the stylet tracks are transformed into special nurse cells (NT1) similar to those described for *A. abietis*.

End of Winter: The Main Feeding Site. The main nurse cells (NT_2) of the pseudofundatrix of *A. abietis* are situated in the cortical tissue of the bud and in the first and second leaf base (Fig. 5). They have been described generally by Plumb (1953) and Meyer (1957) and at the ultrastructural level by Rohfritsch (1977). The earliest observations are from mid-March (first spring molt of the pseudofundatrix nymph). More recent observations show that at the end of autumn and during the winter, slight cell modifications can be noted in the bud near the stylet tips (Rohfritsch 1981).

The nurse cells (NT_2) of the fundatrix of *A. laricis* are also localized in the cortical tissue of the bud (Fig. 6) and in the second and third leaf base. They embrace a larger number of lateral leaf bases than in the case of *A. abietis*. The ultrastructural features of these nurse cells have been briefly described by Rohfritsch (1976). In many points, the induction, evolution, and ultrastructural features of the nurse cells are similar in *A. abietis* and *A. laricis*-induced galls. Each nurse cell type, however, always presents specific features.

In early March, the pseudofundatrix nymph of *A. abietis* initiates an important probing activity: the stylets reach the second leaf base and several lateral leaves and a number of cells are punctured along the stylet tracks, but there is no cell collapse, no necrosis. The stylet movement is facilitated by the secretion of polygalactouronases in the aphid's saliva (McAllan and Adams 1961). In reaction to this aggressive behavior, important cell modifications occur, and the main tissues which nurture the pseudofundatrix develop. Normal cell differentiation is inhibited; the cells become first activated to high proteosynthesis and RNA synthesis. They present a large nucleus with large nucleoli, an extended chromatin, and a dense cytoplasm rich in lipid globules. They have a dense endoplasmic reticulum of smooth and rough types. The ribosomes are abundant; many small vacuoles are present. The very flexuous plastids are perinuclear (Fig. 9, 10, 11, 12).

The young nurse cells first appear as essentially undifferentiated, metabolically active cells which create a sink for water and solutes that the aphid can easily draw upon. The differentiation of resinous canals is inhibited as are all normal cortical structures.

In early April, at the time when the insect needs a high quantity of soluble nutrients, specialized nurse cells differentiate (Rohfritsch 1977). In the most centrally located area, where the cells around the stylet tips are nearly empty of their content, cell autolysis occurs. In these cells, organelles are degenerated, and the plasma membrane is still present along an irregularly thick cell wall. In the numerous pit fields, the pectocellulosic wall is nearly non-existent, and very large plasmodesmata are present (Fig. 13, 14). The differentiation of these cells is similar to the differentiating sieve tube cells of the phloem (Esau 1965, Buvat 1968) or of the transfer cells described by Carde (1973). Around this central area, the cells present more classical nurse cell features (metabolically active cells with a dense cytoplasm rich in small vacuoles of the lysosomal type; an abundant rough, and smooth endoplasmic reticulum; numerous ribosomes and polysomes; a large lobed nucleus with a large nucleolus; and the cell wall is regular). The imago of Adelges laricis feeds on the same two types of nurse cells, with a slightly different location and with some specific characteristics.

The adelgids are cortical parenchyma feeders which can modify the cortical cells and cause them to generate structures similar to those of the phloem which allow an easy transport of the solutes from the vascular bundles of the young shoot and growing leaves toward the aphids' stylets.

By puncturing the cells (without rupture of the plasma membrane) and by loosening the middle lamella with hydrolytic enzymes, the first instar larva has a wounding-like effect on a group of cells in the bud. This group of cells constitutes a sink which is in competition with the meristematic tissues of the bud. The cells engaged in the cecidogenetic field deviate from the normal growth pattern of the shoot; their development is strictly related to the development of the fundatrix.

It is easy to understand the great importance of the location of this group of cells along the normal shoot axis. Their influence will be different if located at the base or in the center of the bud, or on a vigorous, fast growing shoot or on a small, slowly developing one (Fig. 5).

A. laricis generally develops faster than its attacked shoot: a complete young gall emerges from between the scales, the normal development of the shoot being totally and definitely inhibited (Fig. 4). On the other hand, A. abietis and the buds it attacks have a concomitant development. The aphid only partly transforms the normal development of shoot and leaves.

The Resistance Response

During autumn and early winter, it is difficult to see differences in insect behavior and host plant reaction in the spruces that are susceptible or resistant to A. abietis. In a few cases, however, the modified area (cells enriched in cytoplasm and lipids) is more extended in the resistant tree.

At the beginning of March, the differences in reaction between the two types of trees become evident at the histocytological level. In the bud of the resistant tree, a large area of cortical cells and the cells of several leaf bases present evidence of cell hypertrophy and a dense cytoplasm (Fig. 15, 16). The cells are rich in lipid globules but not in starch, which has disappeared. At the ultrastructural level (Fig. 17, 18), the cells present a high density of ribosomes, rough endoplasmic reticulum, very small vacuoles, a large number of autophagic vacuoles, and degenerative structures like curled endoplasmic reticulum. The plastids and mitochondria are similar as in the meristematic tissue. The nucleus with the extremely condensed chromatin has a prepicnotic aspect. This cell type is relatively uniform among all the modified cells. Very seldom is cell death by plasmolysis observed in the attacked area.

At mid-March, the dissection of the buds reveals the to location of the resistant area at the macroscopic level: a white yellowish

Figures 9-14. Figure 9. Cells of the early nutritive tissue (NT_2) of A. abietis as it appears in mid-March. The hypertrophied cells have dense cytoplasm, nucleus (N) with extended chromatin and large nucleoli. The very flexuous plastids (P) are perinuclear. The ribosomes and the endoplasmic reticulum (ER) are abundant. Many lipid globules (LG) are present in the cytoplasm. Figure 10. Normal cortical cells of the bud observed in mid-March. Figure 11. A portion of the nutritive tissue cells (NT_2) of A. abietis showing a salivary track section. Notice thin cellulosic wall and plasma membrane around the sheath (arrows). The nucleus (N) nearly surrounds the salivary sheath. Figure 12. Organelles of a nutritive tissue cell of A. abietis as observed at the end of March. The ribosomes are less numerous than in earlier stages; most of the endoplasmic reticulum (ER) is of the smooth type. LG = lipid globules, D = dictyosomes. Figure 13. Main nutritive tissue cells (NT_2) in a late stage (adult fundatrix) during early April. The central area of the nutritive tissue is constituted of nearly empty cells with degenerated organelles, irregular cell walls, and large plasmodesmata (arrow). Around this central area, cells are activated to high proteosynthesis; they have large nuclei and very dense cytoplasm. Figure 14. Detail of a cell wall (W) of the centrally located cells shown in Fig. 13. The arrow indicates large plasmodesmata.

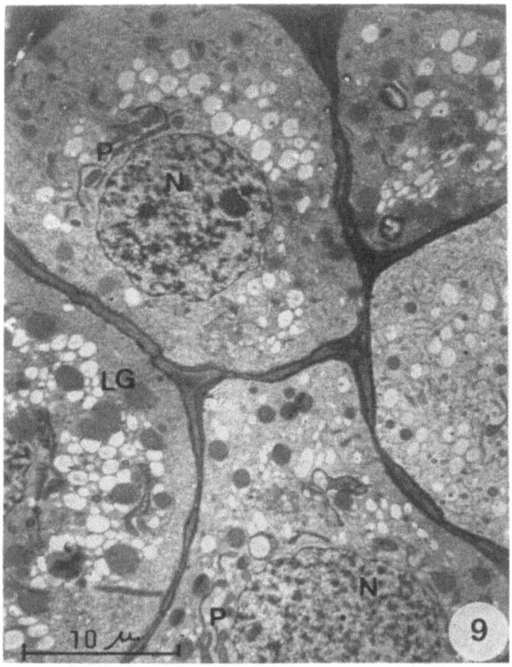
P
N
LG
P
N
10 μ
9

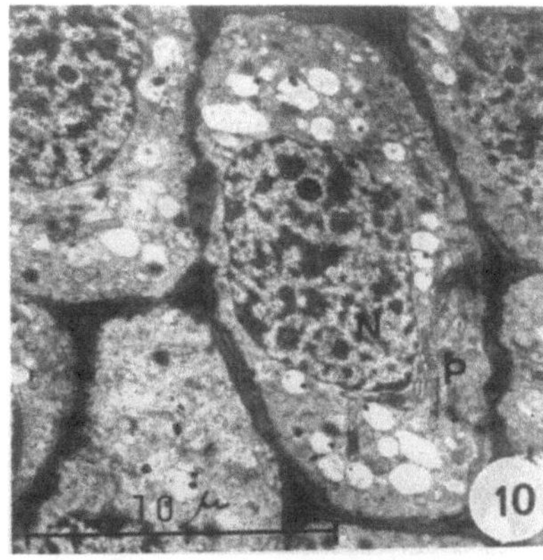
N
P
10 μ
10

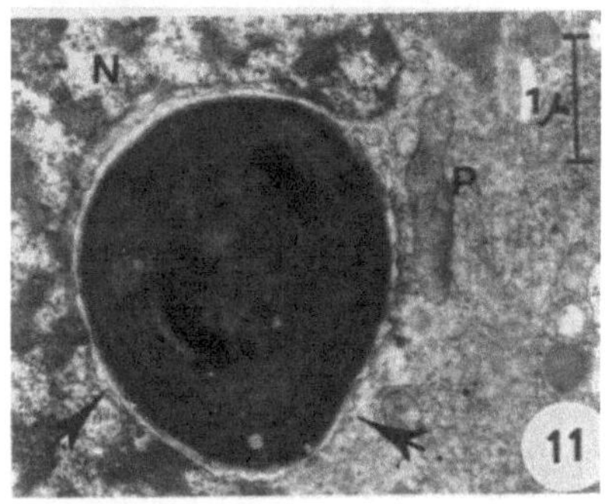
N
1μ
P
11

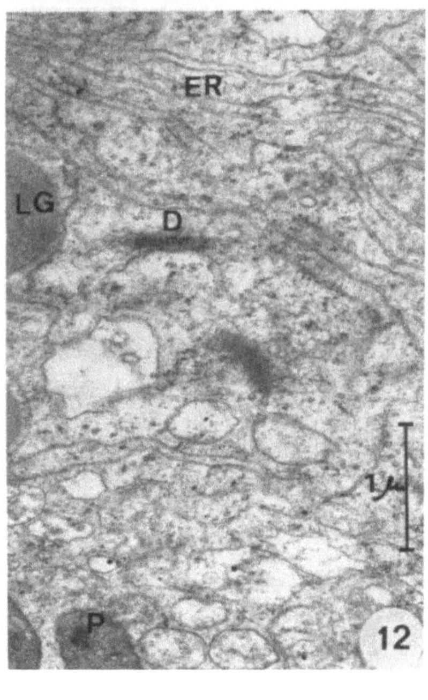
ER
LG
D
1μ
P
12

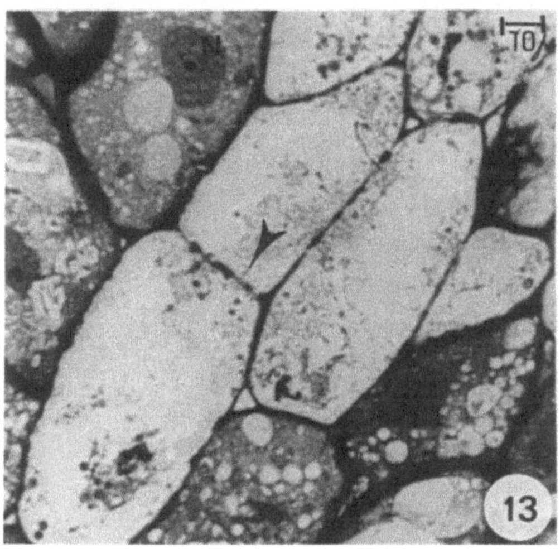
N
10
13

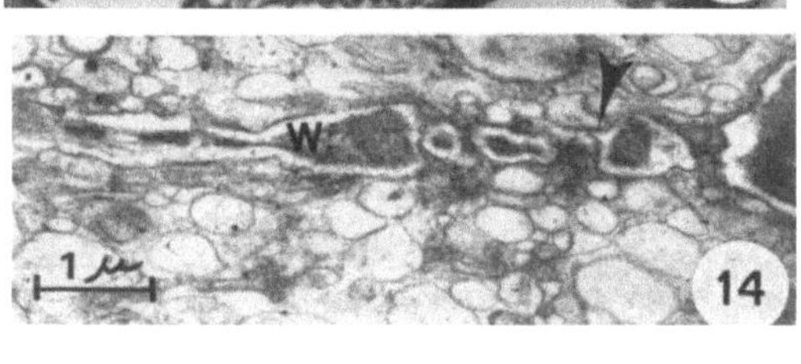
W
1 μ
14

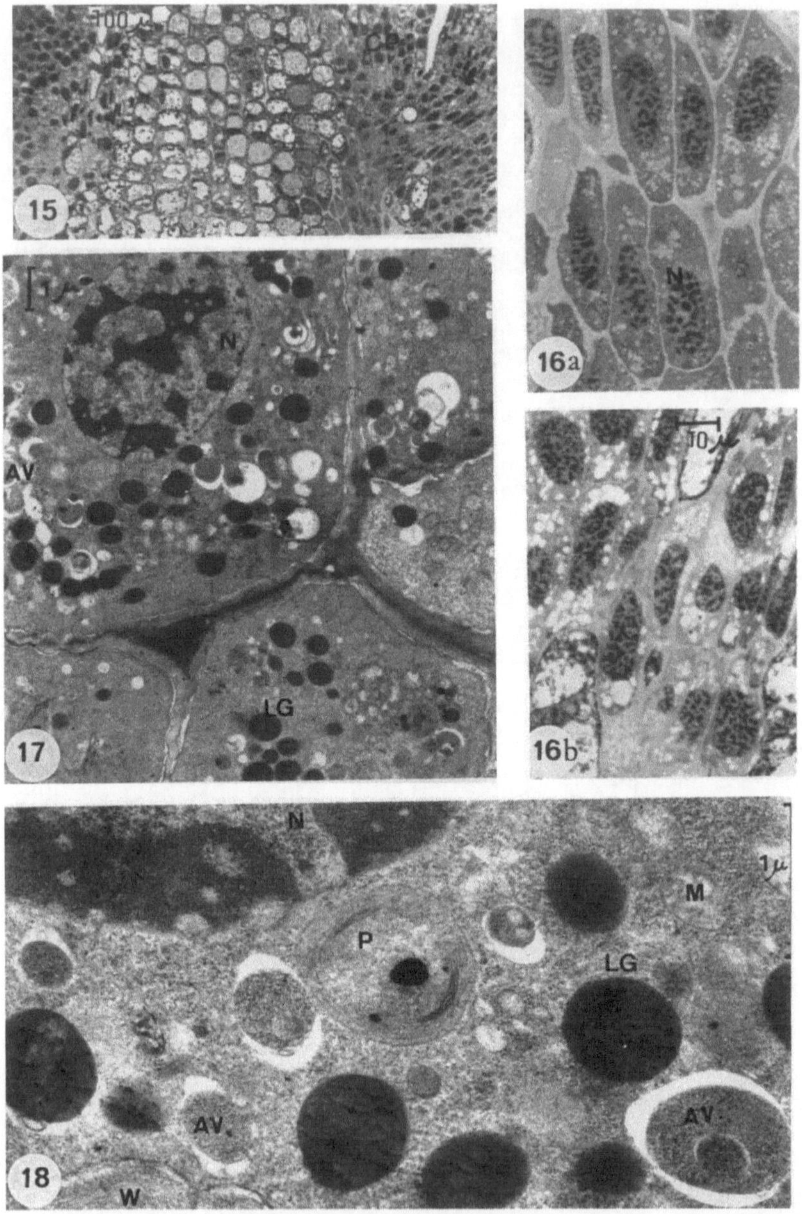

Figures 15-18. Early cell modifications in the resistant bud of <u>Picea excelsa</u> attacked by <u>A</u>. <u>abietis</u>. Figure 15. Section through a young bud--the right side has been attacked, left side remains normal. Figure 16. Magnified views of portions from Fig. 15. 16a. A cell modified by the aphid has dense cytoplasm and a nucleus with very dense chromatin. 16b. Normal cells of the same bud on the side opposite from the attack. Figure 17. A cortical cell enlarged to show the reaction to the attack by <u>A</u>. <u>abietis</u>. In the very dense cytoplasm, there are many lipid globules (LG), numerous autophagic vacuoles (AV), and a nucleus with very dense chromatin. Figure 18. Detail of Fig. 17 showing a part of a nucleus (N) with dense chromatin, a proplastid (P), mitochondria (M), lipid globules (LG), and numerous autophagic vacuoles (AV). The ribosomes are very abundant.

nodule is formed in the bud base around the stylet tracks. The nodule can extend in the first and second leaf base. At the microscopic level, the nodule is composed of a central area of necrotic cells; cell death occurred after plasmolysis. Like the stylet tracks, the necrotic area is branched. Around this central necrotic area, the cells show evidence of high metabolic activity (Fig. 19, 20). These active cells have some features of the normal nurse cells; however, they are smaller, they have less smooth endoplasmic reticulum, and the plastids are more globulous (Fig. 21, 22). Some cells exhibit a high Golgi activity and secrete polysaccharide wall precursors.

In the resistant bud, the pseudofundatrix nymph exhibits a more aggressive behavior: the stylets go higher in the leaves, and they also migrate higher along the bud axis. Many probes are performed in numerous directions. At different places, cells are activated and plasmolyzed.

CONCLUSIONS

The ultrastructural analysis demonstrates that the resistance mechanism does not involve the synthesis of noxious phenolic substances or lignin around the aphid's stylets. The cells surrounding the stylets are first activated to proteosynthesis and to RNA and lipid synthesis. Numerous autophagic vacuoles, together with ribosomes and rough endoplasmic reticulum, constitute the main organelles of the cytoplasm. The autophagic and cell autolytic processes induced at the end of February are later inhibited by cell plasmolysis (in mid-March), so that the insect has no access to the movement of soluble proteins of the host which are now partially immobilized in the necrotic area. This area forms a barrier to the solutes which occur in the activated cells around it. A similar resistance mechanism which first began with cell activation to proteosynthesis and later cell autolysis was described by Wyss _et_ _al_. (1984) in the nematode/ host- plant relationship, _Heterodera_ _schachtii_ in the roots of _Raphanus_ _sativus_ _oleiformis_.

In _A_. _abietis_, the resistance mechanism does not appear to be entirely different from the reaction the insect produces on the susceptible host. The early reaction is more intense and more extended in the resistant than in the susceptible tree. During the first two weeks in March in the susceptible tree, the cells present the characteristics of undifferentiated cells. At the same time in the resistant tree, the cells already present essentially autophagic structures. During the differentiation of main nurse cells in the susceptible

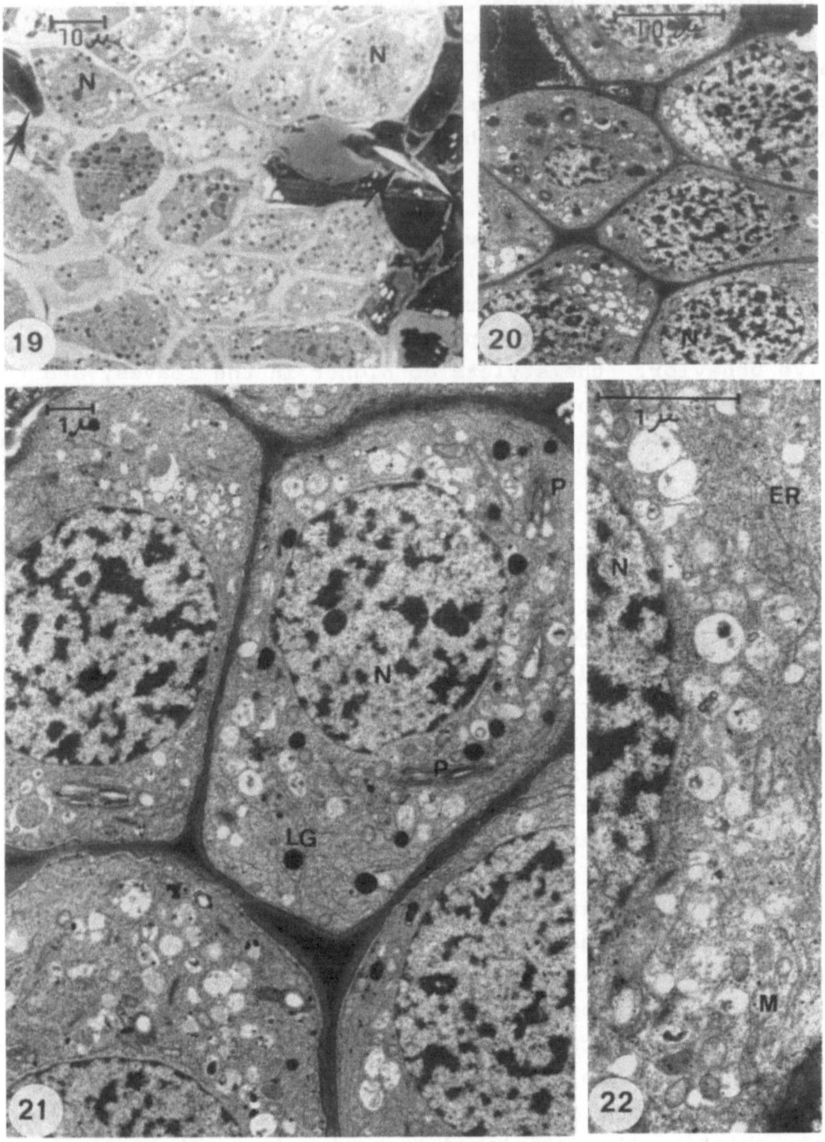

Figures 19-22. Observations of cell modifications in the resistant tree after attack by A. abietis. These reactions were observed in mid-March. Figure 19. Cell necrosis as seen after plasmolysis in the cortical cells and leaf bases along the salivary tracks (arrow). The cells around the necrotic area have dense cytoplasm and a large nucleus with extended chromatin. Figure 20. Cells around the necrotic area appear very active. Figure 21. Higher magnification of the cells shown in Fig. 20. Many features of these cells are comparable to those of the early nutritive tissue (compare with Fig. 9). However, the structure and localization of the plastids (P) are different. The cell is smaller. Figure 22. Detail of the cytoplasm and the nucleoplasm of the cells shown in Fig. 21. The chromatin is extended in a large nucleus (N). The ribosomes and the endoplasmic reticulum (ER) essentially of the rough type are abundant. M = mitochondria.

host, cell autolysis and cell autophagy occur too, although much later in gall development. Because cell plasmolysis deprives the insect of its nurse cells, the reaction on the resistant tree can be considered as a kind of hypersensitive response.

The adelgids, as do most aphids which feed in the parenchyma cells, attack the host partially with hydrolytic enzymes (polygalact-ouronases, cellulases) and partially mechanically (cell punctures with the stylet tips). The hydrolyzed middle lamella, the partially lyzed cell wall, and the mechanical injury caused to the cell could be responsible for the liberation of cell wall fragments of the same type as the oligosaccharides described by Albersheim and Darvill (1985). The oligosaccharides are also produced by the cell after pathogen and mechanical wounding. These cell wall fragments are hypothesized to be a new type of regulatory molecule. They help to control such functions as growth, development, reproduction, and defense against disease. They can elicit cell activation or even cell suicide (see Berryman and also Cheniclet _et al_. in this volume).

Many aphids are known to modify plant cells along their stylet tracks, such as increasing cytoplasmic density or the rate of protoplasm flow. The cell nuclei may swell or increase in density. Plastids may degenerate, cell walls may be modified, and plasmolysis and general necrosis may occur exceptionally (Pollard 1973). Most aphids are phloem feeders that do not normally exploit the activated cell which they may induce in the cortical parenchyma along the stylet tracks. The adelgids, however, are specialized feeders on parenchyma and have "learned" how to exploit the reaction that they induce on the host plant.

While both _A_. _abietis_ and _A_. _laricis_ have managed to control and exploit the plant responses they induce in susceptible hosts, _A_. _laricis_ appears to have adjusted its activity and behavior to the host plant reaction much better. Its choice of secondary small buds and its very lateral way of attack allow it to more easily escape the host plant defense reaction.

REFERENCES

Albersheim, P. and A. G. Darvill. 1985. Oligosaccharins. Sci. Am. 253(3): 44-50.

Bishoff, M., S. B. Ewert, and W. Thalenhorst. 1969. Untersuchungen über die Abhängigkeit der Befallstärke der Gallenlaus _Sacchiphantes_ (L.) vom Austreibetyp der Fichte. Z. Angew. Entomol. 64: 65-85.

Buvat, R. 1968. Différenciation des cellules criblées du protophloème dans les jeunes racines d'orge (_Hordeum_ _sativum_). C. R. Acad. Sci., Paris, série D, 267; 406-408.

Carde, J. P. 1973. Le tissu de transfert dans les aiguilles du Pin maritime. J. Microsc. (Paris) 17(1): 65-87.
Carter, C. I. 1971. Conifer woody aphids (Adelgidae) in Britain. Forest Commission Bull. 42, 50 p.
Eidmann, H. H. and M. Ericsson. 1978. Unterschiede im Befall der Fichtengallenlaus Sacchiphantes abietis L. an Fichten-Kreuzungen. Anz. Schädlingskd., Pflanz., Umweltschutz 51; 177-183.
Esau, K. 1965. Anatomy and cytology of Vitis phloem. Hilgardia 37: 17-72.
Gaumont, R. 1957. Etudes sur la biologie de quelques Chermesidae. Thèse Sciences Nat., Paris, France.
Gazet du Chatelier, G. 1948. Un nouveau réactif pour l'analyse des poudres et des coupes végétales. Ann. Pharm. Fr. 6: 35-39.
McAllan, J. W. and J. B. Adams. 1961. The significance of pectinase in plant penetration by aphids. Can. J. Zool. 39: 305-310.
Meyer, J. 1957. Cécidogenèse comparée de quelques galles d'Arthropodes et évolution cytologique des tissus nourriciers. Thèse, Strasbourg, 321 p., 290 figs.
Plumb, G. H. 1953. The formation and development of the Norway spruce gall caused by Adelges abietis. Connecticut Experiment Station Bull. 566; 1-77.
Pollard, D. G. 1973. Plant penetration by feeding aphids (Hemiptera: Aphidoidea): a review. Bull. Entomol. Res. 62; 631-714.
Rohfritsch, O. 1971. Développement cécidien et rôle du parasite dans quelques galles d'Arthropodes. Marcellia 37: 233-339.
Rohfritsch, O. 1976. Traces de succion de Chermesidae : Chermes abietis L., Chermes strobilobius Kalt., dans les bourgeons de Picea excelsa L. Marcellia 39: 69-84.
Rohfritsch, O. 1977. Ultrastructure of the nutritive tissue of the Chermes abietis L. fundatrix on Picea excelsa L. Marcellia 40: 135-150.
Rohfritsch, O. 1981. A "defense" mechanism of Picea excelsa L. against the gall former Chermes abietis (Homoptera: Adelgidae). Z. Angew. Entomol. 92: 18-26.
Thalenhorst, W. 1972. Zur Frage der Resistenz der Fichte gegen die Gallenlaus Sacchiphantes abietis (L.). Z. Angew. Entomol. 71: 225-249.
Tjia, B. and D. B. Houston. 1975. Phenolic constituents of Norway spruce resistant or susceptible to the eastern spruce gall aphid. For. Sci. 21: 180-184.
Wyss, U., C. Stender, and H. Lehmann. 1984. Ultrastructure of feeding sites of the cyst nematode Heterodera schachtii Schmidt in roots of susceptible and resistant Raphanus sativus L. var. oleiformis. Pers. cultivars. Physiol. Plant Pathol. 25: 21-37.

17

Variations in Susceptibility of *Pinus pinaster* to *Matsucoccus feytaudi* (Homoptera: Margarodidae)

D. Schvester

The scale, Matsucoccus feytaudi, was the primary cause of mortality of about 120,000 hectares of cluster pine stands, Pinus pinaster, from 1962 to 1980 (Carle 1973, Riom 1980) in Provence (Southern France).

M. feytaudi is absolutely specific to P. pinaster. Before its occurrence in the Provence region of France, it occurred mainly in the Landes region, although it was only discovered there in 1938. It has been observed subsequently in Spain, Portugal, Morocco, and along the French Atlantic coast, and even in the Cevennes region along the southeastern border of Massif Central. However, only in Provence and now in Italy have trees been severely damaged since the introduction of this insect into these areas.

M. feytaudi has only one generation per year. The crawlers hatch from late March to mid-May and settle by inserting their stylets into the stem phloem. They moult to the second stage nymph at the end of September. In December, the males give rise to mobile propupae, then pupae, and finally winged adults, whose presence occurs from late January to early February, coinciding with the female's. Females are born directly from the second stage nymph without any intermediate stages.

Unlike other species such as, for example, M. josephi on Aleppo pine, P. halepensis (Mendel 1984) or M. resinosae on red pine, P. resinosa (McLure 1977), M. feytaudi is basically a pest of stems: the crawlers settle at the bottom of the bark crevices, where the "bark plates" of rhytidom appear between one another as narrow fringes of phloem which may be reached by the insect's stylets. Damage to twig extremities (so called "flagging") occurs when there are high populations on the trunk and/or the main branches.

This paper reports on the susceptibility/resistance of different provenances (seed sources) of cluster pine to infestation by the scale (also see Schvester and Ughetto 1986).

MATERIAL AND METHODS

Experimental Design

The provenance plantation of cluster pine was set up in the State Forest of the Maures, in November 1965 at an elevation of about 520 m, using 1-year-old trees.

Six provenances were tested: Genova (Italy), Cuenca (Spain, east of Madrid), Leiria (Portugal), Marghèse (Corsica, France), Tamjoute (Morocco), and Mimizan (Landes, France). The experimental design (complete block) was composed of five replications; each plot unit consisted of 5 x 5 trees spaced at 3 x 3 m. Actually, a statistical design was not necessary because *Matsucoccus* is dispersed by wind during the crawler stage. Therefore, the probability of a tree becoming infested is the same for all trees in an homogeneous stand.

This planting was surrounded by a 6 to 12 meters wide buffer of all the provenances planted at 3 x 3 m. Tree sampling for different observations and the artificial infestation experiments that are reported below were made on these buffer rows (Carle 1973).

Paradoxically, it was impossible to obtain a sufficient amount of seeds of the Maures provenance to include them in the statistical design, so it was impossible to plant more than one unique plot of 75 trees of provenance "Les Mayons" (Var, France) as control. This plot was set up in the immediate vicinity of the provenance plantation. As another control, observations also were made on 50 dominant, naturally regenerated trees of the same age as the planted trees, located close to the experimental site.

During the first two years, some of the trees were seriously attacked by *Hylobius abietis* and uprooted by boars. However, the remaining numbers in each provenance were sufficient to make subsequent reliable observations.

Method of Observation

Observations were made every year in March because the effects of feeding in the previous season appear best at this time just before the beginning of the new growing season. I assessed the damage by giving each tree a numerical score (0-7) reflecting the degree of morbidity. The scale (elaborated in Table 1) varies directly with severity of injury directly.

Other observations were also made on the structure of the cortical tissues and on the scale's population level (estimated by trapping and by counting) according to the provenance. Details of these observations can be found in Schvester and Ughetto (1986).

RESULTS

The first symptoms appeared in 1975 on some trees, 10 years after planting. This delay may seem long, but numerous studies show that on very young trees, the bark is not sufficiently fissured to allow

Table 1. Scoring scale used for assigning damage levels to trees infested by *Matsucoccus feytaudi*.

Symptom	Scores	
	Preliminary[a]	Final[b]
No symptom	0	0
Doubtful or unclear symptoms affecting one or two terminal twigs	1-?	1
Minor resin-exudations on the stem and/or some terminal twigs flagged	1-	2
Some resin flowing and less than a third of terminal twigs flagged or destroyed	1	3
Resin flowing and from a third to a half of the terminal twigs flagged or destroyed	1+	4
Important resin flowing and more than a half of the terminal twigs flagged or destroyed	2	5
Almost all the foliage destroyed	2+	6
Dead tree[b]	3	7

[a]The preliminary scale is used for notation in the field, the final scale for the account of results.
[b]Generally, trees are not directly killed by *Matsucoccus* but by *Pissodes notatus* attacks which are favored by the scale (see Carle 1973).

Matsucoccus to establish itself in sufficient numbers to cause flagging. Detailed damage assessment started in 1979. Symptom levels are given in Table 2 for 2 years--1981 and 1984--for each provenance.

The development of damage during a 7-year period is expressed in Fig. 1, for every year and each provenance, in terms of overall percent morbidity (M), according to the following formula:

$$(M) = \frac{T_i}{N_i \times 7} \times 100$$

Where: T_i is the total sum of the actual indices for all the trees in the provenance being considered, N_i the considered number of trees in the provenance considered, and 7 the maximum possible damage index.

The Morrocan and Spanish provenances (Tamjoute and Cuenca respectively) were very lightly attacked relative to the others (for that reason they do not appear in Fig. 1). In certain years, some symptoms were observed on some trees of these provenances, but they were very light, reversible symptoms, and only rarely occurred on the same trees for 2 consecutive years.

The Italian (Genova) provenance appeared just as susceptible as the S.E. France (Maures) pines. This was not unexpected. Sweet and Thulin (1963) and Destremau et al. (1976) among others consider the Italian ligurian provenances to be closely related to the French Mediterranean ones. It is also known that an M. feytaudi infestation is proceeding at this time in Italy, with the same severe consequences as occurred in France (Fabre 1980).

The French Corsican provenance (Marghèse) appears to be somewhat less susceptible than the Maures or Genova provenances; however, it is not resistant enough to escape serious consequences if M. feytaudi were introduced into Corsica.

The French and Portuguese Atlantic provenances (Mimizan and Leiria) seem to be relatively less susceptible, particularly the former one, in spite of a relatively high proportion of trees with rather advanced symptoms. However, the progression of damage on these provenances slowed greatly in 1984.

It is important to note that the susceptibility ranking of provenances has remained constant for every year. In addition to this, an almost continuous worsening of damage has occurred annually. Likewise, the resistance of Tamjoute and Cuenca provenances has remained constant . It also is interesting to note that these provenances were not damaged by an exceptional frost that occurred in January of 1985.

DISCUSSION

Mendel (1984) also observed differences in the susceptibility of provenances of Aleppo pine to M. josephi, but proposed no hypotheses about the mechanisms governing these differences.

In the case of M. feytaudi, Riom (1980) observed that its multiplication rate was much lower in the Landes region than in the Maures region of France. He attributed part of this difference to the different climatic conditions in the Atlantic Landes region where moisture, particularly the abundant condensation, occurs in coincidence with the crawler's hatching period. This results in the failure of insects to extricate themselves from the wax filaments of the ovisac, thereby causing about 90 percent mortality. Riom (1980) experimentally demonstrated that in the absence of this moisture,

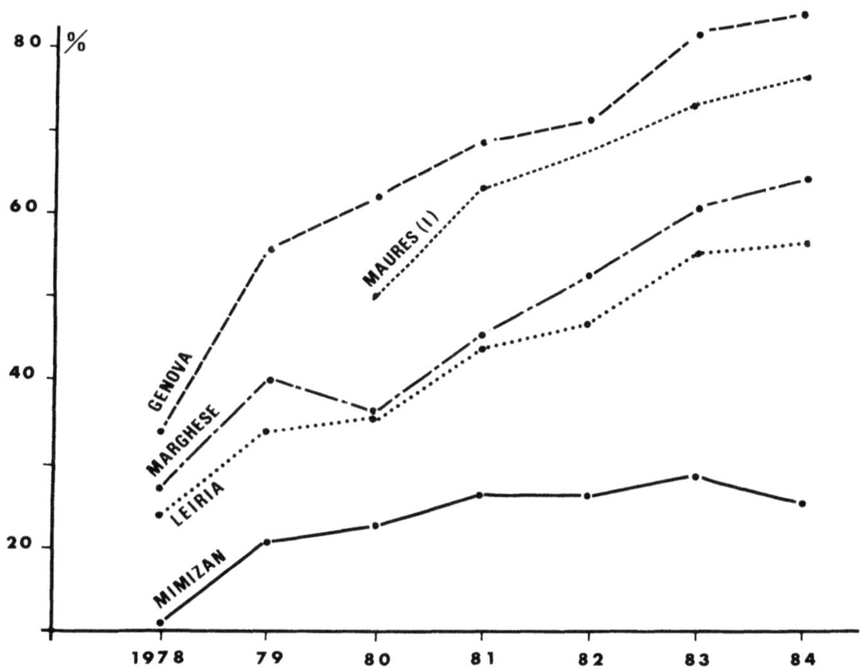

Figure 1. Progression of morbidity index (m) of die-back symptoms due to Matsucoccus feytaudi on diverse provenances of cluster-pine (see text for more explanation).

Table 2. Susceptibility of cluster-pine trees of different provenances to *Matsucoccus feytaudi*: based on the susceptibility index (see Table 1).

Provenances	No. of trees	Yr	Mean susceptibility index (percent of maximum possible damage)							
			0	1	2	3	4	5	6	7
Tamjoute	64	1981	100	0	0	0	0	0	0	0
		1984	100	0	0	0	0	0	0	0
Cuenca	62	1981	90.5	8.0	1.5	0	0	0	0	0
		1984	93.6	6.4	0	0	0	0	0	0
Mimizan	42	1981	28.6	14.3	21.4	28.3	4.8	4.8	0	2.4
		1984	28.6	19.0	31	9.5	4.8	0	0	7.1
Leiria	53	1981	9.4	1.9	11.3	28.3	31.2	11.3	1.9	5.6
		1984	5.7	3.8	18.9	15.1	19.8	9.4	15.1	13.2
Marghèse	63	1981	3.2	4.8	17.5	31.7	31.7	4.8	3.2	3.2
		1984	0	0	9.5	14.3	34.9	14.3	11.1	15.9
Genova	51	1981	0	0	7.7	9.6	38.5	15.4	5.8	23.1
		1984	0	0	1.0	5.8	11.5	21.2	15.4	44.2
Maures I[a]	40	1981	0	0	17.5	22.5	22.5	15.0	2.5	20
		1984	0	0	5	15	15	15.0	22.5	27.5
Maures II[b]	50	1981	0	2	16	14	10	8	2	48
		1984	0	0	12	6	0	0	0	82

[a]Reference plot in the planting.
[b]Natural regeneration near the planting (see text).

there was an important increase in the crawler's survival and the rate of population increase.

Riom (1980) also found in provenance trials located in Mimizan (Landes, France) and in Cuntis (Spain) that the Landes, Maures, and Esterel provenances have nearly equal natural populations of M. feytaudi, and more precisely, that in Mimizan the native pines from Maures and Landes support nearly equal insect populations. On the other hand, he observed that these insect population levels remained lower on the Landes than on Maures sources, even in the case of artificial, massive infestations by egg-masses. These experiments and observations in Landes led Riom (1980) to conclude that the performance of the different provenances with regard to the scale "are not fundamentally different."

But my own observations in the Lambert trial in the Maures, even though relatively sketchy, clearly indicate important differences in the scale populations on diverse provenances. For example, trapping females in the spring of 1981 on 30 trees of each provenance gave an average of only about 4 insects on the Tamjoute provenance and 6 on the Cuenca provenance, versus 42 on the Genova and 32 on the Maures provenances.

In addition, detailed counts were made in November 1982 on 3 trees of each of the resistant Cuenca and Tamjoute provenances, covering approximately 2 m of stem per tree. (The observations were limited to the fissured and cracked parts of the stems, i.e., those that are only able to insure good survival for the scale.) The average density of second instar nymphae was 0.009 per cm^2 for the Spanish provenance and 0.006 per cm^2 for the Moroccan one. Riom (1980) observed as many as 10 per cm^2 in the Maures on native provenance trees.

Therefore it appears, in the case of this trial in the Maures, that the immunity of the tested Moroccan and Spanish provenances is, in fact, related to some traits which make it difficult for Matsucoccus to multiply on these, contrary to what occurs on the Maures or Genova provenances, for example. It seems to be a case of "antibiosis" in the sense of Painter (1958).

It must be noticed that the above mentioned conclusions of Riom (1980) arise from observations in the Landes region where, precisely, the effect of climatic conditions on the multiplication of the scale may contribute to a masking of possible differences related to the characters of the host plant.

Riom (1980) also observed in Mimizan that the structure and the mutual relations of the cortical tissues of trees from the Maures provenance were different from the trees in their native area. The removing and "cleaving" of the rhytidom scales did not occur in so clean a way, seeming to generate only a very small amount of "suitable phloem fringes for the insect. Cadahia and Montoya (1968) made a similar observation in Cuntis and indicated that the bark of the Maures provenance was "thicker" there than in its natural range.

Riom (1980) assumed that edaphic conditions could explain this difference. This suggests the possibility for a "pheno-immunity" in the original sense of the expression of Thiem (in Flanders 1970) caused by "mechanical" barriers.

Actually, in our provenance trial at Maures, the bark structure of the Tamjoute and Cuenca provenances appeared rather different from that of the Maures or Italian provenances. The rhytidom scales are much more difficult to remove when, for example, they are lifted with a large knife. It appears that the Tamjoute and Cuenca provenances offer the scale much smaller amounts of "suitable" phloem fringes than do trees of the Maures provenance, only about 20 percent to 30 percent as much. However, it was observed that only a small fraction of the suitable phloem fringes is effectively colonized on both the Moroccan and Spanish provenances This suggests that other factors of the host-plant (possibly genetically controlled) may affect scale use of these trees.

The results of some experiments by Carle (1973) support this hypothesis. He observed that on some trees of each provenance there was a reaction of the tissues of the twig extremities: a quickly induced differentiation of subero-phellodermic cell layers that often induces the repulsion of the tissues wounded by the piercing stylets. In the Cuenca provenance, there were very important sub-epidermic reactions called "cecidogenetical." Such reactions were weak in the Leiria and Mimizan provenances, and so were tissue lesions caused by the piercing stylets in the Maures, Genova, and Marghèse provenances.

The factors that affect the susceptibly of cluster pines to M. feytaudi appear complex. Susceptibility seems to depend mainly on factors conditioning the survival and the development of the insect. These are (1) mechanical factors (bark structure) that originate by environmental modifications of the genotype (this seems effectively to occur in the Atlantic zone--Mimizan, Cuntis, see above--on the Maures provenance), and/or by more invariant genotypical characters; and (2) biochemical and/or physiological factors, genetically originated, that may or may not be subject to environmental modifications.

We endorse Beck's opinion (1965): "It is doubtful that any example of resistance can be explained on the basis of a simple biological characteristic of the plant."

REFERENCES

Beck, S. D. 1965. Resistance of plants to insects. Annu. Rev. Entomol. 10: 207-231.

Cadahia, D. and R. Montoya. 1968. Prospeccion de Matsucoccus feytaudi Duc y Matsucoccus pini Green (Homoptera: Margarodidae) en la Mitad Norte de Espana. Bol. Serv. Plagas For. 22: 133-134.

Carle, P. 1973. Le dépérissement du pin mésogéen en Provence. Rôle des insectes dans les modifications d'équilibre biologique des forêts envahies par Matsucoccus feytaudi Duc. Thèse Doctorat Sciences Nat., Univ. Bordeaux I, No. 377, 174 p.

Destremau, D. X., H. Jolly, and T. Tahri. 1976. Contribution à la connaissance des provenances de Pinus pinaster. Ann. Rech. For. Maroc 16: 101-153.

Fabre, J. P. 1980. Mortalité dans les peuplements de pin maritime à la suite de l'introduction de Matsucoccus feytaudi Duc. en Italie. L'Italia Forestale e Montana 35(1): 41-42.

Flanders, S. E. 1970. Observations on host plant induced behavior of scale insects and their endoparasites. Can. Entomol. 102: 913-926.

McLure, M. S. 1977. Population dynamics of the red pine scale Matsucoccus resinosae (Homoptera: Margarodidae): the influence of resinosis. Eviron. Entomol. 6(6): 790-795.

Mendel, Z. 1984. Provenance as a factor in susceptibility of Pinus halepensis to Matsucoccus josephi (Homoptera: Margarodidae). For. Ecol. Manage. 9: 259-266.

Painter, H. 1958. Resistance of plants to insects. Annu. Rev. Entomol. 3: 267-290.

Riom, J. 1980. Biologie et écologie des populations de la cochenille du Pin maritime Matsucoccus feytaudi Ducasse 1942 (Coccoidea: Margarodidae). Thèse Doctorat Sciences Nat., Univ. Bordeaux I, No. 660, 253 p.

Schvester, D. and F. Ughetto. 1986. Différences de sensibilité à Matsucoccus feytaudi Duc. (Homoptera: Margarodidae) selon des provenances de Pin maritime (Pinus pinaster Ait.). Ann. Sci. For. 43(4): 459-474.

Sweet, G. B. and I. N. Thulin. 1963. Provenance of Pinus pinaster Ait. A five year progress report on a trial at Woodhill N. Zealand. N. Z. J. For. 8(4): 570-585.

18

Beech Resistance to the Beech Scale: A Variety of Defenses

David Wainhouse, Imogen M. Gate, and David Lonsdale

The scale insect, Cryptococcus fagisuga, is monophagous on Fagus spp. It is indigenous to Europe, principally on F. sylvatica but has been accidentally introduced into North America where it attacks the native F. grandifolia. Other important forest species are also susceptible, for example, F. orientalis in Iran (Adeli 1975). Although we will be concerned exclusively with host resistance and with the ecology of the insect, we should stress that its reputation as a pest of beech is very largely due to its association with a weakly pathogenic fungus, Nectria coccinea. These two organisms together are responsible for the disease syndrome known as beech bark disease. Typically, the bark of trees heavily infested with Cryptococcus becomes infected with Nectria. The subsequent death of the bark may be sufficient to kill the tree. The fungus occasionally attacks trees stressed by factors other than scale infestation, as occurred on mature trees following the extreme drought over much of Europe in 1976 (Lonsdale 1983a). Further details of the complex etiology of this disease can be found in a number of reviews (Ehrlich 1934, Houston et al. 1979b, Lonsdale and Wainhouse 1987).

It is clear that Cryptococcus plays a primary role in beech bark disease and, therefore, some importance can be attached to understanding the causes of population change in this insect and the response of the host to attack.

The host plant seems to occupy a central role in the ecology of Cryptococcus (Wainhouse and Gate 1987). In common with some other highly specialized insects such as the balsam woolly adelgid, Adelges piceae, Cryptococcus is not attacked by parasitoids. Generalist predators such as coccinellids (Schindler 1962, Mayer and Allen 1983) and a host-specific cecidomyid (Wainhouse 1976, Baylac 1980) feed on Cryptococcus, but usually only when it is present at relatively high densities. Hence, they do not appear to exert any control on populations. As well as having a restricted host range, beech scale is parthenogenetic and disperses passively in the crawler stage; all other stages are sessile. Its limited dispersal ability suggests that there is little premium on the colonization of new hosts.

These life history characteristics appear in part to be an evolutionary consequence of the exploitation of an "apparent" or predictable resource (Feeny 1976), individual trees supporting many consecutive generations of insects. We should expect, therefore, an intimate association between insect and host, and there is increasing observational and experimental evidence of a "diversity" of host-related factors that determine the intensity of attack on individual trees.

IMPACT ON THE HOST

Beech is common in Europe, and, in some areas such as southern England, it is a characteristic feature of the landscape. It grows in pure and mixed natural stands as well as in plantations. The timber has a number of important commercial uses. The North American beech, on the other hand, does not normally occur in pure stands, but it is an important component of the northeastern hardwood forests (Crosby and Bjorkbom 1958).

At low to moderate population densities of the scale, there seems to be little impact on the host, but heavy infestations cause dramatic reductions in annual increment (Lonsdale 1980). Local effects on the cambium may lead to considerable stem distortion (Lonsdale 1983b). In Europe, the disease proper has caused significant mortality, although usually only on a local scale. In North America by contrast, the disease has had a dramatic impact on the native beech population, total mortality being as high as 80 to 90 percent (Ehrlich 1934, Houston _et al_. 1979b).

SCALE FEEDING AND NONSPECIFIC DEFENSES

The bark of beech is characteristically smooth and is unusual among temperate hardwoods in that the thin outer primary periderm is normally retained throughout life. As a consequence, _Cryptococcus_, which feeds intracellularly in the bark parenchyma, is able to reach living tissue over most of the main trunk, even on mature trees. During feeding, changes occur in the bark parenchyma which initially appear favorable for scale growth and development. Kunkel (1968) and Lonsdale (1983b) have observed zones of cell proliferation, a kind of internal gall, within the parenchyma near the end of the stylet mouthparts and have suggested that this was a zone of enhanced nutritive value for the insects. Growth hormones secreted by Cryptococcus (Fink and Braun 1980) are probably involved in the formation of these galls.

Gate (1987) has demonstrated that areas previously occupied by scales are often preferred settling sites for crawlers, perhaps due to this induced change in the bark. In a series of artificial incoculation experiments, the distribution of resident scale insects on 2.4 cm diameter areas of bark was recorded photographically. The insects were then removed and the area was enclosed by circular perspex cages similar to those described by was Wainhouse and Howell (1983a). Crawlers were inoculated into the cages during September, and the colonies that became established were photographed in the following August. Many crawlers appeared to settle on or near areas of bark previously occupied by resident colonies (Fig. 1). This correlation is illustrated in Fig. 2, which shows the proportion of each of eight, 45° sectors occupied by indigenous and recolonizing insects.

The host-insect interactions in the early stages of colonization can be regarded as a positive feedback loop of population growth and nutritional facilitation beneath colonies (Wainhouse and Gate 1987), but defensive reactions in the bark are eventually stimulated. Early studies on Cryptococcus noted that heavily infested trees appear to develop "resistance" in the bark to subsequent attack (Brower 1949).

In common with most woody plants, there are nonspecific defensive reactions (Mullick 1977) in beech bark that are induced by wounding. These reactions, which are induced by a range of biotic and abiotic injuries to the bark, have an important role in defense against attack by Cryptococcus.

Necrosis of tissues in the feeding zone appears to be the initial host defensive reaction followed by the development of a secondary necrophylactic periderm (Mullick 1977). This periderm forms underneath the necrotic areas either discretely or extensively, depending on the distribution and intensity of infestation (Braun 1976, 1977; Ostrofsky and Blanchard 1983). This is shown diagrammatically in Fig. 3. The tissues cut off by periderm formation eventually die, forming a rhytidome of dead outer bark which can prevent penetration of the insect's stylets down to the living parenchyma. The formation of continuous necrophylactic periderm may be interrupted, at least in F. sylvatica, by the characteristic sclerified phloem rays (Fig. 3), which project into the cortex (Braun 1976, 1977). During subsequent

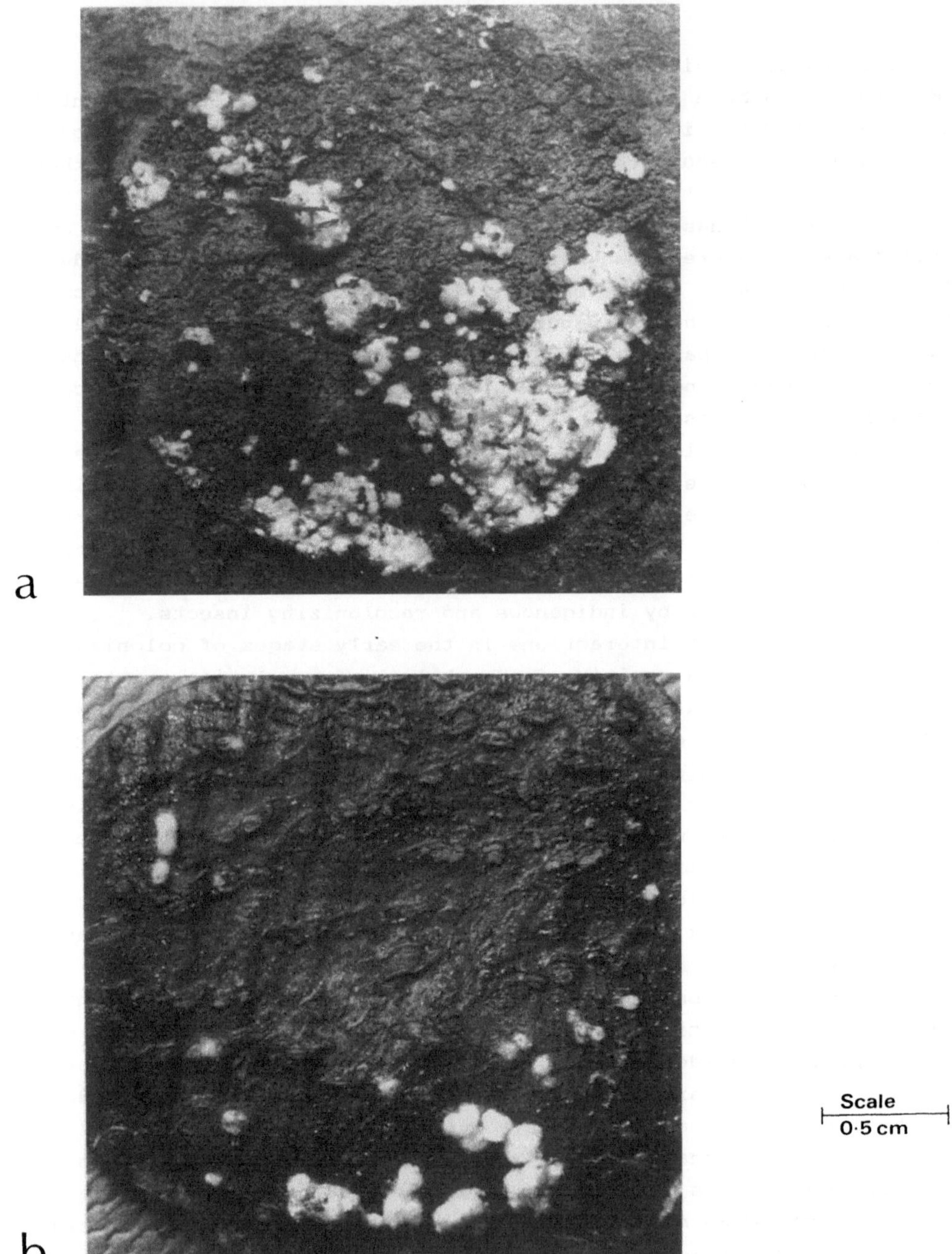

Figure 1. The distribution of (a) indigenous and (b) recolonizing scales on circular areas of bark (see text, from Gate 1987).

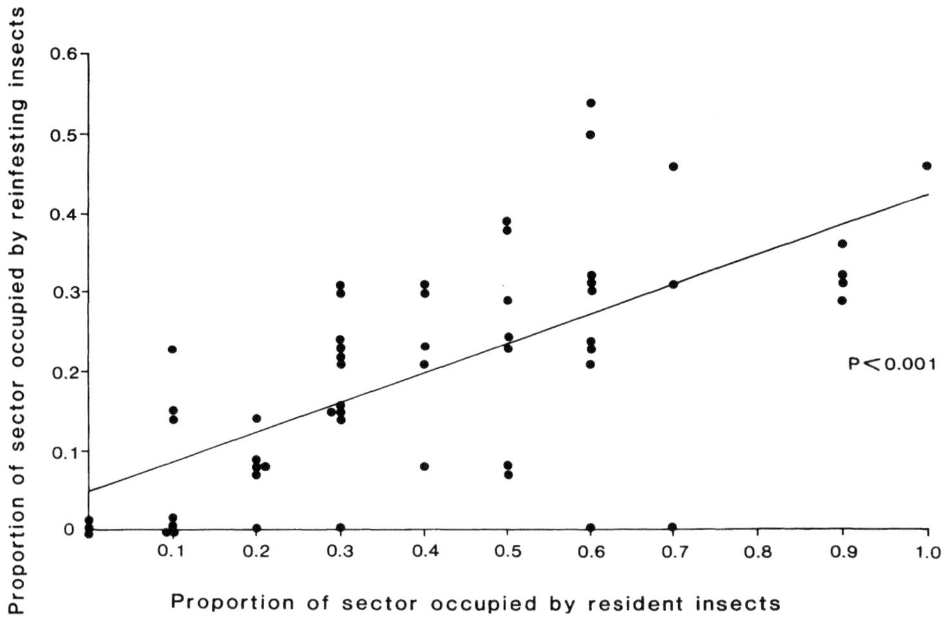

Figure 2. The proportion of different 45° sectors of bark within 2.4 cm diameter cages occupied by scale insect colonies. Data from eight cages on a single tree during 1982 to 1983 (from Gate 1987).

radial growth of the tree, the bark may split at the points where periderm meets the phloem rays so that at the bottom of these fissures, rhytidome is interrupted and the live parenchyma is close to the surface.

These fissures provide a niche for Cryptococcus following its elimination from the general bark surface (Lonsdale 1983b), and it has been shown experimentally that crawlers are able to colonize these fissures. Gate (1987) inoculated crawlers into circular cages placed over fissured and unfissured necrophylactic periderm and found that crawlers settled in the fissures. Their survival and reproduction was significantly higher than that of crawlers on intact periderm ($p < 0.01$) (Table 1). Clearly, necrophylactic periderm formation in beech is an incomplete protection against infestation by Cryptococcus.

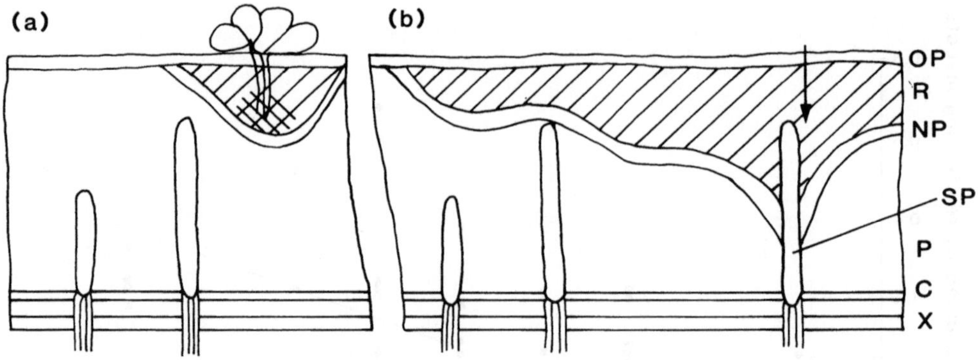

Figure 3. Diagram of necrophylatic periderm formation in beech bark induced by feeding Cryptococcus fagisuga. Periderm formation may be (a) local or (b) extensive, depending on the distribution and intensity of the infestation (see text). Necrotic areas (cross-hatched) that eventually develop in the cortex under (a) scale colonies become isolated in the rhytidome (based on Braun 1976, 1977; Kunkel 1968). Arrow indicates possible point of fissuring (see text). OP, original periderm; R, rhytidome; NP, necrophylactic periderm; SP, sclerotic phloem ray; P, phloem; C, cambium; X, xylem.

Table 1. The survival and fecundity of adults from crawlers inoculated onto fissured and nonfissured periderm. Approximately 600 crawlers were inoculated into each cage (from Gate 1987).

Fissured		Unfissured	
Adults	Fecundity	Adults	Fecundity
8	15.1	2	4.5
17	7.8	1	3.0
40	10.5	7	3.1
9	12.4	0	
4	5.3	0	
19	9.9	2	0
Mean 16.2	10.2	2.0	2.7

These nonspecific defensive reactions occur in all trees and, at least in F. grandifolia, appear not to be related to susceptibility to beech bark disease (Ostrofsky and Blanchard 1983). Of course, there may be genetic variation in the intensity of the wound response between trees, but this has not been studied. It appears that other factors determine initial susceptibility of trees to attack and there is now increasing evidence of genetically determined variation in host resistance to Cryptococcus.

THE HOST PLANT: VARIATION IN CONSTITUTIVE DEFENSES

Genetic Variation in Host Susceptibility

In common with may other scales, Cryptococcus shows considerable tree-to-tree variation in population density. However, the common occurrence of isolated, heavily infested trees among uninfested ones is a consistent and striking feature of Cryptococcus infestations (Boodle and Dallimore 1911, Rhumbler 1914, Thomsen et al. 1949, Kuthe and Kramer 1961). This suggests genetic differences in susceptibility between trees. Other circumstantial evidence points to similar conclusions. For example, grafted trees that have become infested with Cryptococcus often support populations only on the original stock or scion with an abrupt infestation boundary occurring at the graft junction (Wainhouse and Gate 1987).

More direct evidence comes from the observation of Wainhouse and Deeble (1980) that only certain clones of beech in a seed orchard were heavily infested (Fig. 4). Wainhouse and Howell (1983a) found that trees from apparently resistant clones could not be artificially infested. These authors also measured the amount of natural variation in susceptibility among the offspring of single trees (Wainhouse and Howell 1983b). The parent trees had been selected for their desirable silvicultural characteristics, independently of their susceptibility to Cryptococcus. It was found that the Cryptococcus population density varied significantly among their progeny (Table 2), presumably due to inherited differences in susceptibility.

The nature of genetic resistance to Cryptococcus has not been studied in detail. However, there is some histological evidence that layers of stone cells in the bark parenchyma are a physical barrier to stylet penetration and may be an important component of resistance (Lonsdale 1983b, Kunkel 1968, Ehrlich 1934). Lonsdale (1983b) examined sections of bark from relatively resistant and susceptible trees and found that a stone cell layer close to the surface of the bark was more strongly developed in resistant trees (Fig. 5). Based on the thickness of the unlignified parenchyma between the stone cell layers and the continuity of the lignified layers, he developed an index which was thought to reflect the availability of parenchymatous tissue to feeding scales. In most cases, there were distinct differences in this feature between the susceptible and resistant trees (Fig. 6).

The Role of the Environment

There is some evidence that environmental factors can influence the degree of infestation by Cryptococcus and so may modify the expression of resistance. Although there is some anecdotal evidence

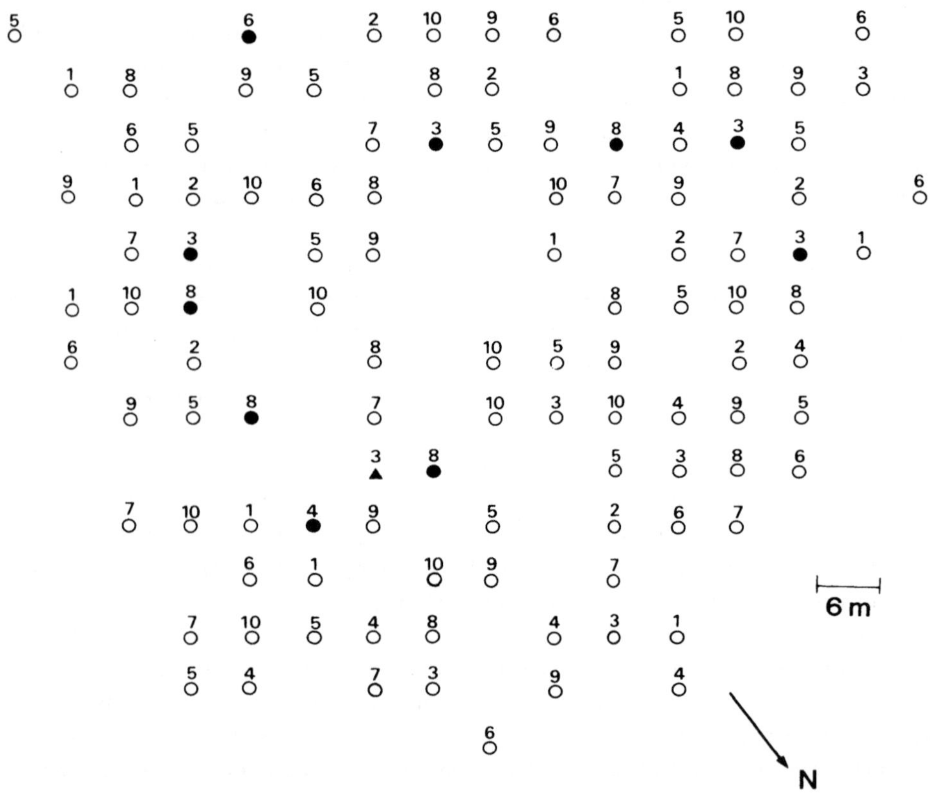

Figure 4. The distribution of Cryptococcus fagisuga infestation in a beech seed orchard in southern England. Ten clones are present represented by 8 to 15 trees. The intensity of Cryptococcus fagisuga infestation is shown by symbols, (triangle) high, (closed circle) moderate and (open circle) low or absent (after Wainhouse and Deeble 1980).

Table 2. Natural infestation of Cryptococcus fagisuga in a Beech tree progeny trial at Andover in southern England (after Wainhouse and Howell 1983b).

Parent "plus" tree from	Mean scale colonies per 36 cm^{-2} adjusted for girth covariate
West Dean 1	2.7
West Dean 2	2.0
Slindon 1	1.9
Slindon 2	1.7
Amberley	1.1
Pennwood 1	1.0
Pennwood 2	1.0
Brecon	1.0
Slindon 3	0.9
Maiden Bradley	0.9

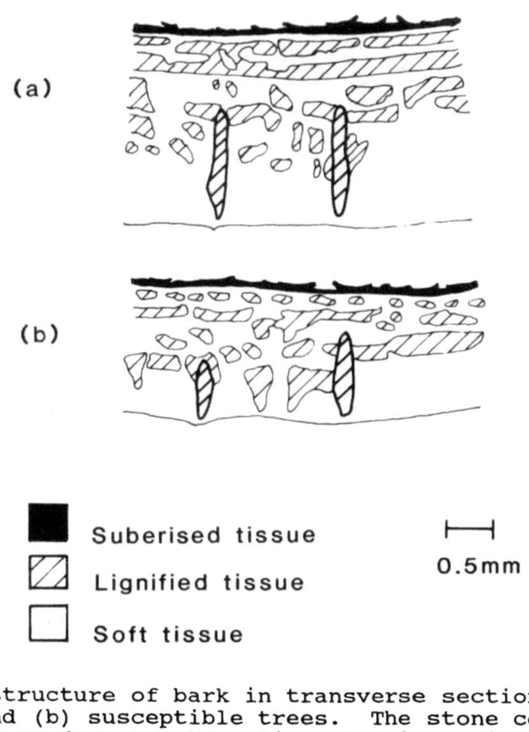

Figure 5. The structure of bark in transverse section from apparently (a) resistant and (b) susceptible trees. The stone cell layers nearest the bark surface are less dissected in resistant trees (see text, from Lonsdale 1983b).

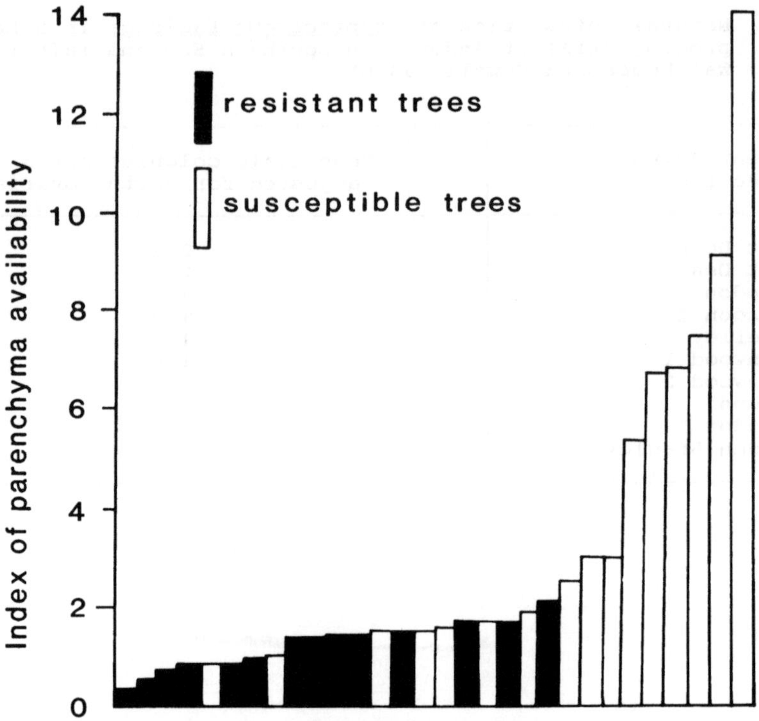

Figure 6. An index of parenchyma availability in apparently resistant and susceptible trees. The index expresses the extent to which the physical barrier of the stone cells prevents access by Cryptococcus fagisuga to the parenchyma (see text, from Lonsdale 1983b).

of site factors affecting populations, the growth of epiphytic organisms on the trunks of beech trees has a more direct influence on Cryptococcus. Houston et al. (1979a) found a positive association between Cryptococcus and the lichen Lecanora conizaeoides which seemed to provide additional niches for settling crawlers on F. grandifolia. Common bark algae such as Desmococcus vulgaris can have a similar sheltering effect. Gate (1987) inoculated crawlers into cages (2.4 cm diameter) enclosing two semi-circular areas of bark, one colonized by D. vulgaris and the other cleaned of all epiphytic growth. Crawlers became established, i.e., started to feed and secrete wax, and subsequently developed into fecund adults predominantly on the algal covered bark (Table 3).

Table 3. The number of established crawlers and fecund adults developing in cages enlosing an area of bark, half of which is colonized by an epiphytic alga Desmococcus vulgaris. The presence of alga had a significant effect (Wilcoxon test $p<0.01$) on the distribution of scales.

	Alga present		Alga absent	
Cage	Established crawlers	Fecund adults	Established crawlers	Fecund Adults
1	7	2	2	0
2	7	0	1	0
3	11	4	4	0
4	7	0	6	1
5	11	6	3	1
6	12	3	4	1
7	29	12	1	0
8	6	0	0	0
9	9	0	4	0
10	8	4	0	0
11	31	11	7	0
12	57	36	3	3
Mean	16.3	6.5	2.9	0.5

On the other hand, some species of lichens appear to prevent colonization by Cryptococcus. In the hardwood forests of the Canadian Maritimes, crustose lichens such as Graphis scripta and Lecanora subfusca appear to be antagonistic to scale establishment (Houston 1983), perhaps as a result of chemicals released by the lichens. Likewise, the fungus Ascodichaena rugosa which grows in the outer layers of the bark can restrict colonization by Cryptococcus (Houston et al. 1979a).

THE BEECH SCALE: GENETIC VARIATION IN POPULATIONS

Evidence for a biochemical component in the resistance of beech to Cryptococcus, in addition to the physical effects of lignin, comes indirectly from a study of variation within populations of Cryptococcus.

Experiments on the transfer of crawlers within and between trees have shown that there is considerable variation in host colonizing ability within populations of Cryptococcus (Wainhouse and Howell 1983a). The survival of crawlers transferred from donor to receptor trees differed significantly ($p < 0.01$) among the receptor trees

(Fig. 7) as would be expected from our discussion of variation between beech trees. Interestingly, there were also highly significant ($p < 0.001$) differences in survival among crawlers from the different donor trees. For example, crawlers from tree 5 were on average the best colonists of new host trees. Further work is needed to determine why crawlers from some trees appear to be superior colonists, but the differences in crawler survival on new receptor trees appear to be a consequence of the adaptation of scale populations to their former individual host tree (Wainhouse and Howell 1983a). This is inferred from the higher survival ($p < 0.05$) of crawlers reinoculated onto their original host tree in experimental transfer of crawlers within and between infested trees (Fig. 8).

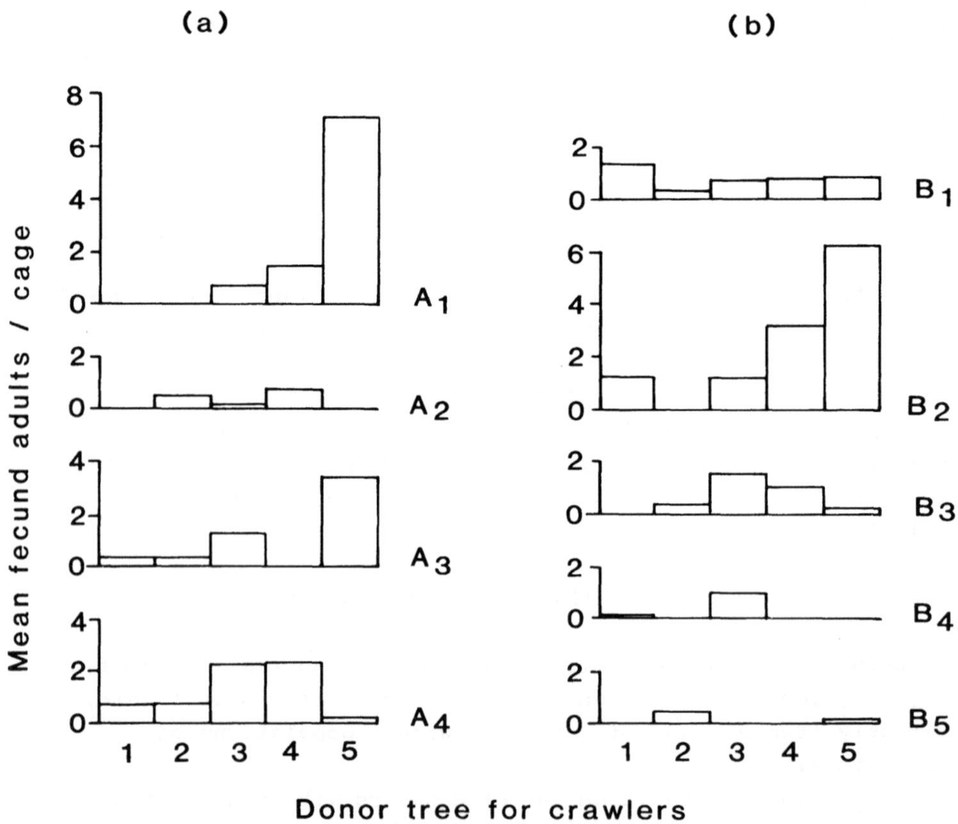

Figure 7. The number of adults developing from different subpopulations of crawlers inoculated onto naturally infested receptor trees (A1-B5) in (a) 1982 or (b) 1984. Crawlers were collected from the same five donor trees (1-5) in both years.

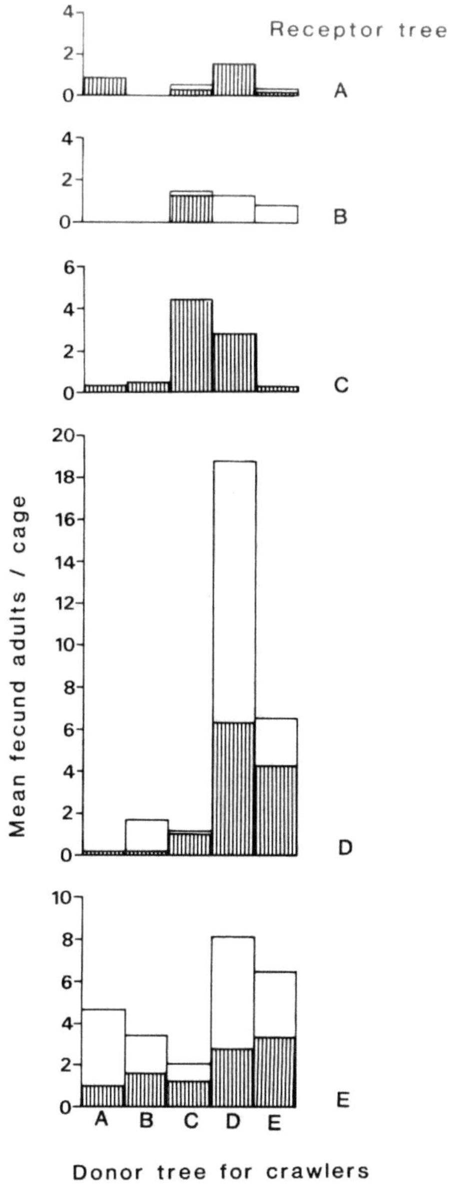

Figure 8. Number of fecund adults developing from crawlers inoculated onto five trees which were both donors and receptors of crawlers. The histograms show results from inoculations made in 2 successive years (from Wainhouse and Howell 1983a, reproduced with the permission of Blackwell Scientific Publications, Ltd.).

The formation of subpopulations of insects adapted to individual trees was demonstrated first for the black pineleaf scales, Nuculapsis californica (Edmunds and Alstad 1978). The phenomenon seems to reflect an underlying variation in biochemical defense between individual trees. The notable difference in general susceptibility between the European F. sylvatica and the American F. grandifolia has been attributed in part to the lack of coevolved defenses in F. grandifolia for which Cryptococcus is an exotic pest (Wainhouse 1983).

DISCUSSION

The level of infestation of individual beech trees is determined by a number of factors of which the most important appear to be the influence of other organisms in the environment, host defensive reactions together with genetically determined variations in susceptibility, and the formation of subpopulations of Cryptococcus.

Epiphytic organisms on the trunk may have both positive and negative effects on scale infestations, depending on the species involved. In Europe, the alga Desmococcus vulgaris, which appears to favor scale establishment, occurs on apparently resistant as well as susceptible trees and is clearly not the main determinant of scale population density, although it may facilitate establishment on trees with only a weak natural resistance. The absence of epiphytes on young trees may be a factor contributing to their general freedom from scale attack.

The initial susceptibility of trees appears to depend in part on physical and biochemical constitutive defenses which vary significantly between trees. Although some trees appear to be completely resistant, they represent one extreme of a spectrum of susceptibility resulting from the interaction between a variable tree population and a variable insect population containing a number of host-adapted genotypes.

Once scale colonies are established on individual trees, the course of the infestation will depend on the efficacy of induced and constitutive host defenses, the origin of the scales, and their ability to evolve adaptations to overcome the host defensive phenotype. A practical consequence of this complex interaction is that, in Europe at least, forests are buffered against extensive outbreaks and only a small proportion of the tree population is likely to be heavily infested at any one time.

The ability of Cryptococcus to evolve adaptations to individual trees suggests that breeding trees for resistance might not be a useful approach to management of this insect. On the other hand, maintaining high diversity within the tree population, which appears to be the main factor limiting growth of Cryptococcus populations, should minimize the impact of this insect in productive forests.

ACKNOWLEDGEMENTS

Part of this work was funded by a N.E.R.C. research studentship to I. M. Gate. We are grateful to R. S. Howell for analysis of the data presented in Fig. 6.

REFERENCES

Adeli, E. 1975. Insects on Oriental beech (Fagus orientalis ssp. macrophylla) in Iran and their importance for forestry practices and wood utilization. Second world technical consultation on forest diseases and insects. F.A.O. Special Pap. No. 8. New Delhi, India; April 7-12, 1975.

Baylac, M. 1980. Faune associée à Cryptococcus fagi (Baer,) (Homoptera: Coccoidea) dans quelques hetraies du nord de la France. Acta Oecologica, Oecol. Applic. 1(2): 199-208.

Boodle, L. A. and W. Dallimore. 1911. Report on investigations made regarding "Beech coccus" (Cryptococcus fagi, Barensprung). Kew Royal Botanic Gardens Bull. Misc. Inf., 8; 332-343.

Braun, H. J. 1976. Das Rindensterben der Buche, Fagus sylvatica L., verursacht durch die Buchenwollschildlaus Cryptococcus fagi Bar. I. Die Anatomie der Buchenrinde als Basis-Ursache. Eur. J. For. Pathol. 6: 136-146.

Braun, H. J. 1977. Das Rindensterben der Buche, Fagus sylvatica L., verursacht durch die Buchenwollschildlaus Cryptococcus fagi Bar. II. Ablauf der Krankeit. Eur. J. For. Pathol. 7: 76-93.

Brower, A. E. 1949. The beech scale and beech bark disease in Acadia National Park. J. Econ. Entomol. 42: 226-228.

Crosby, D. and J. C. Bjorkbom. 1958. Timely salvage can reduce losses from beech scale-Nectria attack. Northeastern Forest Experiment Station, For. Res. Note No. 82, 4 p.

Edmunds, G. F. and D. N. Alstad. 1978. Coevolution in insect herbivores and conifers. Science 199: 941-945.

Ehrlich, J. 1934. The beech bark disease. A Nectria disease of Fagus following Cryptococcus fagi (Baer). Can. J. Res. 10: 593-692.

Feeny, P. 1976. Plant apparency and chemical defense. In: Biochemical interaction between plants and insects (J. W. Wallace and R. L. Mansell, Eds.). Recent Adv. Phytochem. 10: 1-40.

Fink, S. and H. J. Braun. 1980. Die Bedeutung anatomischer Veranderungen bei der Buchenrindennekrose. Ann. Sci. For. 37: 333-343.

Gate, I. M. 1987. Population ecology of the beech scale (Cryptococcus fagisuga Lind.). London, England: University of London; Ph.D. Thesis.

Houston, D. R. 1983. Influence of lichen species on colonisation of Fagus grandifolia by Cryptococcus fagisuga: Preliminary observations from certain Nova Scotian forests. In: Proceedings, IUFRO beech bark disease working party conference (D. Houston and D. Wainhouse, Eds.); 1982; Hamden. Washington, DC: USDA, Forest Service, Gen. Tech. Rep. WO-37; 105-108.

Houston, D. R., E. J. Parker, and D. Lonsdale. 1979a. Beech bark disease: patterns of spread and developement of the initiating agent Cryptococcus fagisuga. Can. J. For. Res. 9: 336-344.
Houston, D. R., E. J. Parker, R. Perrin, and K. J. Lang. 1979b. Beech bark disease: a comparison of the disease in North America, Great Britain, France, and Germany. Eur. J. For. Pathol. 9: 199-211.
Kunkel, H. 1968. Untersuchungen uber die Buchenwollschildlaus Cryptococcus fagisuga Bar. (Insecta Coccina), einen Vertreter der Rindenparenchymsauger. Z. Angew. Entomol. 61: 373-380.
Kuthe, K. and K. Kramer. 1961. Zur Bekampfung der Buchenwollschildlaus (Cryptococcus fagi Bar) mit chemischen Mitteln. Anz. Schaedlingskd. 34: 42-43.
Lonsdale, D. 1980. Nectria infection of beech bark in relation to infestation by Cryptococcus fagisuga Lindinger. Eur. J. For. Pathol. 10: 161-168.
Lonsdale, D. 1983a. Some aspects of the pathology of environmentally stressed trees. International Dendrological Society Yearbook. 1982, 90-97.
Lonsdale, D. 1983b. Wood and bark anatomy of young beech in relation to Cryptococcus attack. In: Proceedings, IUFRO beech bark disease working party conference (D. Houston and D. Wainhouse, Eds.); 1982; Hamden. Washington, DC: USDA, Forest Service, Gen. Tech. Rep. WO-37; 43-49.
Lonsdale, D. and D. Wainhouse. 1987. (In press). Beech bark disease. For. Comm. Bull.
Mayer, M. and D. C. Allen. 1983. Chilocorus stigma (Coleoptera: Coccinellidae) and other predators of beech scale in cental New York. In: Proceedings, IUFRO beech bark disease working party conference (D. Houston and D. Wainhouse, Eds.); 1982; Hamden. Washington, DC: USDA, Forest Service, Gen. Tech. Rep. WO-37; 89-98.
Mullick, D. B. 1977. The non-specific nature of defence in bark and wood during wounding, insect and pathogen attack. Recent Adv. Photochem. 11: 395-441.
Ostrofsky, W. D. and R. O. Blanchard. 1983. Characteristics and development of necrophylactic periderms in mature bark of American beech. In: Proceedings, IUFRO beech bark disease working party conference (D. Houston and D. Wainhouse, Eds.); 1982; Hamden. Washington, DC: USDA, Forest Service, Gen. Tech. Rep. WO-37; 69-79.
Rhumbler, L. 1914. Die Buchenrinden-Wollaus (Cryptococcus fagi) und ihre Bekamfung. J. Neumann, Neudamm, n.d. 32 p.
Schindler, U. 1962. Erfahrungen mit der Buchenwollschildlaus. Der Forst-und Holzwirt 17(15): 290-294.
Thomsen, M., N. F. Buchwald, and P. Hauberg. 1949. Angreb af Cryptococcus fagi, Nectria galligena og andre parasiter paa bog i Danmark 1939-43. Det Forstlige Forsogsvaesen, 18(2): 97-326.
Wainhouse, D. 1976. Forest Entomology: beech scale Cryptococcus fagisuga. Edinburgh, Rep. on Forest Research; 36-37.
Wainhouse, D. 1983. Interaction between beech and beech scale. In: Proceedings, IUFRO beech bark disease working party conference (D. Houston and D. Wainhouse, Eds.); 1982; Hamden. Washington, DC: USDA, Forest Service, Gen. Tech. Rep. WO-37; 31-32.
Wainhouse, D. and R. Deeble. 1980. Variation in susceptibility of beech (Fagus spp) to beech scale (Cryptococcus fagisuga). Ann. Sci. For. 37(4): 279-289.
Wainhouse, D. and I. M. Gate. 1987. (In press). The beech scale, Cryptococcus fagisuga. In: Insects in forest systems: enquiries into the causes of outbreaks (A. A. Berryman, Ed.). New York: Plenum Press.

Wainhouse, D. and R. S. Howell. 1983a. Intraspecific variation in beech scale populations and in susceptibility of their host *Fagus sylvatica*. Ecol. Entomol. 8: 351-359.
Wainhouse, D. and R. S. Howell. 1983b. Distribution of attack by beech scale *Cryptococcus fagisuga* in beech progeny trials. In: Proceedings, IUFRO beech bark disease working party conference (D. Houston and D. Wainhouse, Eds.); 1982. Hamden. Washington, DC: USDA, Forest Service, Gen. Tech. Rep. WO-37; 33-37.

19

Resistance Mechanisms of Loblolly and Shortleaf Pines to Southern Pine Beetle Attack

Stephen P. Cook and Fred P. Hain

The southern pine beetle, Dendroctonus frontalis (Coleoptera: Scolytidae), is probably the most serious pest of pine forests in the southeastern United States. The beetle is capable of attacking and killing all the southern pine species. Of the four major southern yellow pines (loblolly, Pinus taeda; longleaf, P. palustris; shortleaf, P. echinata; and slash, P. elliottii), loblolly and shortleaf appear to be the most susceptible species (St. George and Beal 1929). Of these, shortleaf pine is most susceptible, at least in the Georgia (Belanger et al. 1977) and North Carolina (Cook and Hain 1987) Piedmont. Upon attacking a tree, the beetle introduces into the tree's cambial/sapwood tissue (Bramble and Holst 1935, 1940) several fungi which may play various roles in aiding the beetle to overcome tree defenses (see "FUNGAL ASSOCIATES OF D. FRONTALIS").

Conifer defense against bark beetle/fungal invasion appears to be a three-step sequence of wound cleansing (primary resin flow), infection containment (a necrotic wound response), and wound healing (periderm formation) (Berryman 1972, Hain et al. 1983). In the four major southern yellow pines, resistance to D. frontalis has been related to physical properties of the primary resin including resin flow, viscosity, and crystallization time (Hodges et al. 1979). Loblolly pines that are successfully attacked by the beetle have lower resin flow rates and/or higher percentages of α-pinene in wound response tissue than do unsuccessfully attacked trees (Hain et al. 1985). Successfully attacked shortleaf pines also have lower resin flow rates and longer wound responses than other shortleaf pines (Cook and Hain 1987). Therefore, both the wound cleansing and infection containment steps of host defense appear important in determining if individual trees succumb to D. frontalis attack.

FUNGAL ASSOCIATES OF D. FRONTALIS

Many microorganisms are associated with *D. frontalis*, among which are several fungi which are introduced to host tissue when a female beetle initiates an attack (Bramble and Holst 1935, 1940). Three of these fungal species are *Ceratocystis minor* (Rumbold 1931), *C. minor* var. *barrassii* (Barras and Taylor 1973), and an unidentified basidiomycete (Barras and Perry 1972). The common blue-staining fungus associated with *D. frontalis* is *C. minor*, and it is transported on the body of the beetle in conjunction with phoretic mites (Bridges and Moser 1983). The other two fungi are transported in a mycangium located on the female's prothorax (Barras and Perry 1972).

Ceratocystis minor is believed to play an important role in overcoming tree resistance by disrupting water movement within the attacked tree (Caird 1935, Bramble and Holst 1940, Paine 1984). Indeed, this fungus is capable of causing mortality in seedling and sapling loblolly pine (Basham 1970). Cook and Hain (1985) found that loblolly pine responded more intensely to inoculations of *C. minor* than to inoculations of *C. minor* var. *barrassii*, and they hypothesized that this was due to *C. minor* being more virulent than *C. minor* var. *barassii*.

Lorio and Hodges (1985) have suggested that mass attack by *D. frontalis* may be crucial for successful attack because the beetles must introduce enough fungi to overcome host defenses. The mycangial fungi may be as important as the blue-staining fungus in this regard, because *D. frontalis* can successfully attack trees without *C. minor* being present (Bridges *et al*. 1985). Further, the mycangial fungi are capable of producing a pheromonal synergist (Brand and Barras 1977) and oxidizing one beetle pheromone (Brand *et al*. 1976). Thus, the fungi associated with *D. frontalis* may be important in overcoming tree resistance both directly (by disrupting water movement) and indirectly (by producing compounds which influence beetle attack behavior).

The wound response of trees may not necessarily kill the fungi, but only contain it. Paine (1984) reported that no growth inhibition of *C. minor* occurred when ethanol extracts of ponderosa pine, *P. ponderosae*, were added to the growth medium. However, growth inhibition of other fungi has been reported when resinous or volatile sapwood extracts of lodgepole pine, *P. contorta* var. *latifolia*, were added to the growth medium (Shrimpton and Whitney 1968) or when monoterpenes present in the wound response of grand fir, *Abies grandis*, were added to the growth medium (Raffa *et al*. 1985). Regardless of whether the fungi are killed or contained by the wound response, an attacked tree must defend itself not only against D. frontalis but also against its associated fungi.

EXPERIMENTAL PROCEDURES

Since 1982, our research has primarily been conducted in adjacent loblolly and shortleaf pine stands in the Hill Experimental Forest of North Carolina State University. The forest is located in the North Carolina Piedmont, about 20 km. north of Durham, NC.

We have taken the following tree measurements: total tree height, height to live crown, d.b.h., bark thickness, phloem thickness, age, tree dominance, resin flow rate, and inner bark monoterpene content. Resin flow rate was measured 4 to 5 hours after a resin flow tube (diameter = 0.64 cm) was inserted into a 2-cm-deep hole drilled into a tree at breast height. The exuded resin was captured in a calibrated receptacle and the measurement was converted to a ml/hr flow rate. We measured inner bark monoterpenes by removing an inner bark sample with a cork borer (diameter = 1.3 cm) and immediately placing the sample in 2 ml of n-pentane or CH_2Cl_2. These samples were cold-stored until we could analyze them using a gas chromatograph. An internal standard of 1.0 μl ρ-cymene was used to quantify monoterpene measurements.

We examined induced defenses by inoculating trees with about 1 ml of C. minor in a 2.5 percent malt extract broth and measuring parameters of the induced response 14 days later. The parameters measured were lesion size, monoterpene content, and soluble sugar content. We measured soluble sugars using the Anthrone colorimetric technique and compared them with before-wounding inner bark soluble sugar contents.

We tested tree resistance to D. frontalis by subjecting trees to controlled attack by known numbers of laboratory-reared beetles. The boles of selected trees were tented with nylon-mesh screening, and loblolly pine bolts with ready-to-emerge beetles were placed under the tents. Estimates of beetle emergence were made by sub-sampling the bolts prior to placing them under the tents. Trees were classified as susceptible to D. frontalis if the tree died and there was some beetle brood survival.

TREE RESISTANCE MECHANISMS AGAINST D. FRONTALIS

Tree defense against D. frontalis attack appears to be a three-step sequence, with at least two of the steps (wound cleansing and infection containment) being important in determining tree resistance to the associated fungi. The three steps can also be viewed as two categories of defensive mechanisms, preformed and induced. The preformed defenses are present prior to the tree's exposure to beetle/fungal invasion, while the induced defenses manifest themselves following exposure to the invading organism(s). By induced defenses, we mean that a measurable change in tree physiology (in at least a part of the tree) occurs following wounding/invasion. In loblolly and shortleaf pine, both physical and chemical tree attributes may be important tree resistance mechanisms of both the preformed and induced defenses.

Preformed Resistance Mechanisms

Two preformed physical barriers of loblolly and shortleaf pine against *D. frontalis* that we examined were bark thickness and resin flow rate. Loblolly pine had thicker bark than shortleaf pine, which may be important because the beetles would have to expend more energy to penetrate the thicker-barked trees (Cook and Hain 1986). As the beetle penetrates the outer bark and enters the tree's phloem tissue, resin canals are severed and preformed resin flows down and out through the attack hole, forming a pitch tube around the attack site (Thatcher 1960). If the beetle becomes physically entrapped in this resin, it is prevented from successfully attacking the tree and it is said to be "pitched out" (Vité and Wood 1961). Although shortleaf pine is considered to be more susceptible to *D. frontalis* than loblolly pine (Belanger *et al*. 1977, Cook and Hain 1987), both species had similar resin flow rates in the North Carolina Piedmont (Cook and Hain 1986). However, within each of these species, resistance to *D. frontalis* has been related to high resin flow rates (Hain *et al*. 1985, Cook and Hain 1987).

Preformed resin and inner bark tissue, both of which are encountered by attacking beetles, contain compounds which may be toxic and/or repellant to *D. frontalis*. The most well-known compounds are the monoterpenes α-pinene, β-pinene, camphene, myrcene, limonene, and β-phellandrene, which are present in loblolly and shortleaf pine oleoresin and in the unwounded inner bark (Coyne and Keith 1972, Cook and Hain 1986). All are toxic to southern pine beetle adults (Coyne and Lott 1976) and several are toxic to other bark beetle species (Smith 1965, Raffa *et al*. 1985).

Induced Resistance Mechanisms

As D. frontalis and its associated fungi invade living tissue, the tree responds by forming a necrotic lesion around the infection site. This has been described for some conifers as a rapid necrosis of cells surrounding the infection site, accompanied by the development of traumatic resin ducts, an increased concentration of monoterpenes and phenolics within the response zone (Reid et al. 1967), and a decreased concentration of sugars surrounding the response zone (Shrimpton 1973). The response is highly generalized (Raffa and Berryman 1982) and energy demanding (Wright et al. 1979). It has been observed in both loblolly and shortleaf pines (Cook and Hain 1985, 1986; Stephen and Paine 1985). In both species there is also a decreased concentration of soluble sugars within the response zone, accompanied by a change in monoterpene compositions (Cook and Hain 1986). The decreased sugar concentration represents reduced nutrient availability for invading organisms, while the increased monoterpene concentration represents an accumulation of potential toxins. The changed monoterpene composition has been suggested to be an active defense against bark beetles, not only because of the buildup of toxins (Russell and Berryman 1976), but also because they may negatively influence beetle colonization behavior (Cook and Hain 1986).

Raffa and Berryman (1982) reported that the major difference between resistant and susceptible lodgepole pines to mountain pine beetle, D. ponderosae, was that resistant trees responded more extensively after invasion of their phloem tissue by the fungus Europhium clavigerum. Cook and Hain (1987) found that susceptible loblolly pines had greater than 90 percent of their total wound response monoterpenes as α-pinene. Also, Cook and Hain (1987) found that susceptible shortleaf pine responded to inoculation with Ceratocystis minor by developing significantly longer lesions than did resistant trees. The intensity of the wound response is inversely density dependent in lodgepole pine (Raffa and Berryman 1983) and in Norway spruce (Christiansen 1985), and it has been suggested that mass attack may be crucial to some bark beetles because they must introduce enough fungi into a tree to overcome host defenses (Hornvedt et al. 1983, Lorio and Hodges 1985). The concept of a threshold number of attacks, below which trees can successfully defend themselves has been expressed several times (Berryman 1978, 1982; Mulock and Christiansen 1986; Cook and Hain 1987). If the attack/invasion is unsuccessful, wound periderm forms around the response zone and isolates the area from healthy tree tissue (Mullick 1977). This may be a crucial step in containing the invading fungi which may not be killed, but only contained within the necrotic lesion (see "FUNGAL ASSOCIATES OF D. FRONTALIS").

TREE RESISTANCE TO D. FRONTALIS: A HYPOTHESIS

Resistance to D. frontalis has been related to physical characteristics of the preformed resins in both loblolly and shortleaf pines (Hodges et al. 1979, Hain et al. 1985, Cook and Hain 1987) as well as to the altered monoterpene compositions in wound response tissue (Cook and Hain 1986). The percentage of α-pinene decreased from normal to lesion tissue in shortleaf pine, while it increased in loblolly pine. α-pinene is believed to be the most important volatile host attractant for D. frontalis (Renwick and Vité 1969) partly because of its synergistic effects on frontalin, the beetle's aggregation pheromone (Kinzer et al. 1969, Renwick and Vité 1969). Hence the decreased percentage of α-pinene in shortleaf pine following inoculation with C. minor may influence the mass colonization behavior of D. frontalis following the initial attacks on a host (Cook and Hain 1986). For example, loblolly pine with wound-response monoterpenes dominated by α-pinene ($\geq$ 90 percent) appeared to be more susceptible to controlled attack by D. frontalis. Therefore, both preformed defenses, such as resin flow, and induced defenses, such as quality of the wound response, may be important in determining tree resistance to D. frontalis attack.

Figure 1 represents an hypothesized outcome of beetle attack on a tree, given these variable resistance mechanisms. The graph has been divided into four sections within which trees are classified as susceptible (S) or resistant (R) to D. frontalis attack based upon resin flow (rf) and the induced wound response (wr). The dashed lines separating the categories would not have to be straight lines as depicted, and the lines may shift position with seasonal changes (similar to the hypothesis of Lorio and Hodges 1985) and with changes in beetle density and quality. Beetle population density and quality should be added to this interpretation of tree resistance (Smith 1975). Thus, the dashed lines may be best interpreted as representing transition areas whose exact position varies depending upon several factors.

A highly susceptible tree would be one with low resin flow and a weak wound response. These trees would be in the lower left section of Fig. 1 and may be trees under extreme physical stress such as

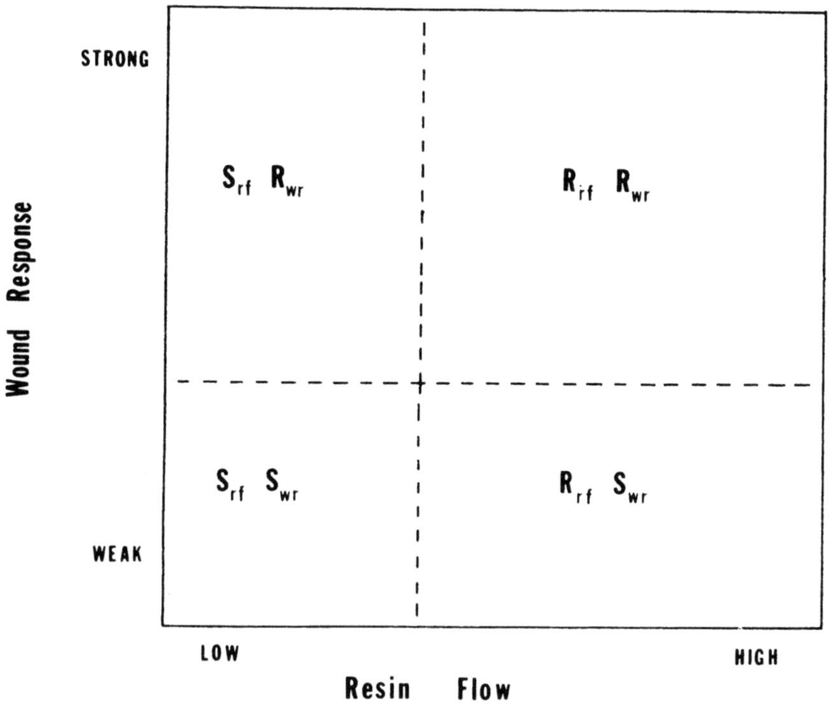

Figure 1. Hypothesized relationship between resin flow (rf) and the induced wound response (wr) in determining relative tree resistance (R) or susceptibility (S) to D. *frontalis* attack.

lightning strike or prolonged drought. Such trees could be overcome by a relatively low number of beetles and may be the resource first utilized in spot initiation. Once an extremely weak tree is overcome, if a large enough beetle brood is produced, trees in the other categories may be successfully attacked.

Trees with a low resin flow and strong wound response are likely to be the second most susceptible to D. *frontalis* attack. Hodges *et al*. (1979) utilized physical characteristics of the oleoresin to classify resistant and susceptible trees. Hain *et al*. (1985) and Cook and Hain (1987) found differences in the wound response of loblolly and shortleaf pines which were resistant or susceptible to D. *frontalis*, but the most important variable for separating trees remained resin flow rate. The third most susceptible category of trees would be those with a high resin flow rate and a weak wound response. These middle two categories may be switched in other bark beetle-conifer systems in which trees defend against few and synchronous beetle generations (Matson and Hain 1985) or where the virulence of the associated fungi may be different. The most resistant category of trees would be those with a high resin flow and a strong wound response. These trees would be capable of withstanding attack by a large number of beetles and would probably succumb to attack only during a D. frontalis epidemic.

ACKNOWLEDGEMENTS

We would like to thank W. Hobbs, G. Morris, P. Nappen, and E. Younan for technical assistance and G. Haven for typing this manuscript. This research was supported by the USDA-sponsored bark beetle IPM program. This is Paper No. 10796 of the Journal Series of the North Carolina Agricultural Research Service, Raleigh, NC, USA.

REFERENCES

Barras, S. J. and T. Perry. 1972. Fungal symbionts in the prothoracic mycangium of Dendroctonus frontalis (Coleoptera: Scolytidae). Z. Angew. Entomol. 71: 95-104.
Barras, S. J. and J. J. Taylor. 1973. Varietal Ceratocysts minor identified from mycangium of Dendroctonus frontalis. Mycopathologia 50: 293-305.
Basham, H. G. 1970. Wilt of loblolly pine inoculated with blue-stain fungi of the genus Ceratocystis. Phytopathology 60: 750-754.
Belanger, R. P., G. E. Hatchell, and G. R. Moore. 1977. Soil and stand characteristics related to southern pine beetle infestations: a progress report for Georgia and North Carolina. In: Proceedings, Sixth South. For. Soils Workshop; 99-107.
Berryman, A. A. 1972. Resistance of conifers to invasion by bark beetle-fungus associations. BioScience 22: 598-602.
Berryman, A. A. 1978. A snoptic model of the lodgepole pine/mountain pine beetle interaction and its potential application in forest management. In: Theory and practice of mountain pine beetle management in lodgepole pine forests (A. A. Berryman, G. D. Amman, R. W. Stark, and D. L. Kibbee, Eds.). Moscow, ID: College of Forest Resources, Univ. Idaho; 98-105.
Berryman, A. A. 1982. Biological control, thresholds, and pest outbreaks. Environ. Entomol. 11: 544-549.
Bramble, W. C. and E. C. Holst. 1935. Microorganisms infecting pines attacked by Dendroctonus frontalis. Phytopathology 25: 7.
Bramble, W. C. and E. C. Holst. 1940. Fungi associated with Dendroctonus frontalis in killing shortleaf pines and their effect on conduction. Phytopathology 30: 881-889.
Brand, J. M. and S. J. Barras. 1977. The major volatile constituents of a basidiomycete associated with the southern pine beetle. Lloydia 40: 398-400.
Brand, J. M., J. W. Bracke, L. N. Britton, A. J. Markovetz, and S. J. Barras. 1976. Bark beetle pheromones: production of verbenone by a mycangial fungus of Dendroctonus frontalis. J. Chem. Ecol. 2: 195-199.
Bridges, J. R. and J. C. Moser. 1983. Role of two phoretic mites in transmission of bluestain fungus, Ceratocystis minor. Ecol. Entomol. 8: 9-12.

Bridges, J. R., W. A. Nettleton, and M. D. Connor. 1985. Southern pine beetle (Coleoptera: Scolytidae) infestations without the bluestain fungus, Ceratocystis minor. J. Econ. Entomol. 78: 325-327.
Caird, R. W. 1935. Physiology of pines infested with bark beetles. Bot. Gaz. (Chicago) 96: 709-733.
Christiansen, E. 1985. Ceratocystis polonica inoculated in Norway spruce: blue-staining in relation to inoculum density, resinosis and tree growth. Eur. J. For. Pathol. 15: 160-167.
Cook, S. P. and F. P. Hain. 1985. Qualitative examination of the hypersensitive response of loblolly pine, Pinus taeda L., inoculated with two fungal associates of the southern pine beetle, Dendroctonus frontalis Zimmermann (Coleoptera: Scolytidae). Environ. Entomol. 14: 396-400.
Cook, S. P. and F. P. Hain. 1986. Defensive mechanisms of loblolly and shortleaf pine against attack by southern pine beetle, Dendroctonus frontalis Zimmermann, and its fungal associate, Ceratocystis minor (Hedgecock) Hunt. J. Chem. Ecol. 12: 1397-1406.
Cook, S. P. and F. P. Hain. 1987. Susceptibility of trees to southern pine beetle, Dendroctonus frontalis Zimmermann (Coleoptera: Scolytidae) Environ. Entomol. 16: 9-14.
Coyne, J. F. and G. C. Keith. 1972. Geographic survey of monoterpenes in loblolly and shortleaf pines. USDA, Forest Service, Res. Pap. SO-79.
Coyne, J. F. and L. H. Lott. 1976. Toxicity of substances in pine oleoresin to southern pine beetles. J. Georgia. Entomol. Soc. 11: 301-305.
Hain, F. P., S. P. Cook, P. A. Matson, and K. G. Wilson. 1985. Factors contributing to southern pine beetle host resistance. In: Proceedings, Integrated pest management research symposium (S. J. Branham and R. C. Thatcher, Eds.); 1985 April 15-18; Asheville, NC. New Orleans, LA: USDA, Forest Service, Southern Forest Experiment Station, Gen. Tech. Rep. SO-56; 154-160.
Hain, F. P., W. D. Mawby, S. P. Cook, and F. H. Arthur. 1983. Host conifer reaction to stem invasion. Z. Angew. Entomol. 96: 247-256.
Hodges, J. D., W. W. Elam, W. F. Watson, and T. E. Nebeker. 1979. Oleoresin characteristics and susceptibility of four southern pines to southern pine beetle (Coleoptera: Scolytidae) attacks. Can. Entomol. 111: 889-896.
Hornvedt, R., E. Christiansen, H. Solheim, and S. Wang. 1983. Artificial inoculation with Ips typographus-associated blue-stain fungi can kill healthy Norway spruce trees. Medd. Nor. Inst. Skogforskning 38: 1-20.
Kinzer, G. W., A. F. Fentiman, Jr., T. F. Page, R. L. Foltz, J. P. Vité, and G. B. Pitman. 1969. Bark beetle attractants: identification, synthesis, and field bioassay of a compound isolated from Dendroctonus. Nature 221: 477-478.
Lorio, P. L., Jr., and J. D. Hodges. 1985. Theories of interactions among bark beetles, associated microorganisms, and host trees (E. Shoulders, Ed.). USDA, Forest Service, Gen. Tech. Rep. SO-54.
Matson, P. A. and F. P. Hain. 1985. Host conifer defense strategies: a hypothesis. In: The role of the host in the population dynamics of forest insects (L. Safranyik, Ed.); Proceedings, IUFRO Conference; 1983 September 4-7; Banff, Alberta. Victoria, BC: Canadian Forestry Service and USDA, Forest Service; 33-42.
Mullick, D. B. 1977. The nonspecific nature of defense in bark and wood during wounding, insect and pathogen attack. Recent Adv. Phytochem. 11: 395-441.

Mulock, P. and E. Christiansen. 1986. The threshold of successful attack by Ips typographus on Picea abies: a field experiment. For. Ecol. Manage. 14: 125-132.

Paine, T. D. 1984. Seasonal response of ponderosa pine to inoculation of the mycangial fungi from the western pine beetle. Can. J. Bot. 62: 551-555.

Raffa, K. F. and A. A. Berryman. 1982. Physiological differences between lodgepole pines resistant and susceptible to the mountain pine beetle and associated microorganisms. Environ. Entomol. 11: 486-492.

Raffa, K. F. and A. A. Berryman. 1983. Physiological aspects of lodgepole pine wound responses to a fungal symbiont of the mountain pine beetle, Dendroctonus ponderosae (Coleoptera: Scolytidae). Can. Entomol. 115: 723-734.

Raffa, K. F., A. A. Berryman, J. Simasko, W. Teal, and B. L. Wong. 1985. Effects of grand fir monoterpenes on the fir engraver, Scolytus ventralis (Coleoptera: Scolytidae) and its symbiotic fungus. Environ. Entomol. 14: 552-556.

Reid, R. W., H. S. Whitney, and J. A. Watson. 1967. Reactions of lodgepole pine to attack by Dendroctonus ponderosae Hopkins and blue stain fungi. Can. J. Bot. 45: 1115-1126.

Renwick, J. A. A. and J. P. Vité. 1969. Bark beetle attractants: mechanism of colonization by Dendroctonus frontalis. Nature 224: 1222-1223.

Rumbold, C. T. 1931. Two blue-staining fungi associated with bark-beetle infestations of pines. J. Agric. Res. 43: 847-873.

Russell, C. E. and A. A. Berryman. 1976. Host resistance to the fir engraver beetle. 1. Monoterpene composition of Abies grandis pitch blisters and fungus-infected wounds. Can. J. Bot. 54: 14-18.

Shrimpton, D. M. 1973. Extractives associated with wound response of lodgepole pine attacked by the mountain pine beetle and associated microorganisms. Can. J. Bot. 51: 527-534.

Shrimpton, D. M. and H. S. Whitney. 1968. Inhibition of growth of blue stain fungi by wood extractives. Can. J. Bot. 46: 757-761.

Smith, R. H. 1965. Effects of monoterpene vapors on the western pine beetle. J. Econ. Entomol. 58: 509-510.

Smith, R. H. 1975. Formula for describing effect of insect and host tree factors on resistance to western pine beetle attack. J. Econ. Entomol. 68: 841-844.

St. George, R. A. and J. A. Beal. 1929. The southern pine beetle: a serious enemy of pines in the south. USDA, Farmers' Bull. 1586.

Stephen, F. M. and T. D. Paine. 1985. Seasonal patterns of host tree resistance to fungal associates of the southern pine beetle. Z. Angew. Entomol. 99: 113-122.

Thatcher, R. C. 1960. Bark beetles affecting southern pines: a review of current knowledge. USDA, Forest Service, Southeastern Forest Experiment Station, Occas. Pap. 180.

Vité, J. P. and D. L. Wood. 1961. A study of the applicability of the measurement of oleoresin exudation pressure in determining susceptibility of second growth ponderosa pine to bark beetle infestation. Contrib. Boyce Thompson Inst. 21: 67-78.

Wright, L. C., A. A. Berryman, and S. Gurusiddaiah. 1979. Host resistance to the fir engraver beetle, Scolytis ventralis (Coleoptera: Scolytidae) 4. Effect of defoliation on wound monoterpenes and inner bark carbohydrate concentrations. Can. Entomol. 111: 1255-1262.

20

Wound-Induced Oleoresins of *Abies concolor:* Is It Part of Host Resistance to the Fir Engraver, *Scolytus ventralis?*

George T. Ferrell

The formation of wound resin in sapwood and phloem by parenchyma cells not normally associated with resin production has been identified as an important induced defense response of conifers to bark beetles and their associated fungi (Reid *et al*. 1967, Berryman 1972). Early work on conifer defenses focused on the preformed resin canal system in unwounded pines (see reviews by Rudinsky 1962, Stark 1965, Callaham 1966, and Smith 1972). The true firs (*Abies* spp.), on the other hand, normally lack such resin canals in the xylem or phloem. The only preformed (in advance of wounding) resin is localized in cortical blisters (Bannan 1936).

The boles of white fir, *Abies concolor*, and other *Abies* spp. in western North America are attacked by the fir engraver, *Scolytus ventralis* (Coleoptera: Scolytidae). The beetles mine into the cambial zone, introducing a pathogenic brown-staining fungus, *Trichosporium symbioticum*. The beetle's biology has been described by Struble (1957) and Ashraf and Berryman (1969), and its association with the fungus has been investigated by Wright (1935, 1938) and Livingston and Berryman (1972).

The responses of white fir resistant to beetle attack (Ferrell 1978) are similar to those of grand fir, *A. grandis* (Berryman 1969, Wong and Berryman 1977). Reactions are characterized by the formation of wound resin, which limits beetle mining, survival, and reproductive success, and simultaneously contains the associated fungus within a small necrotic lesion. Resin in cortical blisters contributes little to this resistance because the fir engraver avoids the cortical blisters when selecting attack sites (Ferrell 1983).

The monoterpene composition of resin formed in wounds infected by associated fungi has been found to differ from that of normal resin found in cortical blisters of grand fir (Russell and Berryman 1976). The same is true for wound and normal sapwood resins of lodgepole pine, Pinus contorta (Shrimpton 1973). Because individual monoterpenes differ in repellency, toxicity, and inhibitory effects on bark beetles and associated fungi (Jantz and Rudinsky 1965, Smith 1965, Cobb et al. 1968, Bordasch and Berryman 1977, Raffa et al. 1985), it is reasonable to assume that differences in resin monoterpene composition may contribute to tree resistance to attack.

Hence, I compared the monoterpene composition of resin from cortical blisters of white fir with that formed in wounds made by the fir engraver and its symbiotic fungus. This provided a further test of the Russell and Berryman (1976) induced toxin/repellent hypothesis.

METHODOLOGY

Attack Wound Sampling

Nine white firs were each subjected to attack by caged fir engravers in one or more tests during the summer months of either 1972 or 1973 (Ferrell 1978). The experimental trees were 9 to 15 cm d.b.h., 6 to 12 m tall, and 40- to 60-years old. They all grew within a radius of 100 m in the understory of a natural stand of scattered large ponderosa pine, Douglas-fir, and white fir near Hat Creek, Shasta County, in northeastern California.

The fir engraver beetles used in the tests were reared from nearby naturally infested white firs. Emerging beetles were collected from the walls and ceiling of a screen house at 1800 h daily and were stored in tissue paper-lined petri dishes at 4^0 for 1 to 2 weeks. To begin a test, the dishes were allowed to warm for 30 to 60 minutes, and the more active beetles were selected for testing.

For each test, I installed 1-m-tall sleeve cages on the boles of two or more trees. Each cage was a 20-mesh plastic screen taped at top and bottom to two 7.5-cm-thick polyurethane foam collars, which were carefully fitted at heights of 1 and 2 m on portions of the bole smoothed by lightly shaving the bark. This design allowed the beetles to move freely over the caged bole surface. Fifteen or 20 unsexed beetles were placed in each cage.

After 12 to 15 days, I removed the cages and located the attack wounds by observing either resin droplets or boring dust on the bole surface near beetle entrance tunnels. I used a cork borer to remove a plug of bark and phloem 15 mm in diameter around the entrance tunnel. The desired sample size was 10 wounds per tree; in practice, this varied from 2 to 16, depending on the number of entrance tunnels located. The outer corky bark was peeled off the plug, and the resin in the remaining phloem disc was extracted in 2 cc of chromatographic quality pentane (4h, 4° C). The extracts were stored (7 mo., 4° C) in tightly sealed vials for monoterpene analysis. Dissected attack wounds were sealed with caulking compound, and the cork borer was wiped with an ethyl alcohol-soaked cotton swab to remove resin before dissecting the next wound.

Within 2 days, the cages were reinstalled and the next test was begun. Two tests with two trees were performed in 1972, and three tests with seven trees in 1973, but the number of tests' run on each tree varied with the availability of beetles. Over both years, a combined total of 171 wounds--all evidencing a resistant resinous reaction--were sampled for resin analysis.

Cortical Blister Sampling

At the end of testing in each year, a 5-ml sample of resin from cortical blisters was collected from each tree by pressing the lip of a screw-cap vial against slits made in blisters on older portions of the stem. Pooling of blister resin is acceptable because monoterpene composition varies little between blisters on individual white firs, except in portions of the stem less than 20 years old (Zavarin 1968). The vials were tightly sealed and stored (7 mo., 4° C). For analysis of monoterpene composition, one drop of resin was dissolved in 2 ml of chromatographic quality pentane.

Monoterpene Analysis

The monoterpenes were analyzed by injecting one microliter of each sample into an Aerograph A90P3 gas chromatograph with a thermal conductivity detector. The columns used were 1/8-inch OD, 2.1 m stainless steel tubing packed with 5 percent β, β' oxydipropionitrile suspended on 80/100 mesh, acid-washed Chromosorb W. The oven temperature was 78° C and temperatures at injector and detector were 145° and 155° C, respectively. The filament current was 180 ma, and the carrier gas was helium (He).

Nine peaks eluted within 6 min. Retention times of 8 peaks agreed with those identified as α-pinene, camphene, β-pinene, delta-3-carene, myrcene, limonene, β-phellandrene, and terpinolene in a sample of Pinus ponderosa resin (Smith 1964) analyzed with the same column and conditions. Retention time of the remaining peak agreed with that identified as sabinene in a sample of ponderosa pine resin (Smith 1977).

Peak heights on chromatograms were measured ($\pm$ 0.1 cm), then normalized and converted to percentages of the total monoterpene fraction (Smith and Greene 1971). Normalization avoided variation that was due to quantitative variation in the phloem disc, the resin, the pentane extractant, and the sample volume injected into the column and allowed the analysis to be based on a single determination of each sample. Data from each year were similar and were combined for analysis.

Data Analysis

Variations among trees, tests, and wounds were compared by nested analysis of variance (Steel and Torrie 1960). Each of the monoterpenes was analyzed separately, although the values, being percentages, were, of course, not independent. In view of this relationship and the large number of comparisons made (nine compounds and three sources of variation), only F-ratios with probabilities of 1 percent or less were accepted as significant.

MONOTERPENE COMPOSITION

Attack Wound Resin

The results indicated that, for most of the monoterpenes of wound resin, variation among trees was significantly greater than that among tests or wounds. Within-tree variation was therefore ignored as inconsequential, and the mean wound resin composition, over all the tests of each tree, was compared directly with the composition of the tree's cortical blister resin.

Alpha-pinene was the major monoterpene constituent of the wound resin, averaging 60 percent of the monoterpene fraction in trees sampled. (Table 1). Next highest in concentration were β-pinene, averaging 18 percent and myrcene, averaging 14 percent. Camphene, delta-3-carene, sabinene, limonene, β-phellandrene, and terpinolene were minor components, all found at levels averaging less than 3 percent.

In cortical blisters, β-pinene was the major constituent, averaging 72 percent of the monoterpene fraction, with α-pinene and β-phellandrene averaging 14 percent and 8 percent, respectively. Camphene, limonene, and myrcene were all minor constituents, averaging less than 3 percent, and terpinolene was found in only one tree (0.3 percent). The average composition in the sample trees agreed closely

Table 1. Monoterpene composition of resins from attack wounds and cortical blisters in nine white firs caged with fir engraver beetles in 1972 or 1973.

Monoterpene	Attack wounds[a]		Cortical blisters[b]	
	Mean	Range	Mean	Range
	Percent[c]			
α-pinene	60.3	43.6 - 70.1	13.6	10.4 - 20.2
Camphene	1.4	0.0 - 3.2	2.0	0.5 - 3.2
β-pinene	17.9	7.9 - 37.5	71.8	59.7 - 78.0
Delta-3-carene	1.4	0.0 - 4.5	0.0	---
Sabinene	2.1	0.0 - 5.6	0.0	---
Myrcene	14.0	0.0 - 37.4	0.4	0.0 - 5.0
Limonene	2.3	0.0 - 7.3	2.5	1.0 - 6.8
β-phellandrene	0.7	0.0 - 2.5	7.7	5.5 - 17.0
Terpinolene	0.1	0.0 - 0.4	0.1	0.0 - 0.3

[a]Based on averages of 2 to 35 wounds per tree. Total wounds sampled was 171.
[b]Sample of pooled blisters from each tree.
[c]Total monoterpene basis.

with that reported for cortical blister resin from other nearby white firs, except that some delta-3-carene--less than 1 percent--was found in the latter trees (Zavarin et al. 1975).

DISCUSSION AND CONCLUSIONS

The monoterpene composition of resin from fir engraver attack wounds differed markedly from that in cortical blisters. In all trees, wound resin consistently had higher percentages of α-pinene and myrcene and lower percentages of β-pinene and β-phellandrene than the blister resin. The greatest differences between wound and blister resins were in α-pinene and β-pinene. Wound resin averaged 46.7 percent more α-pinene and 53.9 percent less β-pinene than blister resin. Wound resin also averaged 13.1 percent more myrcene and 8.8 percent less β-phellandrene. Also, delta-3-carene and sabinene were detected (at low levels) in wound resin but not in blister resin. Volatilization from the entrance tunnels bored by the beetles might have contributed to those differences, but the high concentration of α-pinene--the most volatile monoterpene in the attack wounds--suggests otherwise.

White fir, like grand fir, produces wound resin that differs markedly from cortical blister resin. In both species, α-pinene, myrcene, and delta-3-carene were more prevalent in wound resin than in blister resin (Russell and Berryman 1976). In contrast to white fir, however, wound resin of grand fir lacked both camphene and sabinene, and the proportion of β-pinene was not different from that in blister resin.

Laboratory bioassays of beetle and fungal responses to individual monoterpenes (Table 2) only partially supported the induced toxin/repellent hypothesis of Russell and Berryman (1976) which states that conifers respond to fungus infection by producing monoterpenes that are more toxic, repellent, and (or) inhibitory to bark beetles and their associated fungi. For example, α-pinene, myrcene, limonene, and β-phellandrene were the monoterpenes found to be most repellent, toxic, and/or inhibitory to the fir engraver and its fungal symbiont

Table 2. Monoterpenes ranked (1 = most, 6 = least) by volatility, concentration in _Abies concolor_ resins, and antibiotic effects on the fir engraver beetle and its fungal symbiont.

Monoterpene	Vol.	Resin		Beetle		Fungal
		Wound	Blister	Repellency[a]	Toxicity[b]	Inhibition[b]
α-pinene	1	1	2	3	1	?
Camphene	2	4	5	6	6	3
β-pinene	3	2	1	5	4	4
Delta-3-carene	4	6	-	2	5	4
Myrcene	5	3	6	4	3	2
Limonene	6	5	4	1	2	1
β-phellandrene	7	7	3	?	3	?

[a]Bordasch and Berryman 1977
[b]Raffa _et_ _al_. 1985

(Raffa et al. 1985, Bordasch and Berryman 1977). However, in white fir wound resin, limonene and β-phellandrene occurred at the same or lower relative abundance as in blister resin. Moreover, delta-3-carene, also one of the more repellent compounds, occurred only at low concentration in wound resin.

The studies of monoterpenes from both white fir and grand fir wound resin do not fully support the Russell and Berryman (1976) hypothesis. This suggests that the quantity (Berryman 1969, Ferrell 1978) rather than the monoterpene composition of resin formed in wounds may be more important in governing host resistance to the fir engraver and its fungal symbiont. Laboratory bioassays of Bordasch and Berryman (1977) and Raffa et al. (1985) somewhat support this. However, other unmeasured components of the resin, such as sesquiterpenes and resin acids may yet support the induced toxin/repellent hypothesis (see Cheniclet et al. in this volume).

REFERENCES

Ashraf, M. and A. A. Berryman. 1969. Biology of Scolytus ventralis (Coleoptera: Scolytidae) attacking Abies grandis in northern Idaho. Melanderia 2: 1-23.

Bannan, M. W. 1936. Vertical resin ducts in the secondary wood of the Abietinae. New Phytol. 35: 11-46.

Berryman, A. A. 1969. Response of Abies grandis to attack by Scolytus ventralis (Coleoptera: Scolytidae). Can. Entomol. 101: 1033-1041.

Berryman, A. A. 1972. Resistance of conifers to attack by bark beetle-fungus associations. BioScience 22: 598-602.

Bordasch, R. P. and A. A. Berryman. 1977. Host resistance to the fir engraver beetle, Scolytus ventralis (Coleoptera: Scolytidae) 2. Repellency of Abies grandis resins and some monoterpenes. Can. Entomol. 109: 95-100.

Callaham, R. Z. 1966. Nature of resistance of pines to bark beetles. In: Breeding pest resistant trees (H. D. Gerhold, R. E. Mcdermott, B. J. Schreiner, and J. A. Winjeski, Eds.). New York: Pergamon Press; 197-201.

Cobb, F. W., Jr., M. Drstic, E. Zavarin, and H. W. Barber, Jr. 1968. Inhibitory effects of volatile oleoresin components on Fomes annosus and four Ceratocystis species. Phytopathology 58: 1327-1335.

Ferrell, G. T. 1978. Moisture stress threshold of susceptibility to fir engraver beetles in pole-size white firs. For. Sci. 24: 85-92.

Ferrell, G. T. 1983. Host resistance to the fir engraver, Scolytus ventralis (Coleoptera: Scolytidae): Frequencies of attacks contacting cortical resin blisters and canals of Abies concolor. Can. Entomol. 115: 1421-1428.

Jantz, O. K. and J. A. Rudinsky. 1965. Laboratory and field methods for assaying olfactory responses of the Douglas-fir beetle, Dendroctonus pseudotsugae Hopkins. Can. Entomol. 97: 935-941.

Livingston, R. L. and A. A. Berryman. 1972. Fungus transport structures in the fir engraver, Scolytus ventralis (Coleoptera: Scolytidae). Can. Entomol. 104: 1793-1800.

Raffa, K. F., A. A. Berryman, J. Simasko, W. Teal, and B. L. Wong. 1985. Effects of grand fir monoterpenes on the fir engraver, Scolytus ventralis (Coleoptera: Scolytidae), and its symbiotic fungus. Environ. Entomol. 14: 552-556.

Reid, R. W., H. S. Whitney, and J. A. Watson. 1967. Reactions of lodgepole pine to attack by Dendroctonus ponderosae Hopkins and blue stain fungi. Can. J. Bot. 45: 1115-1126.

Rudinsky, J. A. 1962. Ecology of Scolytidae. Annu. Rev. Entomol. 7: 327-348.

Russell, C. E. and A. A. Berryman. 1976. Host resistance to the fir engraver beetle. 1. Monoterpene composition of Abies grandis pitch blisters and fungus-infested wounds. Can. J. Bot. 54: 14-18.

Shrimpton, D. M. 1973. Extractives associated with wound response of lodgepole pine attacked by the mountain pine beetle and associated micro-organisms. Can. J. Bot. 51: 527-534.

Smith, R. H. 1964. Variations in the monoterpenes of Pinus ponderosae laws. Science 143: 1337-1338.

Smith, R. H. 1965. Effect of monoterpene vapors on the western pine beetle. J. Econ. Entomol. 58: 509-510.

Smith R. H. 1972. Xylem resin in the resistance of the Pinaceae to bark beetles. USDA, Forest Service, Gen. Tech. Rep. PSW-1.

Smith, R. H. 1977. Monoterpenes of ponderosa pine xylem resin in Western United States. USDA, Forest Service, Tech. Bull. 1532.

Smith, R. H. and L. E. Greene. 1971. Use of peak heights from a fast column for rapid approximation of the normalized monoterpene composition of pine resin. J. Chrom. Sci. 9: 755-756.

Stark R. W. 1965. Recent trends in forest entomology. Annu. Rev. Entomol. 10: 303-324.

Steel, R. G. D. and J. H. Torrie. 1960. Principles and procedures of statistics. New York: McGraw-Hill.

Struble, G. R. 1957. The fir engraver, a serious enemy of western true firs. USDA, Prod. Res. Rep. No. 11.

Wong, B. and A. Berryman. 1977. Host resistance to the fir engraver beetle. 3. Lesion development and containment of infection by resistant Abies grandis inoculated with Trichosporium symbioticum. Can. J. Bot. 55: 2358-2365.

Wright, E. 1935. Trichosporium symbioticum, a wood-staining fungus associated with Scolytus ventralis. J. Agric. Res. 50: 525-538.

Wright, E. 1938. Further investigations of brown-staining fungi associated with engraver beetles (Scolytus) in white fir. J. Agric. Res. 47: 759-773.

Zavarin, E. 1968. Chemotaxonomy of the genus Abies. II. Within tree variation of the terpenes in cortical oleoresin. Phytochemistry 7: 92-107.

Zavarin, E., K. Snajberk, and J. Fisher. 1975. Geographic variability of monoterpenes from cortex of Abies concolor. Biochem. Syst. Ecol. 3: 191-203.

21

Elicitation of Defensive Reactions in Conifers

François Lieutier and Alan A. Berryman

There is a general understanding about the different kinds of induced defensive reactions in herbaceous plants, and some hypotheses have been proposed for the possible mechanisms of their induction (Sequeira 1983, Darvill and Albersheim 1984). Two reactions have been distinguished: a localized one and a systemic one. The localized or hypersensitive reaction is seen only in close proximity to the site of wounding and is characterized by a local accumulation of phytoalexins. This reaction is generally caused by the presence of microorganisms (bacteria or fungi) in the wound because sterile wounds do not exhibit this kind of response. Phytoalexins, which play an important role in restricting the extent of penetration by the microorganisms, are released by host plant cells in response to various elicitors, usually compounds from pathogen or plant cell walls (Hadwiger et al. 1981, Sequeira 1983, Darvill and Albersheim 1984). These elicitors are nonspecific and are generally polysaccharides or glycoproteins. The systemic reaction is observed at sites in the host-plant distant from the point of damage or infection and some time after its induction. In these circumstances, the plant is usually more resistant to a challenge inoculation after the original inducing inoculation than to the original one itself. The elicitors responsible for this reaction originate from broken cell walls of the plant and diffuse throughout the plant. They can be released by a simple wound that is caused, for example, by the feeding of chewing phytophagous insects (Ryan et al. 1985).

In conifers, many forms of induced resistance have been reported against insects and microorganisms. For example, resistance may be expressed in the increased lignification of cells in the needles, thus conferring them a low food quality for defoliating insects (Baltensweiler et al. 1977), or it may take the form of an accumula- tion of terpenes and polyphenols close to the vicinity of the attack in the case of microorganisms associated or not with insects (Coutts and Dolezal 1966, Shain 1971, Shain and Hillis 1971, Berryman 1972). These compounds may stop the development of the aggressor either by their toxic or inhibitory properties or by isolating it from essential nutrients (Wong and Berryman 1977). Parenchyma cells have been observed to play an important role in the synthesis of these compounds (Fig. 1) (Reid et al. 1967, Berryman 1969, Lieutier and Berryman 1987).

Only recently, however, have the mechanisms of elicitation of defensive reactions in conifers been investigated (Miller et al. 1986). To further study this problem, we inoculated seven species of western North American conifers with Ceratocystis clavigera, a fungus associated with the mountain pine beetle, Dendroctonus ponderosae, and with two chemical elicitors--chitosan and the proteinase inhibitor inducing factor (PIIF). Chitosan is a glucosamine polymer constituent of the cell wall of many fungi and has been demonstrated to be an elicitor of hypersensitive responses in herbaceous plants (Hadwiger and Beckman 1980, Hadwiger et al. 1981). PIIF is a plant cell wall

Table 1. Longitudinal extension (in mm) of resin-impregnated phloem in seven species of conifers 14 days after inoculation with a fungus and two chemical elicitors.

Conifer	Kind of inoculation			
	Ceratocystis clavigera	Chitosan	PIIF	Buffer alone
Pinus ponderosa	50	>55	5	5
Pinus contorta	95	45	10	10
Pinus monticola	>30	20	5	<5
Larix occidentalis	0	0	0	0
Pseudotsuga menziesii	10	5	5	0
Abies grandis	0	0	0	0
Thuya plicata	0	0	0	0

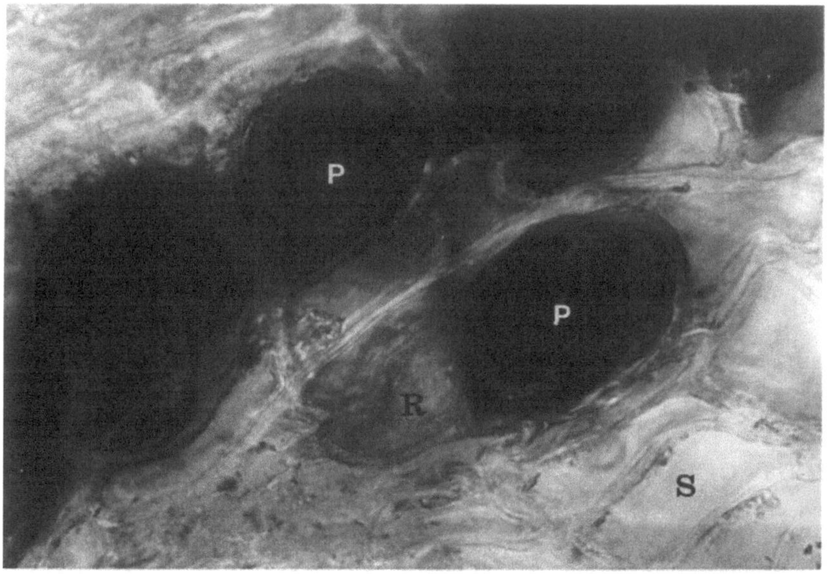

Figure 1. Transversal section in Pinus monticola phloem at the edge of the defense reaction, 7 days after a chitosan inoculation, 20 cm away longitudinally from the inoculation site. Notice the sieve cell filled with resin close to the parenchyma cells. P = parenchyma cell, R = resin in the sieve cell, S = normal sieve cell.

derived pectic oligomeric fragment which has been demonstrated to induce a systemic response in herbaceous plants (Green and Ryan 1972, Ryan et al. 1985). The conifer species inoculated were Pinus ponderosa, Pinus contorta, Pinus monticola, Larix occidentalis, Pseudotsuga menziesii, Abies grandis and Thuya plicata.

Histological observation of sections of phloem and sapwood (Lieutier and Berryman 1987) indicated that chitosan and fungus inoculations elicit very similar reactions (Table 1). In the pines, hypersensitive reactions were well developed with a large number of the conductive cells being filled with resin in both phloem and sapwood. Resin soaking of the conductive tissues begins close to parenchyma cells (Fig. 1) and then spreads rapidly into more and more distant cells. This suggests that a diffusion process is involved. But, because of its high viscosity, it is difficult to imagine diffusion of the resin itself. In addition, parenchyma cells are not observed to contain resin (Lieutier and Berryman 1987). We therefore hypothesize that parenchyma cells synthesize a less viscous precursor and that transformation of this precursor into resin takes place in the lumens of the conductive cells (Fig. 2).

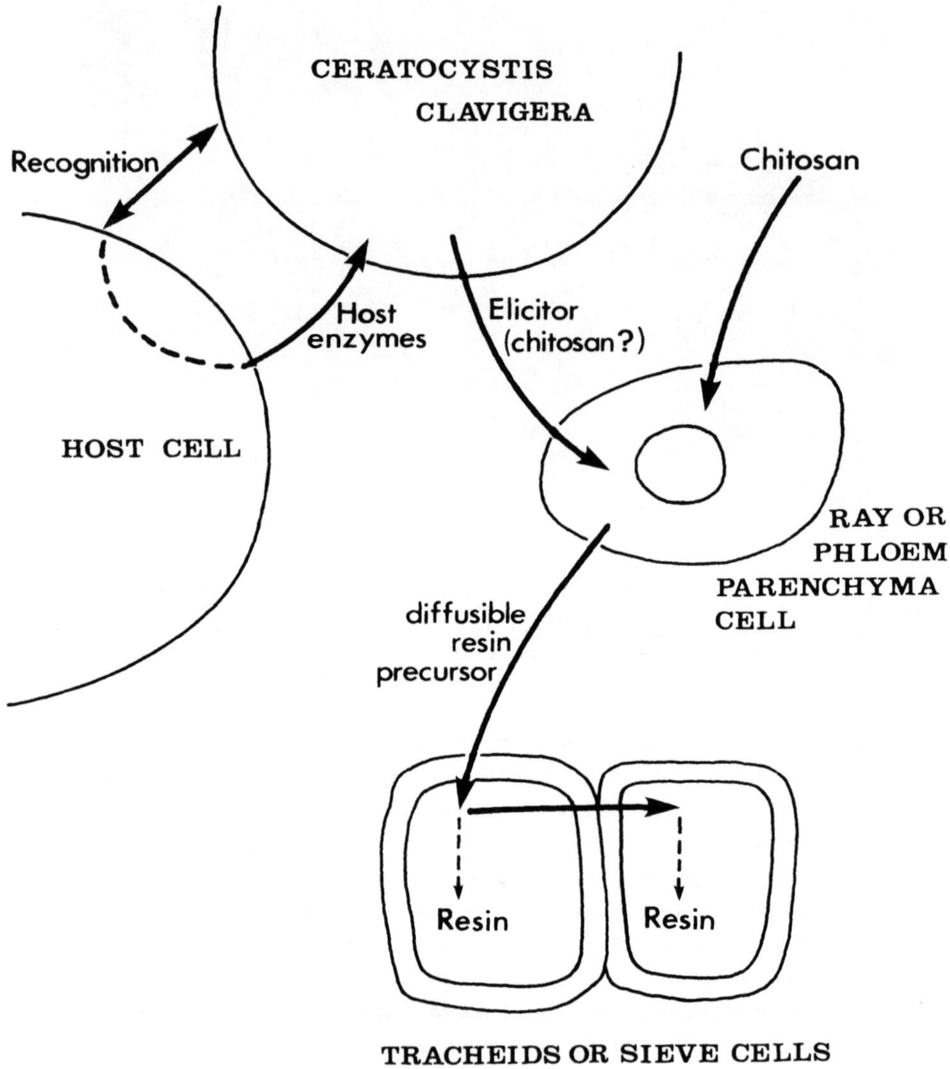

Figure 2. Possible mechanisms involved in the hypersensitive reaction of pines to <u>Ceratocystis clavigera</u> and chitosan.

The similarity of the defense reactions of *Pinus* to both fungus and chitosan suggests that a similar mechanism is involved in both cases. In fungus inoculations, the synthesis of resin precursors by parenchyma cells is probably induced, therefore, by a substance of fungal origin, possibly chitosan. When pea pods are infested by the fungus *Fusarium solani*, the chemical elicitor of the plant response is apparently chitosan released from fungus cell walls by the action of plant enzymes (Hadwiger and Beckman 1980, Hadwiger *et al*. 1981). The same mechanism may be involved in the relationships between pines and *Ceratocystis clavigera* (Fig. 2).

In conifers other than pines, the hypersensitive reaction to *C. clavigera* and chitosan is absent or only very limited (Table 1). The absence of a response to the fungus may be explained by the fact that these conifers are not the usual host species of *Dendroctonus ponderosae*, and so its mutualistic fungus, *C. clavigera*, would not be recognized as a pathogenic fungus. Growth of the fungus in these hosts would probably be limited by constitutive defensive chemicals or lack of essential nutrients, and the fungus would not be adapted to penetrating the living tissues of its host. Nevertheless, these conifers are generally attacked by other bark beetles/fungi associations, e.g., *Abies grandis* attacked by *Scolytus ventralis* and its fungal symbiont, *Trichosporium symbioticum*. In this case, a vigorous defense reaction is induced by the insect-fungus infection (Berryman 1969, Wong and Berryman 1977), proving that this host is capable of recognizing at least some pathogenic invasions. The absence of a response to chitosan in *A. grandis* suggests that this chemical is certainly not the only elicitor by which pathogenic fungi induce hypersensitive reactions in conifers.

The hypersensitive response of all the conifers to inoculation with PIIF appeared to be no different from that to control inoculations (buffer solution alone). Thus, in spite of the fact that PIIF can induce localized reactions in some herbaceous plants (Walker-Simmons *et al*. 1983, Nothnagel *et al*. 1983), it seems more likely to be involved in the systemic reaction of conifers.

The elicitation of the defensive reactions in conifers seems to be basically the same as that in herbaceous plants. It is possible that closely related elicitors occur in these two groups of plants. Chitosan, for example, might have a very widespread action and might play a role in pines as well as peas. From this point of view, it may be surprising that differences between related genera (for example *Abies* and *Pinus*) were observed in our study while, on the contrary, similarities occur between two distant genera like *Pinus* and *Pisum*.

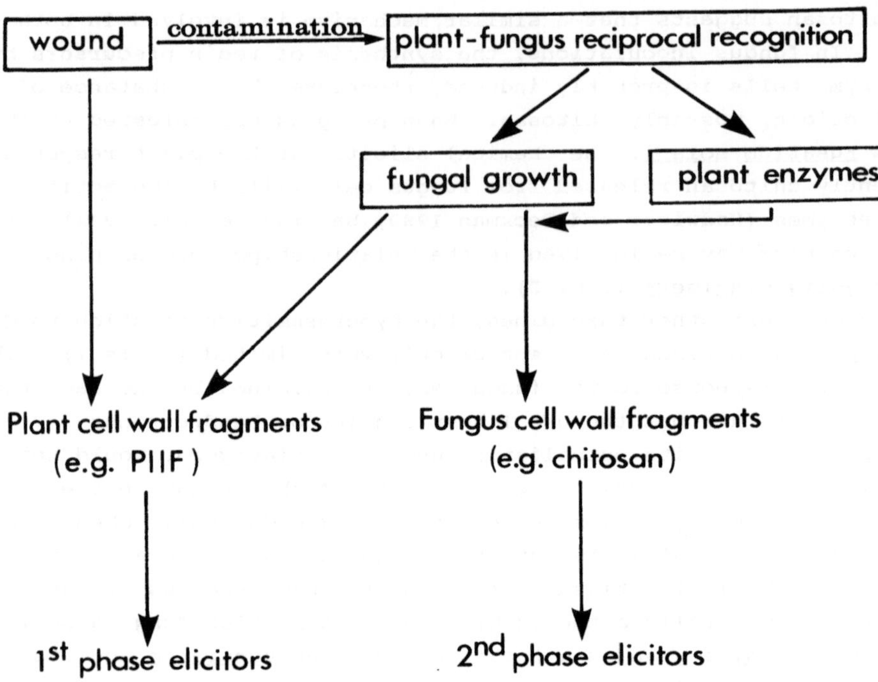

Figure 3. Hypothetical pathways eliciting induced defensive reactions in conifers and other plants.

Yet, notwithstanding the difference in the nature of the elicitors, the hypersensitive reaction seems to be a general mechanism of defense which is induced by compounds released from pathogen cell walls (e.g., chitosan). We hypothesize that the wound alone, in the absence of pathogenic contamination, induces a systemic reaction by the release of elicitors from host cell walls (e.g., PIIF) (Fig. 3). These "first phase" elicitors of plant origin would be released by both mechanical injury, such as is caused by a defoliating insect, as well as by microorganisms penetrating plant cells. However, other "second phase" elicitors may be released in the latter case as plant enzymes react with the cells of the penetrating microorganism (Fig. 3). We hypothesize that these "foreign" elicitors are necessary for inducing the intense local defensive reaction often called the hypersensitive response. This hypothesis fits with the ultrastructural changes in parenchyma cells observed by Lieutier and Berryman (1987) and

Cheniclet *et al*. (in this volume). This unifying theory is developed in more detail by Berryman (in this volume).

REFERENCES

Baltensweiler, W., G. Benz, P. Bovey, and V. Delucchi. 1977. Dynamics of larch bud moth populations. Annu. Rev. Entomol. 22: 79-100.

Berryman, A. A. 1969. Responses of *Abies grandis* to attack by *Scolytus ventralis* (Coleoptera: Scolytidae). Can. Entomol. 101: 1033-1041.

Berryman, A. A. 1972. Resistance of conifers to invasion by bark beetle-fungus associations. BioScience 22: 599-601.

Coutts, M. P. and J. E. Dolezal. 1966. Polyphenols and resin in the resistance mechanism of *Pinus radiata* attacked by the wood wasp, *Sirex noctilio* and its associated fungus. Commonwealth Australia, Forestry and Timber Bureau Leaflet 101, 19 p.

Darvill, A. G. and P. Albersheim. 1984. Phytoalexins and their elicitors--a defense against microbial infection in plants. Annu. Rev. Plant Physiol. 35: 243-275.

Green, T. R. and C. A. Ryan. 1972. Wound-induced proteinase inhibitor in tomato leaves. Plant Physiol. 51: 19-21.

Hadwiger, L. A. and J. M. Beckman. 1980. Chitosan as a component of pea-*Fusarium solani* interactions. Plant Physiol. 66: 205-211.

Hadwiger, L. A., J. M. Beckman, and M. J. Adams. 1981. Localization of fungal components in the pea-*Fusarium* interaction detected immunochemically with anti-chitosan and anti-fungal cell wall antisera. Plant Physiol. 67: 170-175.

Lieutier, F. and A. A. Berryman. 1987. (In press). Histology of the defense reactions of three pine species to *Ceratocystis clavigera* and two chemical elicitors. Can. J. For. Res.

Miller, R. W., A. A. Berryman, and C. A. Ryan. 1986. Biotic elicitors of defense reactions in lodgepole pine. Phytochemistry 255: 611-612.

Nothnagel, E. A., M. McNeil, P. Albersheim, and A. Dell. 1983. Host-pathogen interactions. XXII. A galacturonic acid oligosaccharide from plant cell walls elicits phytoalexins. Plant Physiol. 71: 916-926.

Reid, R. W., H. S. Whitney, and J. A. Watson. 1967. Reactions of lodgepole pine to attack by *Dendroctonus ponderosae* Hopkins and blue stain fungi. Can. J. Bot. 46: 1115-1126.

Ryan, C. A., P. D. Bishop, M. Walker-Simmons, W. E. Brown, and J. S. Graham. 1985. Pectic fragments regulate the expression of proteinase inhibitor genes in plants. In: Cellular and molecular biology of plant stress (A. R. Liss, Ed.); 319-334.

Sequeira, L. 1983. Mechanisms of induced resistance in plants. Annu. Rev. Microbiol. 37: 51-79.

Shain, L. 1971. The response of sapwood of Norway spruce to infection by *Fomes annosus*. Phytopathology. 61: 301-307.

Shain, L. and W. E. Hillis. 1971. Phenolic extractives of Norway spruce and their effects on *Fomes annosus*. Phytopathology. 61: 841-845.

Walker-Simmons, M., L. Hadwiger, and C. A. Ryan. 1983. Chitosans and pectic polysaccharides both induce accumulation of the antifungal phytoalexin pisatin in pea pods and antinutrient proteinase inhibitors in tomato leaves. Biochem. Biophys. Res. Commun. 110: 194-199.

Wong, B. L. and A. A. Berryman. 1977. Host resistance to the fir engraver beetle. 3. Lesion development and containment of infection by resistant *Abies grandis* inoculated with *Trichosporium symbioticum*. Can J. Bot. 55: 2358-2365.

22

Do Fungi Influence the Establishment of Bark Beetles in Scots Pine?

François Lieutier, Annie Yart, Jacques Garcia, Blandine Poupinel, and Jean Levieux

Most aggressive bark beetle species (Coleoptera: Scolytidae) are associated with fungi which play an important role in the establishment of these beetles on conifers. The success or failure of establishment appears to depend on the capability of the tree to defend itself, especially the so-called hypersensitive reaction directed against the associated fungi (Reid *et al*. 1967; Berryman 1972; Safranyik *et al*. 1975; Raffa and Berryman 1982, 1983; Christiansen and Hornvedt 1983). However, almost nothing is known about the mechanisms of the establishment of the European bark beetles on their usual host trees except for *Ips typographus* in Norway spruce.

Herein, we present our exploratory research on the establishment of two European bark beetles, *Tomicus piniperda* and *Ips sexdentatus*, on Scots pine, *Pinus sylvestris*. We present a series of observations and experiments showing a parallel between the two bark beetles species (Lieutier and Levieux 1985).

FUNGI ISOLATED FROM *TOMICUS PINIPERDA* AND *IPS SEXDENTATUS*

All fungi were isolated either from adult beetles (flying or attacking) or from their galleries a short time after their establishment. In addition to several saprophytic fungi, three species of possibly pathogenic fungi were found with each beetle species. In the case of *T. piniperda*, they were *Hormonema dematioides*, a known pathogen of the pine shoots, *Verticicladiella* sp., which is an imperfect form of *Ceratocystis*; and a *Ceratocystis* species closely related to *C. minor* which will be named *C.* (*minor*) in the following discussion. In the case of *I. sexdentatus*, they were *Ceratocystis brunneo-ciliata*, *Ceratocystis* sp. 1; and *Ceratocystis* sp. 2. In addition, we have observed that *Verticicladiella* sp., *C. minor* and *C. brunneo-ciliata* are related to the blue stain occurring in the sapwood of Scots pine.

Constancy of the Fungi in the Population of Beetles

For T. piniperda, the percentage of beetles carrying fungi is variable from one year to another, but for a given year it is consistently high and comparable from one site to another for H. dematioides; consistently low and comparable from one site to another for Verticicladiella sp.; and very variable for C. (minor) (Table 1). It is interesting to observe that the presence of C. (minor) in a locality seems to be positively correlated with the presence of a mortality spot in this locality. Because of its high variability, it seems very unlikely that C.(minor) plays a role in the establishment of T. piniperda.

For I. sexdentatus, it is difficult to define an exact percentage of beetles carrying the different species of fungi because the fruiting bodies of the fungi were difficult to obtain. We can only conclude that the fruiting bodies of C. brunneo-ciliata were the most frequently observed. However, the total frequency for the three Ceratocystis species together was very high and not variable.

Aggressiveness of the Different Species of Fungi on Scots Pine

Trees were inoculated at breast height with 2- to 3-week-old malt-agar cultures of the fungi. All trees chosen had about the same vigor according to their periodic growth ratio (PGR) and to Waring's

Table 1. Percentage of beetles carrying different species of fungi in different years.

	Tomicus piniperda						Ips sexadentatus	
	Hormonema dematioides		Verticicladiella sp.		Ceratocystis (minor)		Ceratocystis spp.	
	1985	1986	1985	1986	1985	1986	1986 May	1986 July
Swarming beetles	--	38	--	4	--	0	100	100
Attacking beetles	88	42	11	4	14	13	94	94

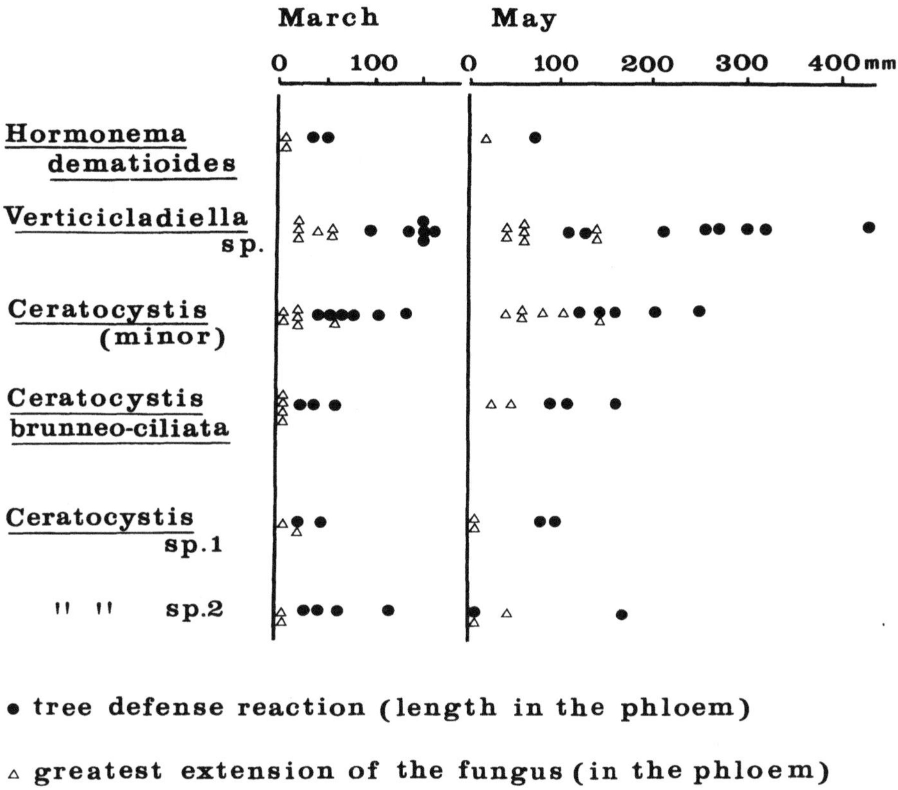

Figure 1. Aggressiveness of different species of fungi associated with Tomicus piniperda and Ips sexdentatus measured by the total length of the resinosis and the maximum extension of the fungi in the phloem 3 weeks after inoculations on two dates (March and May). Each symbol represents a single tree.

index (Mahoney 1978, Waring and Pitman 1980). The inoculations were done twice per year on the same trees, at the time of swarming for each beetle species (March for T. piniperda and May for I. sexdentatus).

At each time, each fungus was inoculated into at least two trees. Three weeks later, the aggressiveness of each fungus was evaluated by measuring the length of the induced resinosis (resin impregnated phloem/sapwood) and the extent of the fungus in the phloem (Fig. 1).

For those fungi associated with T. piniperda, Verticicladiella sp. was the most aggressive and H. dematioides was least aggressive. C. (minor) fell between these two. For those fungi associated with I.

sexdentatus, C. brunneo-ciliata and C. sp. 2 were the most aggressive species.

We conclude that the fungi which are most likely to play a role in the bark beetle and Scots pine relationship are as follows: Verticicladiella sp. is the best candidate for T. piniperda, because of its strong aggressiveness. However, its variability in the beetle population was rather high. C. (minor) was far too variable from place to place, and H. dematioides was basically unaggressive. C. brunneo-ciliata seems to be the best candidate for I. sexdentatus. It has about the same aggressiveness as C. sp. 2 but its variability was much lower. C. sp. 1 had low aggressiveness as well as high variability.

ROLE OF THE PRIMARY DEFENSE REACTION IN THE SCOTS PINE AND BARK BEETLE RELATIONSHIP

In March, we introduced 96 females of T. piniperda into 8 pines having nearly the same vigor (according to their PGR and Waring's index). We made small holes with a drill up to the cambium level and then covered both beetle and hole with a small cage. Males were added the next day. Using this same method in May, we introduced 102 pairs of I. sexdentatus into 5 pines. At the same time, we measured resin-flow at 2 cms away from the beetle hole--on its right side for T. piniperda and just under it for I. sexdentatus. The galleries of the beetles were examined 4 weeks later.

Results for Ips Sexdentatus

All Ips attacks failed: one insect was found dead, the rest left the hosts. For Ips, the boring activity begins with a nuptial chamber. Thus the length of their gallery appears as a wide and oblique cavity rather than a true narrow gallery. Nevertheless, the data clearly show that the boring activity of beetles was greatest when the quantity of primary resin was lowest (Fig. 2). Cases where there was only small boring activity as well as a small quantity of resin probably indicate that some factors other than the primary resin inhibited the beetles. We hasten to point out that we did not study a natural attack. The artificial characteristics of the "inoculation" hole could be a confounding factor in our experiment. We conclude that, to some extent, the primary resin accounts for the failure of the Ips attacks, but most beetles are apparently not killed--they abandon the host.

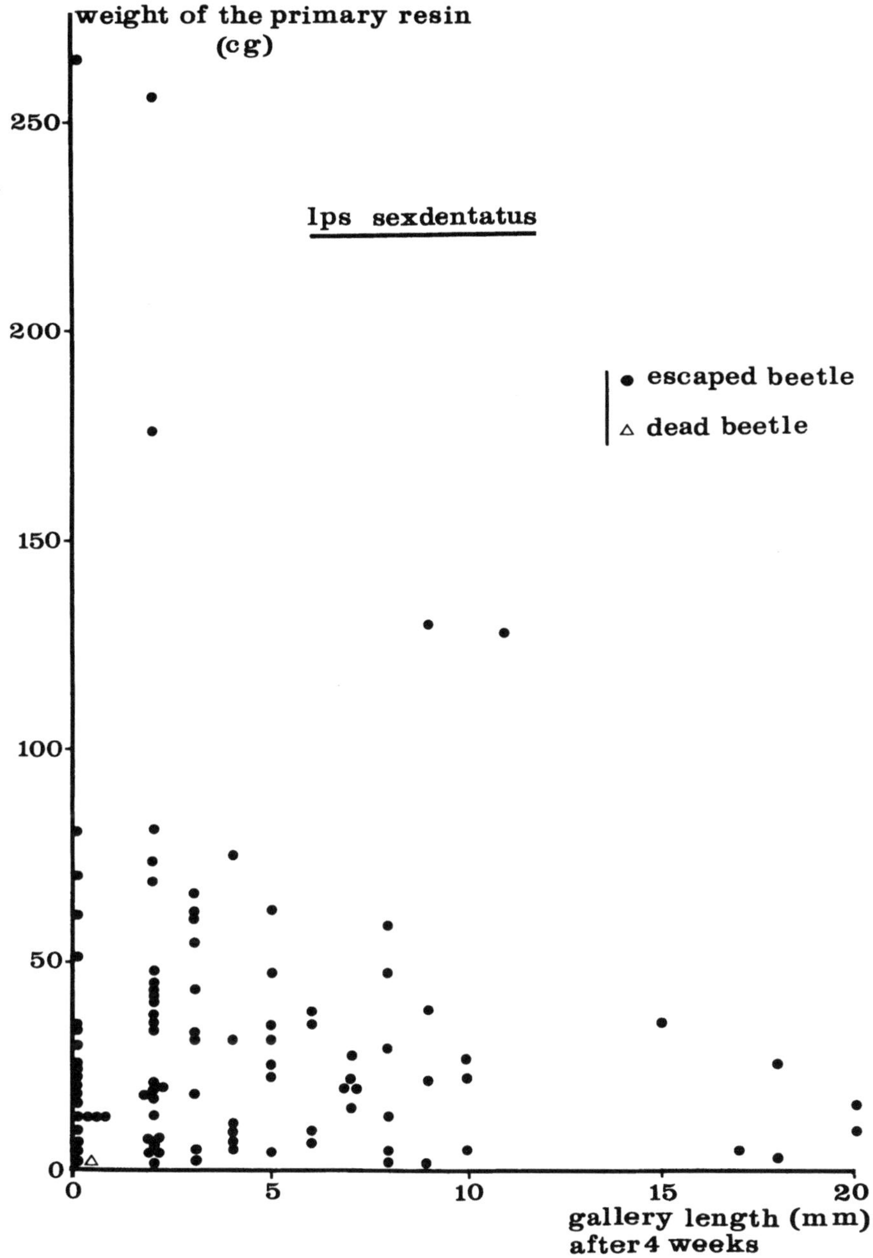

Figure 2. Quantity of primary resins (resin flow measured in grams on 7 days in May) measured at 2 cms away from the beetle (I. sexdentatus) hole, in relation to the length of the corresponding galleries (artificial attack).

Results for Tomicus Piniperda

As was true for Ips, all Tomicus attacks failed. There was no relation between the length of the gallery, the number of dead beetles, and the quantity of the primary resin (Fig. 3). Thus, the primary resin did not play a role in the establishment of T. piniperda. However, in this experiment, resin-flow was measured on the side of the beetle hole, which is probably a less accurate estimation of the primary resins encountered by the beetles than by a measurement under the beetle hole. Because of this, we cannot reject the role of the primary resins in beetle establishment.

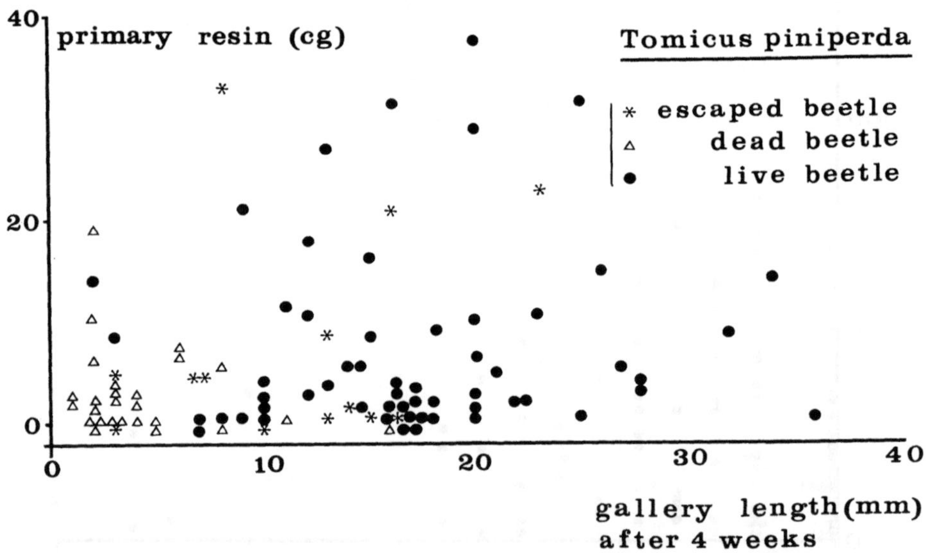

Figure 3. Quantity of primary resins (resin flow measured in grams on 7 days in March) measured at 2 cms away from the "inoculation" hole of the beetle (T. piniperda) in relation to the length of the corresponding galleries (artificial attack).

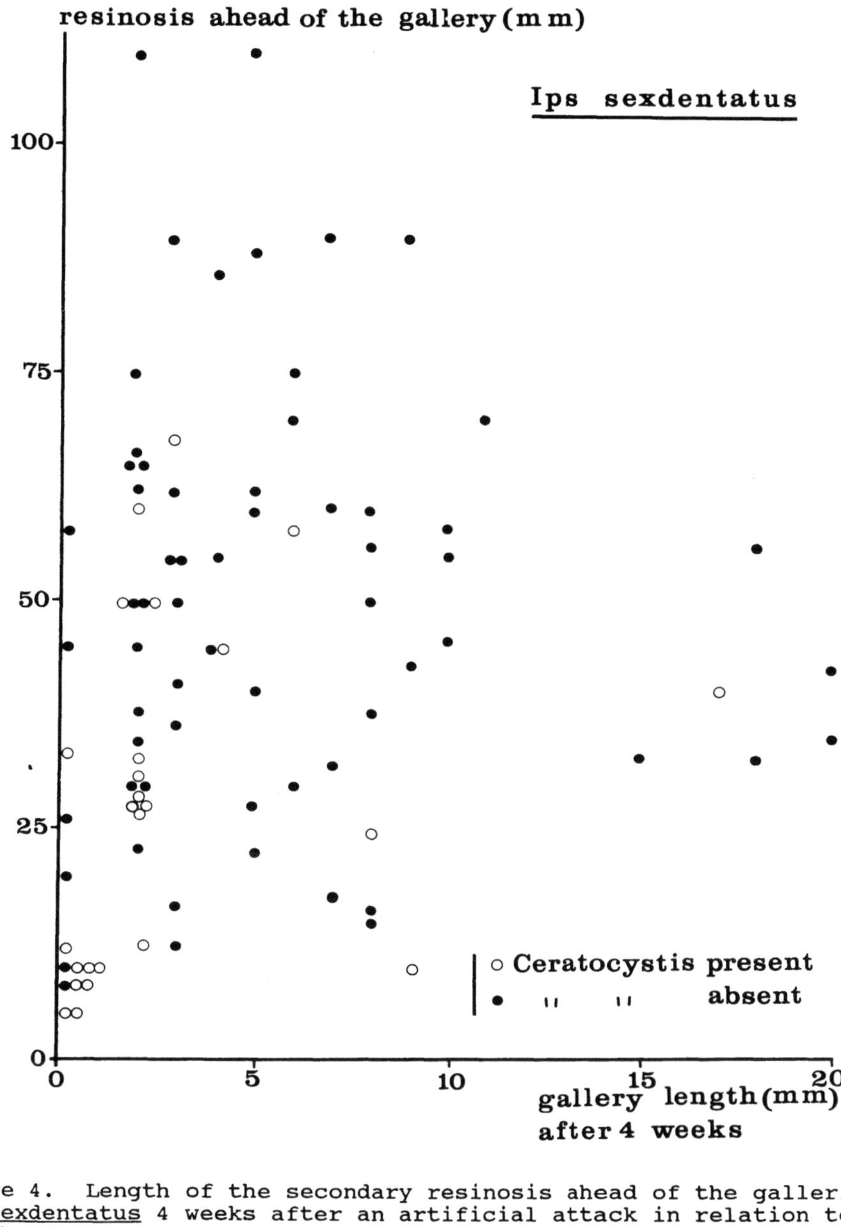

Figure 4. Length of the secondary resinosis ahead of the galleries of *Ips sexdentatus* 4 weeks after an artificial attack in relation to the length of the corresponding galleries.

ROLE OF THE SECONDARY DEFENSE REACTION

Ips Sexdentatus

The length of the resinosis ahead of the *Ips* galleries seems to increase with the presence of a *Ceratocystis* in the gallery (Fig. 4). In addition, the longer the gallery, the more fungi that were associated with it. According to these observations, one would expect a long gallery to be associated with a considerable secondary defense reaction. But the contrary was observed (Fig. 4). After the action of the primary resin, the success or failure of the beetle boring in the phloem could depend upon the following (1) an early inoculation of the phloem with the fungus which induces an immediate secondary defense reaction which in turn caused the insect to cease boring and to leave or (2) a delayed inoculation of the phloem with fungi which causes the secondary defense reaction but only after some galleries have become very long. This might explain the higher constancy of the fungus in the longer galleries.

Tomicus Piniperda

We studied natural attacks induced by attracting the beetles to living trees in March and examined the results 8 weeks later in both a resistant and a susceptible tree.

In the case of the susceptible tree, the density of the attacks was 69 beetles/m^2 of bark surface. We measured 45 successful and 38 unsuccessful attacks. The occurrence of the fungi was the same in the successful as well as in the unsuccessful attacks (Table 2), which clearly suggests that the establishment of the beetles does not depend on the presence of a fungus. It probably depends only on the innate capacity of the tree to defend itself. This was confirmed by the clustered distribution of the successful attacks on the tree--all the failures occurred on one side, whereas all the successes were on the other side. Plotting the length of the resinosis against the length of the galleries, stratified by the absence or the presence of the fungi (Fig. 5), shows that (1) There was little or no resinosis regardless of the length of gallery for successful attacks. (2) On the other hand, the length of resinosis increased directly with the length of the gallery for the failed attacks. This was also true for another tree where all the attacks failed (density 60 attacks/m^2 of bark) (Fig. 6). (3) There was no relation between the length of the gallery and the presence of the fungi, either for the successful or

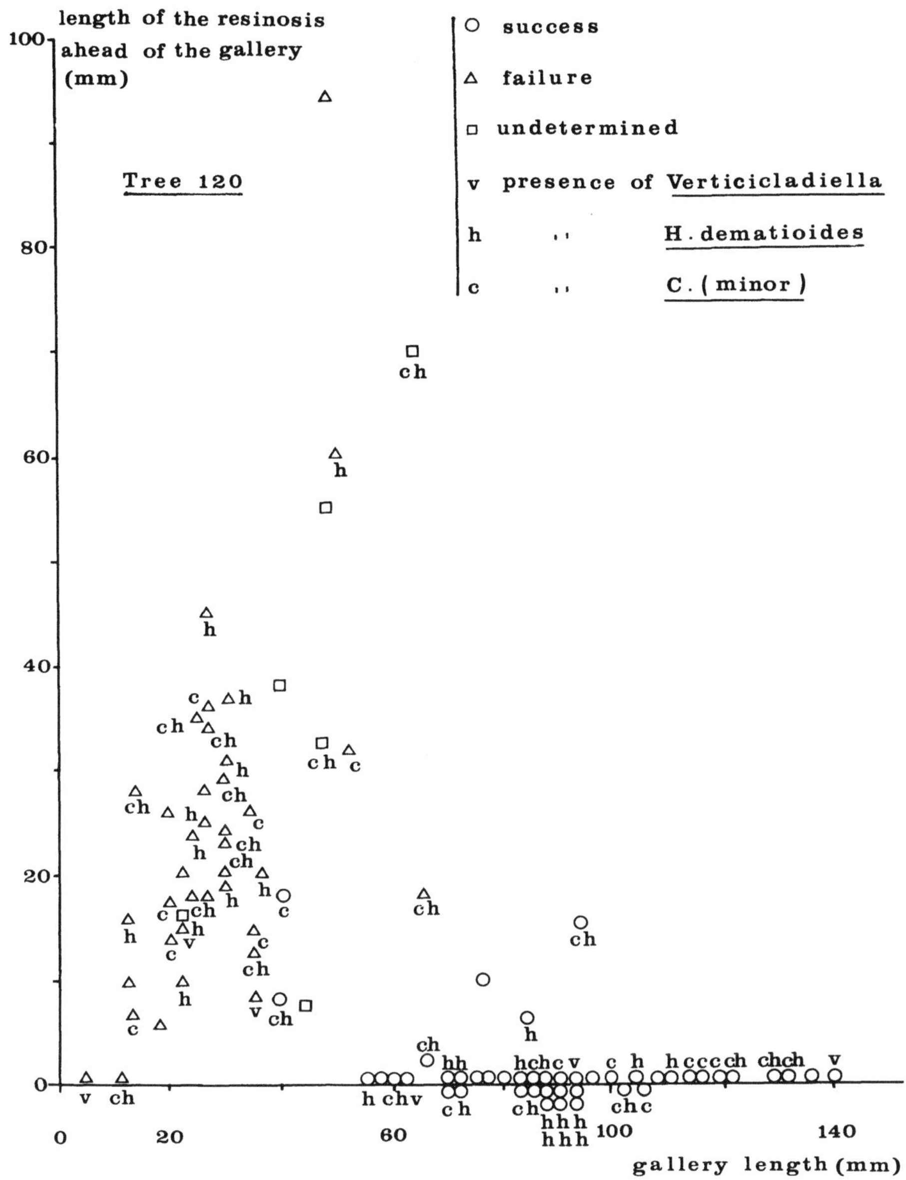

Figure 5. Length of the secondary resinosis ahead of the galleries of T. piniperda 8 weeks after a natural attack in relation to the length of the corresponding galleries in the case of a susceptible tree for different kinds of attacks.

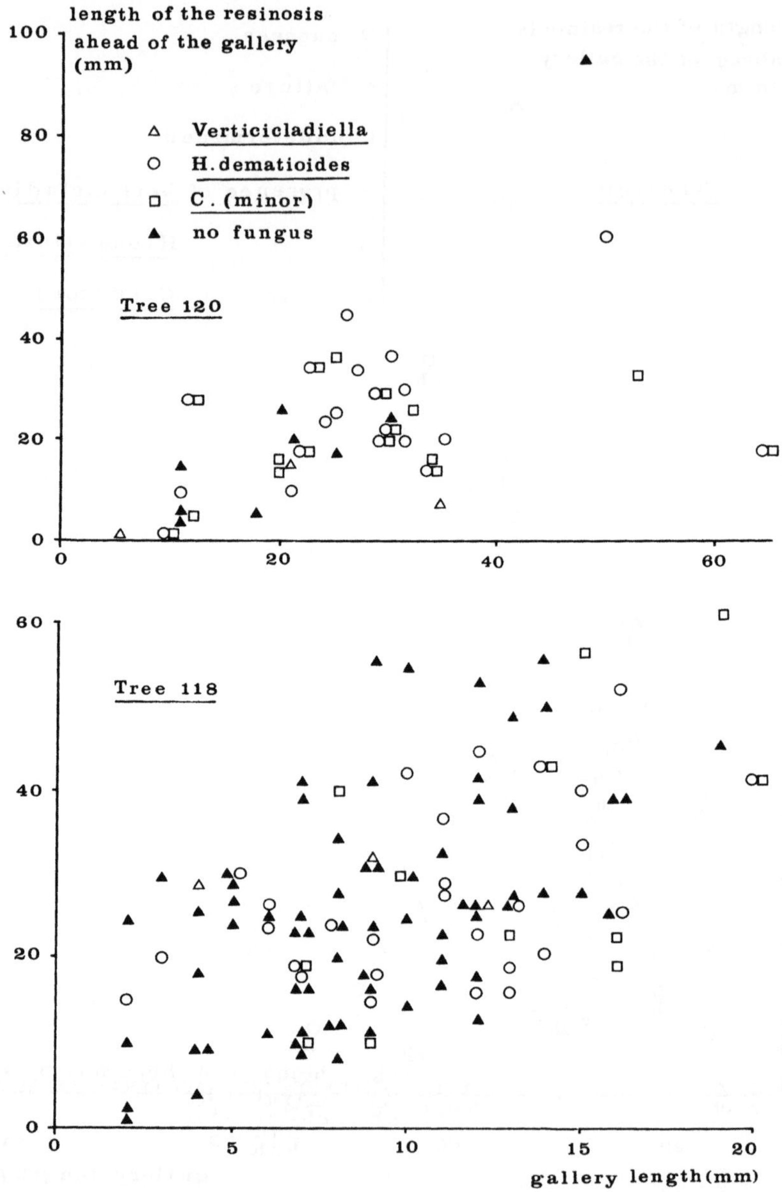

Figure 6. Length of the secondary resinosis ahead of the galleries of T. piniperda 8 weeks after a natural attack and length of the corresponding galleries. 6a. Same susceptible tree as in Fig.5, but only for the failed attacks. 6b. Case of a resistant tree (all the attacks failed).

Table 2. Percentage of beetles contaminated by the different species of fungi for the successful and failed attacks in a susceptible tree.

	Verticicladiella	H. dematioides	C. (minor)
Success (n = 45)	7	51	42
Failure (n = 38)	5	50	45

the failed attacks. Thus, for T. piniperda, the secondary defense reaction of the tree seems to play a major role in the success of its attacks. This reaction seems to be directly related to the importance of the mechanical wounding induced by the boring activity of the beetle and not to the presence of any associated fungus considered in the assay. We conclude that these fungi do not have an important role in the establishment of T. piniperda.

These results are completely opposite from those obtained with I. sexdentatus. In order to further investigate this contrast, we studied the dose-effect in the response of the tree to Verticicladiella sp. and to C. brunneo-ciliata. We inoculated two trees having about the same vigor with various quantities of spores of these two species of fungi (in March for Verticicladiella sp. and the Tomicus model, and in May for C. brunneo-ciliata and the Ips model). For each fungus, the various quantities of spores (0 to 10^7) were obtained by diluting the surface of a malt-agar culture of the fungus in sterile water. For each concentration, each tree received two inoculations. The response of the tree was measured by the concentration of resin in the phloem within the first 25 mm from the inoculation site.

The tree response to Verticicladiella sp. was very weak until there were very large quantities of inoculum. It differed significantly from the response to the sterile water only after the quantity of inoculum was equal to or higher than 15,000 spores (Fig. 7a). The response to C. brunneo-ciliata, on the other hand, was strong and rapidly increased to the maximum intensity. It differed significantly from the response to the sterile water even for a quantity of inoculum as low as 100 spores (Fig. 7b). In both cases, the response to an inoculation of a malt-agar culture of the fungi was the same as those obtained with the water suspension of an identical number of spores.

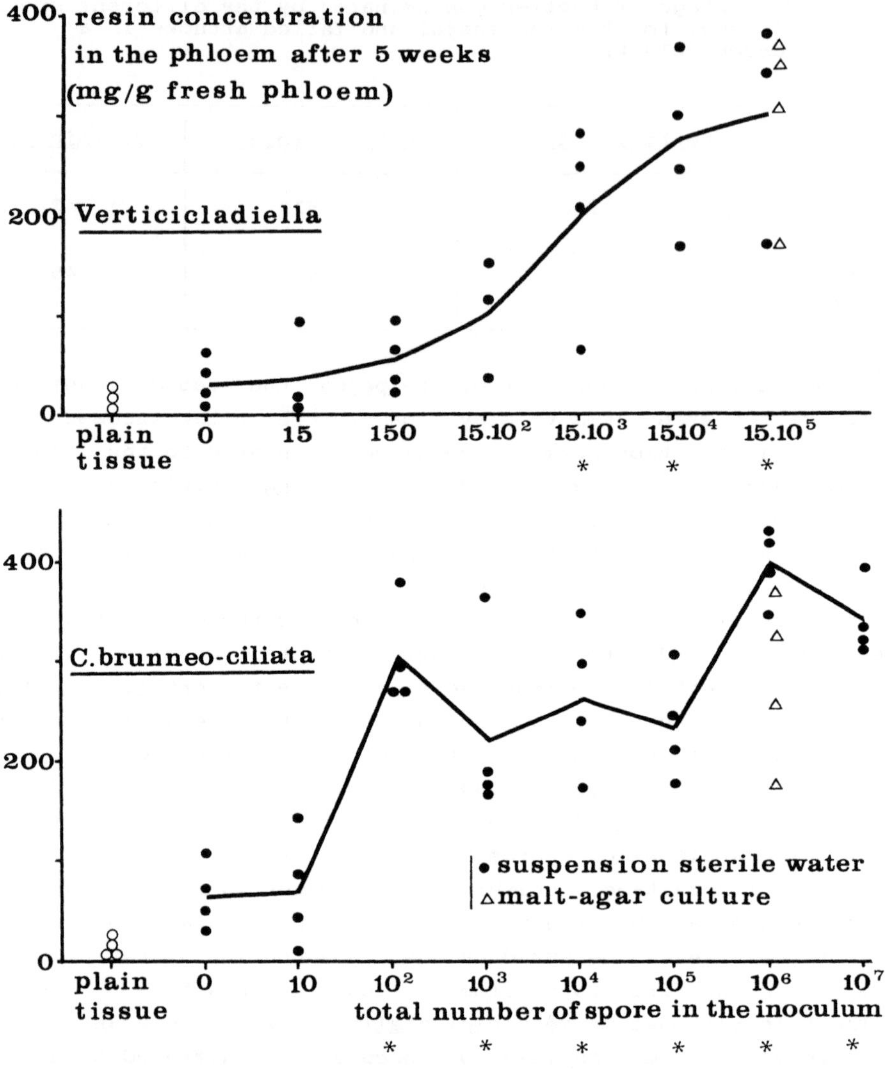

Figure 7. The secondary response of _Pinus sylvestris_ in relation to different doses of _Verticicladiella_ sp., a fungus associated with _T. piniperda_ (7a) and _C. brunneo-ciliata_, a fungus associated with _I. sexdentatus_ (7b). The quantities of inoculum corresponding to a concentration of resin in the phloem that are significantly different from the concentration induced by sterile water alone are asterisked.

Because Verticicladiella needs at least 15,000 spores to induce a significant response and there is only a low probability that an insect carries such a very high number of spores, we can understand why the tree's secondary response to T. piniperda does not depend on the presence of the fungus and why it probably has no role in the establishment of T. piniperda. In the case of Ceratocystis, most Ips beetles probably carry far fewer than 100 spores, thus explaining why the amount of secondary reaction against I. sexdentatus is directly related to the presence of the Ceratocystis and why this fungus appears to have a role in the establishment of Ips sexdentatus on Scots pine.

In summary, the mechanisms of establishment of the two bark beetles Ips sexdentatus and Tomicus piniperda on Scots pine thus appear to be very different from each other.

T. piniperda carries a very aggressive fungus which has a very low constancy in the beetle population. This fungus does not seem to play a role in the establishment of the beetle, at least partly because of the high number of spores required to induce an important defense reaction from the tree. Nevertheless, the tree's secondary defense reaction seems to play an important role in establishment of Tomicus.

I. sexdentatus carries three species of Ceratocystis: at least one has a high constancy in the beetle population and is moderately aggressive. This fungus seems to play a role in the establishment of the beetle, at least partly because of the low number of spores required for the elicitation of an important defensive response from the tree. Both the primary resins as well as the secondary resins are essential in the tree's defense against I. sexdentatus.

ACKNOWLEDGEMENTS

The authors thank the Office National des Forêts, particularly the Head, and the Offices of the Management Centre of Orléans for giving them the free disposition of the trees and plots needed in the field experiments.

REFERENCES

Berryman, A. A. 1972. Resistance of conifers to invasion by bark beetle-fungus associations. BioScience 22: 599-601.

Christiansen, E. and R. Hornvedt. 1983. Combined Ips/ceratocystis attack on Norway spruce, and defensive mechanisms of the trees. Z. Angew. Entomol. 96: 110-118.

Lieutier, F. and J. Levieux. 1985. Les relations conifères-Scolytides: importance et perspectives de recherches. Ann. Sci. For. 42: 359-370.

Mahoney, R. L. 1978. Lodgepole/mountain pine beetle risk classification methods and their application. In: Theory and practice of mountain pine beetle management in lodgepole pine forests (A. A. Berryman, G. D. Amman, R. W. Stark, and D. L. Kibbee, Eds.). Moscow, ID: Univ. of Idaho, College of Forest Resources; 106-113.

Raffa, K. F. and A. A. Berryman. 1982. Accumulation of monoterpenes and associated volatiles following inoculation of grand fir with a fungus transmitted by the fir engraver, Scolytus ventralis (Coleoptera: Scolytidae). Can. Entomol. 114: 797-810.

Raffa, K. F. and A. A. Berryman. 1983. The role of host resistance in the colonization behavior and ecology of bark beetles (Coleoptera: Scolytidae). Ecol. Monogr. 53: 27-49.

Reid, R. W., H. S. Whitney, and J. A. Watson. 1967. Reactions of lodgepole pine to attack by Dentroctonus ponderosae Hopkins and blue stain fungi. Can. J. Bot. 45: 1115-1126.

Safranyik, L., D. M. Shrimpton, and H. S. Whitney. 1975. An interpretation of the interaction between lodgepole pine, the mountain pine beetle, and its associated blue stain fungi in Western Canada. In: Management of lodgepole pine ecosystems (D. M. Baumgartner, Ed.). Pullman, WA: Washington State Univ. Coop. Ext. Serv.; 406-428.

Waring, R. H. and G. B. Pitman. 1980. A simple model of host resistance to bark beetles. Forest Research Laboratory Res. Note 65, 2 p.

23

The Toxicity of Norway Spruce Monoterpenes to Two Bark Beetle Species and Their Associates

Claude Everaerts, Jean-Claude Grégoire, and Joël Merlin

Monoterpenes are involved in the preformed and induced defenses of conifers against bark beetles. They are produced in the preconstituted resin system of the trees as well as in the tissues subject to induced wound reaction. While it is well-known that these compounds are generally toxic to arthropods, their effect on bark beetles is less clear, and contradictory statements appear in the literature. On the one hand, bark beetles are supposed to be relatively immune to terpene toxicity because of their long coevolution with conifers. Monoterpenes belong to the so-called "qualitative defenses" of plants to which specialist herbivores are able to adapt (Cates and Alexander 1982). On the other hand, there are some experimental studies and observations which suggest that some monoterpenes remain sufficiently toxic to bark beetles to significant-ly influence their ecology. For example, studies by Smith (1975) and by Sturgeon (1979) in the *Pinus ponderosa*/*Dendroctonus brevicomis* association suggest that tree resistance is linked to a higher limonene content. The hypothesis is that in areas of intensive tree killing by *D. brevicomis*, selective pressure exerted by the insects led to an increase in the proportion of trees having a high limonene content.

So far, the toxicity and repellency of conifer monoterpenes have been tested mainly on American *Dendroctonus* spp., on *Scolytus ventralis*, and on *Ips paraconfusus* (Smith 1961a, 1961b, 1963, 1965, 1975; Coyne and Lott 1976; Bordash and Berryman 1977; Byers 1981; Raffa *et al*. 1985). These insects are well-known tree killers (Wood 1982) which invade the tree *en masse*, and cause its death directly or by inoculation of pathogenic fungi. The tests performed on these bark beetles revealed that all the monoterpenes tested had some toxicity or repellency and that several compounds consistently were more potent than others.

These gregarious species appear to respond to the defenses of the trees by converting some of the host monoterpenes into aggregation pheromones with at least two results: (1) Those compounds used as pheromone precursors are detoxicated, and (2) The mass attack elicited by the aggregation pheromones causes the rapid exhaustion of the tree's primary resin followed by the tree's death under the combined action of beetle feeding and the fungal mutualists. The consequences of this host colonization strategy are that the adult beetles manage to share and reduce the total impact per individual beetle of the tree's defenses and to reduce the period during which the defenses are effective by draining the resin ducts and rapidly weakening and killing the host, putting an end to the hypersensitive wound reaction.

There is, however, another host colonization strategy among primary bark beetles. Some species, such as the Eurasian Dendroctonus micans, are solitary colonizers of green trees (Grégoire 1985). In D. micans, only one or at most a few females attack the same spruce, Picea abies, tree, (no pathogenic fungi are inoculated) and the resulting larvae which are gregarious (up to 200 per female) spend their whole life feeding more or less side-by-side in an amoeboid-like patch within the living bark. One would expect such species to have developed their own ways of coping with host tree defenses. Because they cannot avoid them or stop their production, they must have been obliged over evolutionary time to coexist with them.

Yet another look may be taken at the interaction between host monoterpenes and bark beetle ecology from the third trophic level. Just as these different types of relations with the host may determine different adaptations among the scolytids to the host's defenses, the same may also be true regarding their parasitoids and predators. One would expect that natural enemies of solitary colonizers would have had to develop a higher resistance to terpenes than natural enemies of gregarious colonizers that kill trees.

MATERIALS AND METHODS

Insects

Two behaviorally different, sympatric spruce bark beetle species were compared: Dendroctonus micans, a solitary colonizer, and Ips typographus, a gregarious, occasional tree killer associated with Ceratocystis pathogenic fungi (Christiansen and Horntvedt 1983, Horntvedt et al. 1983).

Two sympatric species of bark beetle associates were also compared: Rhizophagus grandis and Rhizophagus dispar. The former is a specific predator of D. micans and spends its whole life with its prey in the living bark of spruce, whereas the latter is associated with several bark beetle species (among which, one is Ips typographus) and is both an occasional predator and a fungivore in aging Ips galleries (Merlin et al. 1986).

As a control, insects with little or no normal contacts with monoterpenes were also tested: the Hemipteran, Dysdercus cingulatus, the ant, Formica rufa, and the beetle, Tenebrio molitor. Among these three species, only the ant has some contacts with monoterpenes, since its nests are made with conifer needles.

Chemicals

We tested the major monoterpenes identified by Heemann and Francke (1977) in spruce bark samples: (-)-α-pinene, (+)-α-pinene, β-pinene, delta-3-carene, limonene, myrcene, α-terpinene, and camphène. The chemical purity of these compounds was always greater than 93 percent.

Exposure to Vapors

The experiments were made in a hermetical set-up consisting of two chambers separated by a piece of wire netting. The test compounds were introduced in the lower chamber in relatively high quantities (about 60 μl), so that the set-up was permanently saturated with vapors, as attested by the presence of residual liquid monoterpenes during the whole experiment. For each species, 20 to 30 individuals were used per test. After 24 hours, the dead and paralysed insects were counted.

Topical Application Tests

Prior to the experiments, the insects were immobilized by a short period of exposure to cold (-18 °C). Pure monoterpenes were applied in measured amounts on the sternal area of each adult or on the whole body of each larva. For treatments with large amounts of the compounds, several successive applications were made. After total disappearance of the liquid from the cuticular surface, the insects were kept in Petri dishes with moist paper, and after a 20 hour period, the number of dead and paralysed insects were counted.

Each LD_{50} was computed as follows. For each compound, the mortality per dose was plotted on a graph. The plots corresponding to the straight, intermediate part of the resulting sigmoid curves were fitted to a linear function, and the LD_{50} was obtained from this. For each LD_{50}, at least 10 doses were tested, each of them on at least 15 insects. For D. micans and R. grandis, however, the insects' high tolerance/resistance prevented us from ever reaching a substantial mortality. For R. dispar, the limited number of insects available allowed us to test only two doses, one corresponding to the highest dose for R. grandis and a lower one.

RESULTS

Exposure to Vapors

Both larvae and adults of D. micans exhibited total resistance to vapors, whereas substantial mortality occurred in Ips typographus. Mortality among the control insect species, Formica, Tenebrio, and Dysdercus, was much higher still. The two bark beetle associates, Rhizophagus grandis and R. dispar, displayed the largest difference in their resistance to terpenes. R. grandis was not affected, whereas R. dispar suffered very high mortality, at least as much as the control species (Table 1).

Topical Applications

Among bark beetles, D. micans adults proved almost totally resistant to contact toxicity, with monoterpene doses equal to a quarter of their own weight. Their larvae, however, suffered some mortality. On the other hand, doses of the same magnitude caused 50 percent mortality in adult Ips typographus, except for myrcene and α-terpinene which were even more toxic. Both bark beetles were more resistant to terpenes than were the control species (Table 2).

The resistance of R. grandis to topical monoterpene applications was almost total in spite of the large quantities applied (equivalent to half the insects' weight). The same doses caused 100 percent mortality in R. dispar. Due to shortage of living material, LD_{50}'s were not established; some very small-scale tests with decreasing doses (not reported here) were made with a few individuals which allowed an approximate determination of the highest dose at which no mortality occurred for each compound. A full test was then made. The high toxicity of myrcene is noticeable.

Table 1. Percent mortality of insects submitted to saturated monoterpene vapors during 24 hours (n= 20 or 30).

Monoterpene	D. micans		I.[a]	R. grandis		R. dispar		D.[b]	F.[c]	T.[d]
	Adults	Larvae	Adults	♂	♀	♂	♀			
(-)α-pinene	5	0	6.6	0	0	100	100	100	100	100
(+)α-pinene	0	0	26.4	0	0	100	100	100	100	100
β-pinene	10	0	13.2	0	0	100	100	100	100	100
Delta-3-carene	5	0	19.8	0	0	80	100	85	100	40
Limonene	5	0	6.6	0	0	90	100	20	100	0
Myrcene	5	0	6.6	0	0	100	100	35	100	0
α-terpinene	5	0	19.8	0	5	90	100	20	100	0
Camphène	0	0	0	0	0	100	100	100	100	100
Control	10	0	0	0	0	0	0	0	0	0

[a]Ips typographus
[b]Dysdercus cingulatus
[c]Formica rufa
[d]Tenebrio molitor

As with the bark beetles, the Rhizophagus species were much more resistant to monoterpene contact toxicity than the control species (Table 3).

DISCUSSION

The insects with some links to intracortical life in conifers all proved more resistant to both fumigant and contact monoterpene toxicity than the other species. This was not unexpected because a certain degree of adaptation to the host tree toxins must occur in the organisms inhabiting spruce trees.

Comparing the two scolytid species, the adults of Ips typographus were affected by contact toxicity (larvae were not tested), whereas both adults and larvae of D. micans were not, even when treated with a quarter of their weight in monoterpenes! In the case of Dendroctonus frontalis, Coyne and Lott (1976) found LD_{50}'s 100 times lower than those we found for Ips typographus. Unfortunately, accurate comparisons are impossible due to differences in the experimental methods. Coyne and Lott (1976) simultaneously tested contact and fumigant

Table 2. Mortality of insects submitted to monoterpene topical applications (doses: mg/mg; n = 20).

Monoterpene	D. micans				I.[a]	D.[b]	F.[c]	T.[d]
	Larvae		Adult ♀♀		Adults	Ad.	Ad.	Ad.
	Dose	% Mort.	Dose	% Mort.	LD_{50}[e]	LD_{50}	LD_{50}	LD_{50}
(-)α-pinene	286	30	287	10	208	8.1	27.5	14
(+)α-pinene	286	5	287	0	167	15.1	40.1	25.8
β-pinene	291	15	292	0	231	11.7	17.5	17.8
Delta-3-carene	289	0	289	0	182	10.4	26.5	14.7
Limonene	281	15	282	10	168	7.3	53.8	30.5
Myrcene	267	0	268	20	69	24.6	48.7	51
α-terpinene	284	10	285	15	60	9.7	46	25.7
Control		0		10	/	/	/	/

[a] Ips typographus
[b] Dysdercus cingulatus
[c] Formica rufa
[d] Tenebrio molitor
[e] Computation of all LD_{50} with at least 15 insects/pt. and 10 pts.

toxicity, and they applied the monoterpenes diluted in acetone, which possibly resulted in increased cuticular permeability to monoterpenes.

Fumigant toxicity tests caused some mortality in Ips typographus, similar to that observed by Smith (1965) for Dendroctonus brevicomis. D. micans was unaffected by these treatments. These results suggest a substantial difference between D. micans and I. typographus and the North American scolytids tested so far.

Such differences in terpene toxicity may very well reflect the different ecological strategies adopted by primary bark beetles. The gregarious tree killers do not appear to have evolved total resistance; they are sensitive to most compounds and suffer greatly from some of them (Smith 1965, 1975; Coyne and Lott 1976). Their adaptation to monoterpene toxicity seems to rely to a great extent upon

Table 3. Mortality of insects submitted to monoterpene topical applications (doses: mg/mg; n = 15).

Monoterpene	*R. grandis*				*R. dispar*				*D.*[a]	*F.*[b]	*T.*[c]
	♂		♀		♂		♀		Ad.	Ad.	Ad.
	Dose	% Mort.	Dose	% Mort.	Dose	% Mort.	Dose	% Mort.	LD_{50}[d]	LD_{50}	LD_{50}
(-)α-pinene	564	0	650	0	151 564	0 100	191 650	0 100	8.1	27.5	14
(+)α-pinene	564	0	650	6.6	151 564	0 100	191 650	0 100	15.1	40.1	25.8
β-pinene	569	0	655	0	152 569	0 100	192 655	0 100	11.7	17.5	17.8
Delta-3-carene	568	0	654	0	152 568	0 100	192 654	0 100	10.4	26.5	14.7
Limonene	553	10	637	0	148 553	0 100	187 637	0 100	7.3	53.8	30.5
Myrcene	526	0	607	0	/ 70	/ 100	/ 86	/ 100	24.6	48.7	51
α-teripinene	559	6.6	645	6.6	149 559	0 100	189 645	0 100	9.7	46	25.7
Control		0		0		0		0	/	/	/

[a]*Dysdercus cingulatus*
[b]*Formica rufa*
[c]*Tenebrio molitor*
[d]Computation of all LD_{50} with at least 15 insects/pt. and 10 pts.

upon avoidance mechanisms. They limit their exposure to high levels of toxins by quickly killing the host, and, furthermore, some tend to prefer trees containing less of the most toxic compounds (Smith 1975, Hodges *et al.* 1979, Sturgeon 1979, Gollob 1980). Their avoidance mechanism is linked to their capacity to communicate with conspecific adults. For example, pioneers choose suitable hosts (perhaps with lesser amounts of toxic compounds), and emit aggregation pheromones which allow other individuals to rapidly aggregate onto and quickly kill these trees. Mutualistic microorganisms may also contribute to monoterpene detoxification (Brand *et al.* 1975, 1976, 1977).

Solitary colonizers have no such possibility of avoiding the trees' defenses. Spending their whole life in a living host, they had to develop individual mechanisms of overcoming or tolerating toxins. An impervious cuticle may be one such adaptation, and chemical detoxication of the compounds entering the gut and the tracheae may be another.

Strikingly, D. micans was resistant to all compounds tested. This generalized resistance is possibly a way of facing intraspecific variation in Norway spruce because D. micans does not rely upon pioneers to select the less harmful hosts. Each individual has to find a host by itself, a most demanding task for this species, which is a poor flier (Vouland et al. 1984). Moreover, there is so far no evidence of long distance primary stimuli helping D. micans to find suitable defense-poor trees. Therefore, we can assume at least provisionally that it proceeds by random landing as has been suggested by Moeck et al. (1981) for other bark beetle species. On the other hand, there is indeed some indication that intraspecific variability in monoterpene composition occurs in Norway spruce (Heemann and Francke 1977), as observed also in other conifers (Cates and Alexander 1982). The beetle's probability of survival would thus markedly decrease if it had to reject a tree because of its high content of a more toxic compound.

In the case of D. micans, the host's wound response (if any) might be elicited by and directed to the insect alone, since no pathogenic fungi appear to be associated with the bark beetle. This hypothetic reaction would be sustained during the scolytid's whole life-cycle. Our tests suggest that D. micans is well able to cope with the monoterpenes produced by the hypersensitive reaction. On the other hand, the gregarious feeding behavior of its larvae may allow them to progress fast enough to keep ahead of the other "quantitative" defenses produced by the wound reaction in the form of digestibility-reducing tannins, polyphenols, and resins.

The resistance of the Rhizophagus species to monoterpenes seems closely linked to the nature of their association with bark beetles. R. grandis showed complete immunity. Unpublished field observations suggest that this species is the only predator regularly associated with D. micans, and this lack of competitors may perhaps be attributed to the general abundance of toxic monoterpenes permeating D. micans' brood chambers. R. grandis might have won a well-protected niche at the cost of evolving resistance to monoterpenes. Resistance to all compounds may enable it to follow its prey everywhere, in spite of variations in the host tree's monoterpene composition. On the other hand, R. dispar was much less resistant. This species probably does not encounter any great quantity of monoterpenes because its normal habitat is degraded, aging bark.

REFERENCES

Bordash, R. P. and A. A. Berryman. 1977. Host resistance to the fir engraver beetle, Scolytus ventralis (Coleoptera: Scolytidae) 2. Repellency of Abies grandis resins and some monoterpenes. Can. Entomol. 109: 95-100.

Brand, J. M., J. W. Bracke, L. N. Britton, A. J. Markovetz, and S. J. Barras. 1976. Bark beetle pheromones: production of verbenone by a mycangial fungus of Dendroctonus frontalis. J. Chem. Ecol. 2: 195-199.

Brand J. M., J. W. Bracke, A. J. Markovetz, D. L. Wood, and L. E. Browne. 1975. Production of verbenol pheromone by a bacterium isolated from bark beetles. Nature 254: 136-137.

Brand, J. M., J. Schultz, S. J. Barras, L. J. Edson, T. L. Payne, and R. L. Hedden. 1977. Bark beetle pheromones: enhancement of Dendroctonus frontalis (Coleoptera: Scolytidae) aggregation pheromone by yeast metabolites in laboratory bioassays. J. Chem. Ecol. 3: 657-666.

Byers, J. A. 1981. Pheromone biosynthesis in the bark beetle, Ips paraconfusus, during feeding or exposure to vapours of host plant precursors. Insect Biochem. 11(5): 563-569.

Cates, R. G. and H. Alexander. 1982. Host resistance and susceptibility. In: Bark beetles in North American conifers (J. B. Mitton and K. B. Sturgeon, Eds.). Austin, TX: Univ. of Texas Press; 212-263.

Christiansen, E. and R. Horntvedt. 1983. Combined Ips/Ceratocystis attack on Norway spruce and defensive mechanisms of the tree. Z. Angew. Entomol. 96: 110-118.

Coyne, J. F. and L. H. Lott. 1976. Toxicity of substances in pine oleoresin to southern pine beetles. J. Ga. Entomol. Soc. 11(4): 297-301.

Gollob, L. 1980. Monoterpene composition in bark beetle-resistant loblolly pine. Naturwissenschaften 67: 409.

Grégoire, J.-C. 1985. Host colonization strategies in Dendroctonus: larval gregariousness vs mass attack by adults? In: The role of the host in the population dynamics of forest insects (L. Safranyik, Ed.); Proceedings, IUFRO Conference; 1983 September 4-7; Banff, Alberta. Victoria, BC: Canadian Forestry Service and USDA, Forest Service; 147-154.

Heemann, V. and W. Francke. 1977. Gaschromatographisch-massenspektrome-trische Untersuchungen der flüchtigen Rindeninhaltsstoffe von Picea abies (L.) Karst. Planta Med. 32(4): 342-346.

Hodges, J. D., W. W. Elam, W. F. Watson, and T. E. Nebeker. 1979. Oleoresin characteristics and susceptibility of four southern pines to southern pine beetle (Coleoptera: Scolytidae) attacks. Can. Entomol. 111: 889-896.

Horntvedt, R., E. Christiansen, H. Solheim, and S. Wang. 1983. Artificial inoculation with Ips typographus-associated blue-stain fungi can kill healthy Norway spruce trees. Medd. Nor. Inst. Skogforskning 38: 1-20.

Merlin, J., C. Parmentier, and J.-C. Grégoire. 1986. The feeding habits of Rhizophagus dispar (Col., Rhizophagidae), an associate of bark beetles. Meded. Fac. Landbouwwet. Rijksuniv. Gent. 51/3a: 915-923.

Moeck, H. A., D. L. Wood, and K. Q. Lindahl. 1981. Host selection behavior of bark beetles attacking Pinus ponderosa, with special emphasis on the western pine beetle, Dendroctonus brevicomis. J. Chem. Ecol. 7: 49-83.

Raffa, K. F., A. A. Berryman, J. Simasko, W. Teal, and B. L. Wong. 1985. Effects of grand fir monoterpenes on the fir engraver, Scolytus ventralis (Coleoptera: Scolytidae) and its symbiotic fungus. Environ. Entomol. 14: 552-556.

Smith, R. H. 1961a. Techniques for determining the toxicity of pine resin vapors to Dendroctonus brevicomis and D. jeffreyi. J. Econ. Entomol. 54(2): 359-364.

Smith, R. H. 1961b. The fumigant toxicity of three pine resins to Dendroctonus brevicomis and D. jeffreyi. J. Econ. Entomol. 54(2): 365-369.

Smith, R. H. 1963. Toxicity of pine resin to three species of Dendroctonus bark beetles. J. Econ. Entomol. 56(6): 827-831.

Smith, R. H. 1965. Effect of monoterpene vapors on the western pine beetle. J. Econ. Entomol. 58(3): 509-510.

Smith, R. H. 1975. Formula for describing effect of insect and host tree factors on resistance to western pine beetle attack. J. Econ. Entomol. 68(6): 841-844.

Sturgeon, K. B. 1979. Monoterpene variation in ponderosa pine xylem resin related to western pine beetle predation. Evolution 33: 803-814.

Vouland, G., M. Giraud, and D. Schvester. 1984. La période ténérale et l'envol chez Dendroctonus micans Kug. (Coleoptera: Scolytidae). In: Proceedings, EEC seminar on the biological control of bark beetles (Dendroctonus micans) (J.-C. Grégoire and J. M. Pasteels, Eds.); 1984 October; Brussels; 68-79.

Wood, D. L. 1982. The role of pheromones, kairomones and allomones in the host selection and colonization behavior of bark beetles. Annu. Rev. Entomol. 27: 411-446.

24

Traumatized Hosts: Their Influence on the Population Dynamics of the Southern Pine Bark Beetle Guild

Richard O. Flamm and Robert N. Coulson

There is considerable interest worldwide in understanding the interactions between plants and insects. Typically, studies focus on the interactions of individual plants and insects and then extrapolate to the population level. This extrapolation may be misleading because studies at the level of the individual necessarily simplify and overlook many abiotic and biotic factors of the environment which affect population-level performance. Therefore, population-level predictions formed from studies at the individual level may differ substantially from actual observations made at the population level. In this chapter, we study host/insect interactions directly at the population level. We compare parameters of bark beetle population dynamics in traumatized trees (host defenses presumed to be largely removed) and in naturally infested pines (defenses presumed to be relatively intact) to examine the role of disturbed trees in the epidemiology of the southern pine bark beetle guild. Specifically, we consider (1) arrival densities, (2) attack densities, (3) colonization distributions, (4) emergence densities, (5) oviposition, (6) brood production, and (7) survivorship of bark beetles.

BARK BEETLES AND PINE TREES

The southern pine bark beetle guild consists of five species: *Dendroctonus frontalis*, *D. terebrans*, *Ips avulsus*, *I. grandicollis*, and *I. calligraphus* (Coleoptera: Scolytidae). Successful colonization of pines, which entails adults overcoming host defenses (Blanche *et al*. 1983), is crucial to the population dynamics of these insects. The ability to overcome host defenses is related in part to how many beetles are available for rapid host colonization during a particular time frame. Generally, in expanding infestations, the large number of beetles available allows successful *en masse* colonization of fully defended trees. On the other hand, when beetle populations are low, environmental events that diminish the effectiveness of tree defense systems (Cates and Alexander 1982) may be necessary for successful colonization. Disturbances constitute such events (also see Lorio in this volume).

DISTURBANCE

Disturbances have long been associated with bark beetle infestations (Hetrick 1949, Rykiel 1985). Only recently, however, have specific disturbance regimes been linked to bark beetle population dynamics. For example, Coulson *et al*. (1983) hypothesized that lightning disturbance was central to the epidemiology of the southern pine bark beetle guild and developed a conceptual model of bark beetle epidemiology around this theme (Coulson *et al*. 1985, 1986).

Lighting and Pine Trees

In a forest, tall trees are more prone to lightning strikes than short trees (Komarek 1964). In the southern pine forest, which contains both pines and hardwood species, pines are usually taller, and more numerous, and therefore are the most frequent targets of cloud-to-ground lightning strikes.

Throughout the geographical range of the southern pine bark beetle guild, the number of thunderstorm days varies from 45 to 90 per year (Brown and Davis 1973). The Lightning Protection Institute estimated that the number of cloud-to-ground lightning strikes in a particular square mile area can be computed roughly by assigning one or two lightning strikes per thunderstorm day (Komarek 1964). By this formula, about 45 to 180 lightning strikes can be expected per square mile of forest in one year, the targets of most of these strikes being pine trees. Not all pines struck by lightning are killed, but surviving trees are considered severely disturbed and generally are susceptible to bark beetle colonization. Hodges and Pickard (1971) have documented changes in phloem chemistry in trees struck by lightning. Many of these changes occur in trees undergoing other types of stress (Blanche *et al*. 1983, 1985).

Lightning-Struck Pines and Bark Beetles

Lightning strikes occur in consistent seasonal and annual patterns. Out of the many forest disturbances that can lead to bark beetle colonization, only lightning occurs with sufficient regularity to be considered as a primary component of the life history strategy of *D. frontalis* and the other members of the bark beetle guild (Coulson *et al*. 1983). However, little is known about how bark beetles respond to disturbed trees (Coulson *et al*. 1986). Trees with diminished defenses may provide refuge for beetles (Coulson *et al*. 1983) and act as foci for beetle infestations (Lorio and Bennett 1974).

METHODS

Experimental

Data were collected from pines infested as a result of being traumatized in 1983 using the lightning strike simulation technique (Miller 1983), and from pines naturally infested with *D. frontalis* in 1977 and 1978. In 1983, lightning-simulation trials were initiated on February 17, June 8, August 4, and September 14 to explore seasonal variation in the response of the bark beetles to host disturbance (Coulson *et al*. 1986). Each trial contained five plots of two disturbed trees and one control. All trees were mass attacked within 2 weeks of treatment except for trees traumatized in February, which were colonized at the same time as trees newly traumatized in June. Trees selected for comparison from the 1977/78 data set were colonized either in late May and June (MAY/JUN) or August and early September (AUG/SEP) to correspond to treatment dates in 1983. Interception traps were used to sample arriving beetles in 1983 (Coulson *et al*. 1986), while both field studies used bark disks and emergence traps to sample the remaining life stages (Coulson *et al*. 1975, McClelland *et al*. 1978).

Analytical

1983 Populations. We used the frustum estimation procedure (Pulley *et al*. 1977) to calculate densities of attacking beetles, emerging beetles, and gallery length from ground level to 11.0 m bole height for each tree. Frustum estimates of gallery length were calculated at individual sample heights (0.5, 3.5, 6.5, 9.5 m) to examine the spatial pattern of colonization. Egg densities were estimated by multiplying gallery density by 1.59 (Foltz *et al*. 1976) and 1.44 (Flamm *et al*. 1987) for *D. frontalis* and *I. avulsus* respectively. *I. calligraphus* egg densities were estimated directly from egg counts.

We summarized the data by averaging over the ten treatment trees in each trial. Estimates of the population parameters were calculated for D. frontalis and the three Ips species.

1977/78 Populations. We used the topological estimation procedure to calculate the population parameters from the ground level to 11.0 m bole height (Pulley et al. 1976). Gallery distribution, in contrast to the 1983 data, was estimated by distributing total gallery over the eleven meters, using the model of Foltz et al. (1976). Averages for the variables listed above were calculated for the MAY/JUN trees and the AUG/SEP trees. Population parameters were calculated for D. frontalis only.

RESULTS

Arrival Density

Arrival density gives an indication of the abundance of bark beetles available for host colonization (Fig. 1). Arrival density of D. frontalis increased in each successive trial in 1983 (Feb. to Sept.), indicating a seasonal increase in D. frontalis abundance. Such an increase may be a typical feature in the natural history of this insect, or it may reflect an ongoing population surge that eventually peaked in 1985 with a record high number of bark beetle infestations in Texas. In either case, D. frontalis populations have a large capacity for growth.

There was a declining numerical response of the Ips species after the June trial. This was due either to an actual decrease in Ips abundance or, more likely, to competitive displacement by D. frontalis to unmeasured areas (above 11.0 meters) of the tree. Because D. frontalis is the most aggressive colonizer in the guild, it is often the first species to arrive en masse, colonizing the midbole quickly, and thereby largely excluding the Ips species. Therefore, Fig. 1 may reveal a diminishing role for Ips during the initiation of an infestation owing to rapid increases in abundance of D. frontalis. These results suggest that (1) There may be seasonal variation in the establishment of infestations (Coulson et al. 1986), and (2) Trees with depressed defenses may be especially important in the winter and spring because at this time beetle numbers are normally low and, furthermore, their numerical response to the tree occurs over a long

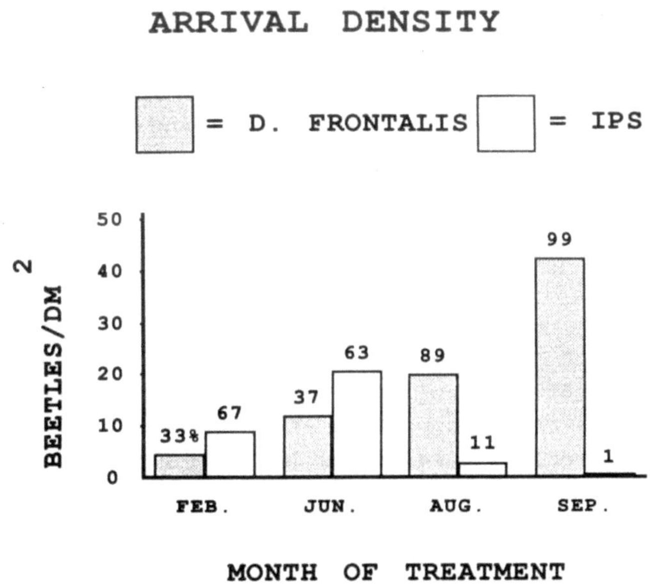

Figure 1. Arrival densities (beetles/unit surface area of bole) of Dendroctonus frontalis and the combined densities of Ips avulsus, I. calligraphus, and I. grandicollis on traumatized trees at different treatment dates. Numbers above each column show the percentage of arrivals between Ips and Dendroctonus at each treatment date.

period of time. Lorio (in this volume) argues that most trees do indeed have diminished defenses at this time because they are in a growth mode which, by its nature, precludes strong defensive systems.

Attack Density

Among the four trials of 1983, the proportion of attacking D. frontalis and Ips changed although combined attack densities for the Ips and D. frontalis were not significantly different (Fig. 2). From February to September, Ips densities decreased while D. frontalis densities increased, suggesting again that Ips beetles play a decreasing role in the establishment of infestations as D. frontalis increases in abundance.

Overall, attack densities in the traumatized trees were lower than in the nontraumatized infestation trees. However, the seasonal trends for D. frontalis were similar in both experiments, even though populations were rising during 1982 to 1985 and declining in 1977 and 1978. These results suggest that colonization of traumatized and nontraumatized trees was different because of differences in the size and composition of the respective beetle populations. In addition, the increases in D. frontalis populations from spring to autumn are a typical feature of its natural history. Nothing is known about the density of Ips in the nontraumatized trees, but considering the large densities of D. frontalis, it is probable that Ips populations were negligible below 11.0 meters.

Gallery Distribution

Gallery length is the single parameter that best illustrates successful bark beetle colonization because it represents the establishment of a brood population (Fig. 3). Seasonal trends of total gallery showed the same trends as total attack: in both traumatized and nontraumatized trees, D. frontalis dominated the lower bole, largely excluding the Ips species. However, gallery densities in the nontraumatized trees were higher. These findings suggest that the

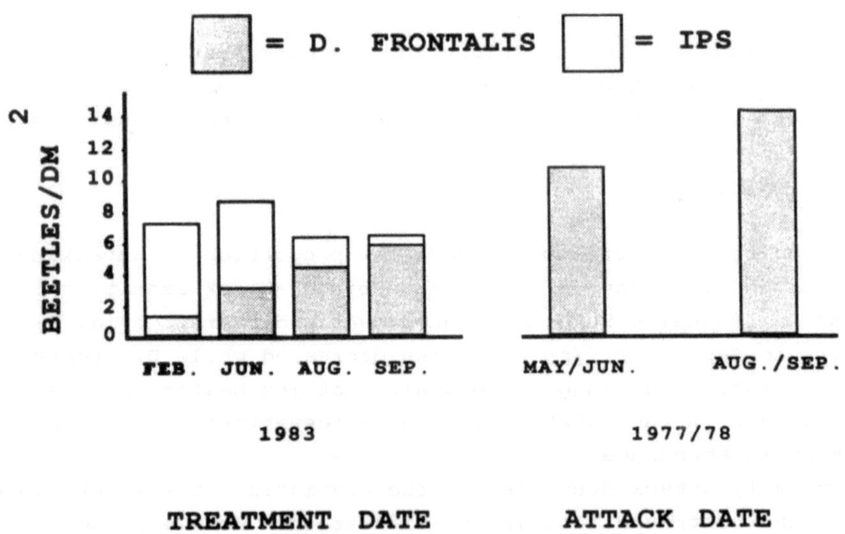

Figure 2. Total attack densities of Dendroctonus frontalis and the combined densities of Ips avulsus, I. calligraphus, and I. grandicollis in traumatized trees (1983) and attack densities of D. frontalis in nontraumatized infestation trees (1977-78).

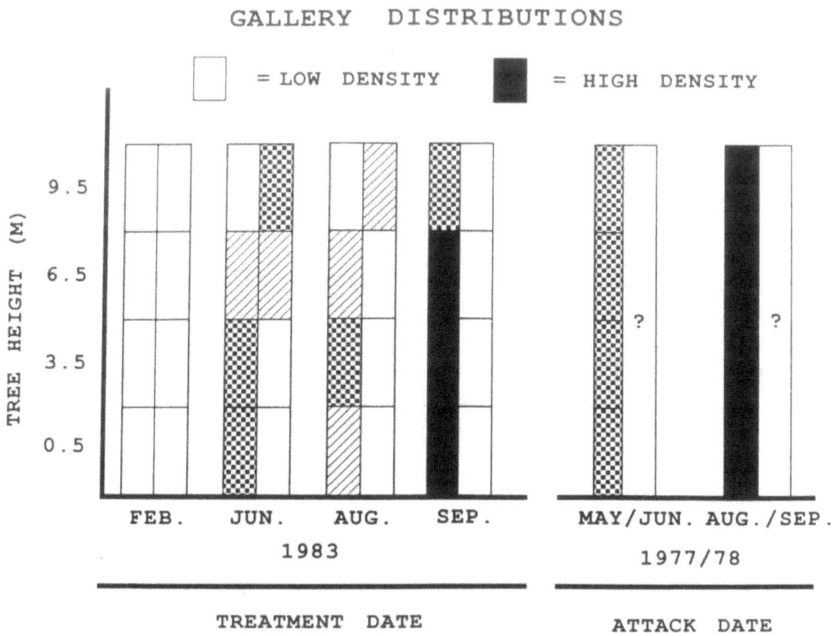

Figure 3. Gallery distribution of Dendroctonus frontalis (left half of each bar) and the combined gallery of Ips avulsus, I. calligraphus, and I. grandicollis (right half) in traumatized trees (1983) and gallery distribution of D. frontalis in nontraumatized infestation trees (1977-78). Four classes: 1-20 cm gallery/dm^2 = open; 21-40 = hachured; 41-60 = checkered; 61-80 = black.

Ips species may play a larger role in overcoming host defenses of traumatized than of nontraumatized trees probably because D. frontalis populations are somewhat lower in the former.

Emergence Density

Emergence density is a parameter that reflects the response of the developing brood to their environment (Fig. 4). In 1983, there was significant variability in emergence among the traumatized trees, while not so in the nontraumatized, undisturbed, natural-infestation trees. Using all six sets of 1983 trees, only February and September trees were significantly different from one another.

Poor host quality may have caused the low emergence density in the February trees. Host quality may have been affected by the time of treatment, the severity of trauma, the long length of time between treatment and colonization, or some combination of these factors (Coulson et al. 1986). In the September trees, the very high emergence density is evidence of the seasonal increase in D. frontalis

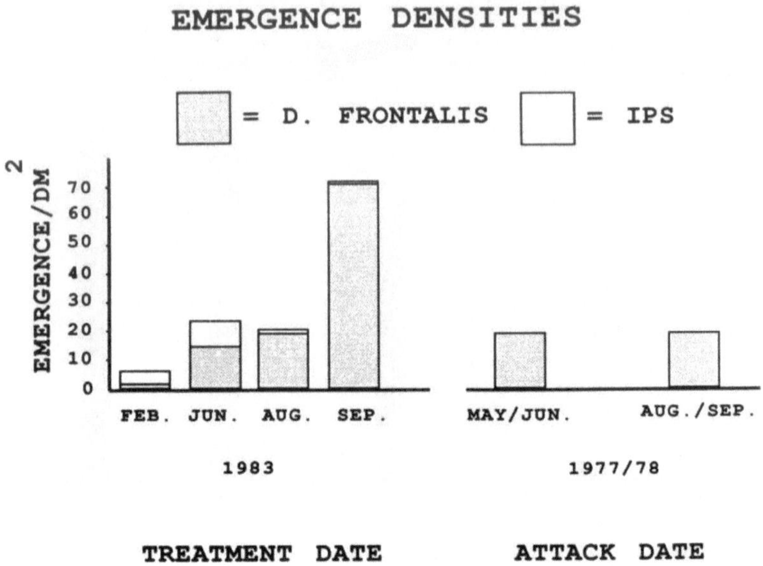

Figure 4. Total emergence densities of *Dendroctonus frontalis* and the combined densities of *Ips avulsus*, *I. calligraphus*, and *I. grandicollis* in traumatized trees (1983) and the emergence densities of *D. frontalis* in nontraumatized infestation trees (1977-78).

populations. Such high emergence was not observed in 1977/78, a period when beetle populations wre declining.

Oviposition Per Parent Beetle

The oviposition per parent beetle parameter helps explain the individual beetle's contribution to the production of a brood population (Fig. 5). Within each study, total eggs per parent *D. frontalis* were not significantly different. Oviposition per parent *Ips* beetle was variable, probably influenced by *D. frontalis* coloni-zation. When both studies are compared, significantly more eggs were laid per *D. frontalis* in the traumatized trees than in the nontraumatized infestation trees. In general, as attack densities increase, the amount of gallery, and hence eggs, produced per beetle in a single host decreases (Coulson *et al*. 1976, Flamm *et al*. 1987).
The significance of this result is that regardless of the attack density, large numbers of eggs are laid, a necessary life history feature if the infestation is to expand.

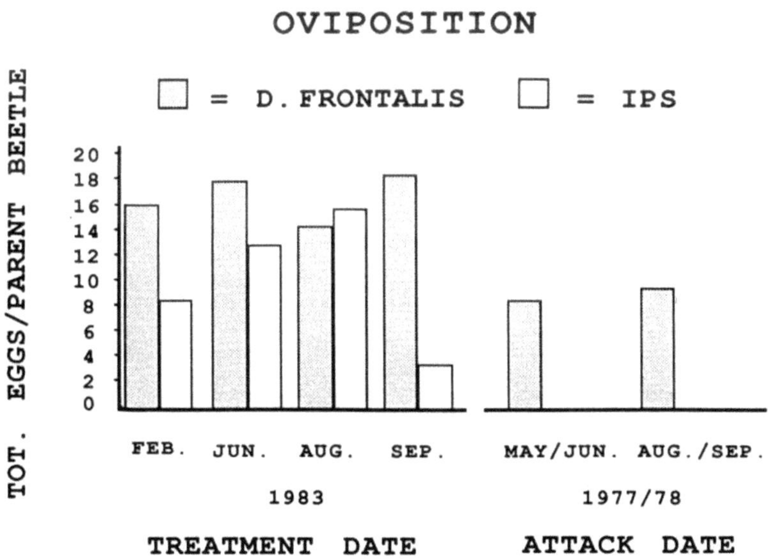

Figure 5. Oviposition (total eggs ÷ total parent beetles) by Dendroctonus frontalis and the combined oviposition of Ips avulsus, I. calligraphus, and I. grandicollis in traumatized trees (1983) and oviposition by D. frontalis in nontraumatized infestation trees (1977-78).

Brood Production

Brood production (emergence per parent beetle) examines population growth (Fig. 6). Any production ratio greater than one (excluding between-tree mortality) suggests a growing population. Except for the February trial, brood production in the traumatized trees was significantly higher than in the natural-infestation trees.

Production ratios are also a function of attack density because more brood can be produced per individual at low than at high attack densities. In growing infestations, where attack densities are high, brood production measured on a per tree basis is low. Brood production per beetle must be assessed by following its emergence and oviposition in subsequent trees. At the initiation phase of a bark there are only enough beetles available to colonize simultaneously one or two traumatized trees.

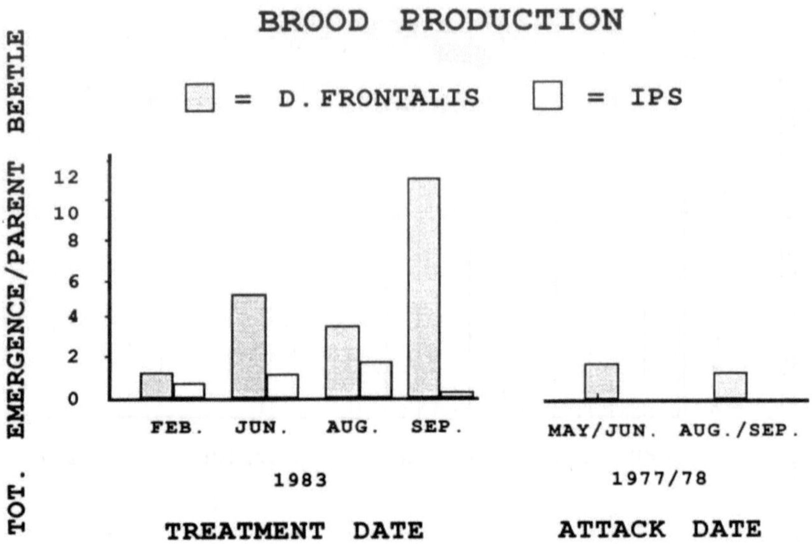

Figure 6. Brood production (total emerging beetles ÷ total parent beetles) for Dendroctonus frontalis and Ips avulsus, I. calligraphus, and I. grandicollis in traumatized trees (1983) and nontraumatized infestation trees (1977-78).

Survivorship

Survivorship reflects the interaction of the brood beetles with their environment (Fig. 7) which includes temperature (Wagner *et al*. 1987, In press 1987), natural enemies (Moore 1971, Berisford 1981, Linit and Stephen 1983), and host characteristics (Amman 1969, 1972; Berryman 1976; Haack *et al*. 1984a, 1984b). Of the six groupings of trees (four from 1983, two from 1977/78), only the February and September trials of 1983 had significantly different survivorship. Poor host quality may have caused the low survivorship in the February trial, whereas a combination of factors may have caused the high survivorship in the September trial. It is difficult to assess the exact effect of our disturbance treatment on developing broods because both traumatized and nontraumatized trees are usually dead by the time the eggs hatch, in what appears to be a very similar environment.

CONCLUSIONS

From the population parameters we measured, three conclusions can be made about traumatized trees. First, most of the beetle population

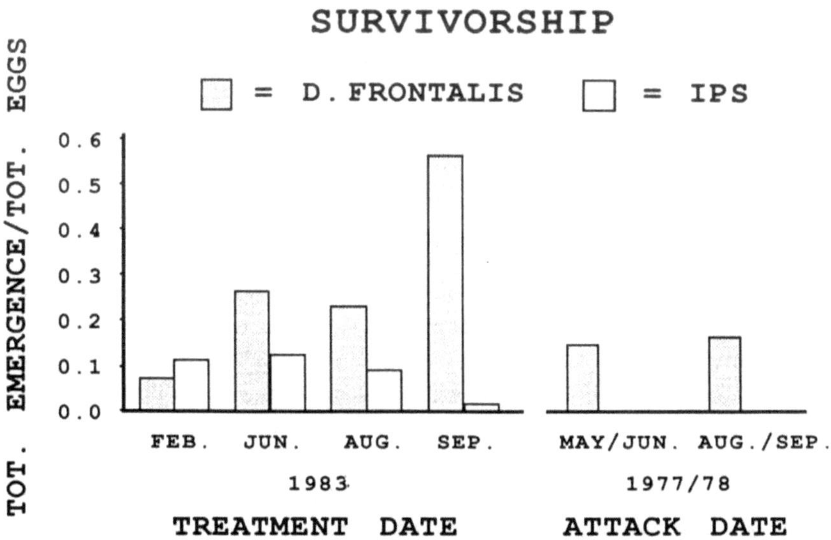

Figure 7. Survivorship (total emerging beetles ÷ total eggs) for Dendroctonus frontalis and Ips avulsus, I. calligraphus, and I. grandicollis in traumatized trees (1983) and nontraumatized infestation trees (1977-78).

parameters showed high seasonal variation. Second, although most parameters in the traumatized trees showed distinct differences from those in the naturally infested trees, it was due more to difference in beetle background populations than to differences in hosts themselves. Third, D. frontalis can exhibit explosive population growth in traumatized trees.

Comparison of Parameters

Population parameters associated with beetle attack (attack density, gallery distribution, and probably arrival density) were lower in the traumatized trees. This suggests that the background beetle populations around the traumatized trees of 1983 were lower than around the naturally mass-infested trees of 1977/78. The significance here is that small numbers of beetles are capable of successfully colonizing traumatized trees, supporting the hypothesis that traumatized trees probably act as refugia for the endemic beetle populations which are not usually large enough to colonize and overwhelm undisturbed trees. Reproduction parameters (oviposition per beetle and brood production) were higher in the traumatized trees. This simply reflects lower beetle attack densities in such trees, and furthermore indicates that these hosts are highly suitable substrates, thereby allowing bark beetles to increase their populations quickly, a significant life history feature if eventual colonization of adjacent undisturbed trees is to occur.

Explosive Population Growth

D. frontalis exhibited high survivorship and emergence densities from trees traumatized in September, while that of *Ips* was never very large. Emergence seems to be generally high during autumn and winter for *D. frontalis* compared to other times of the year, but no previous studies have reported equivalently high rates of survivorship and emergence that we observed in traumatized trees colonized in the September trial. This study supports our hypothesis that traumatized trees, as may occur after lightning strikes, are as suitable for bark beetles as nontraumatized trees whose defenses are sometimes overwhelmed by large numbers of bark beetles attacking *en masse*. In other words, the results suggest that stressed trees are different from unstressed trees (from the perspective of bark beetles) in that the former have lower defenses. Otherwise, they are both equally capable of supporting bark beetles.

REFERENCES

Amman, G. D. 1969. Mountain pine beetle emergence in relation to depth of lodgepole pine bark. USDA, Forest Service, Res. Note INT-96, 8 p.

Amman, G. D. 1972. Mountain pine beetle brood production in relation to thickness of lodgepole pine phloem. J. Econ. Entomol. 65: 138-140.

Berisford, C. W. 1981. Natural enemies and associated organisms. In: The southern pine beetle (R. L. Thatcher, J. L. Searcy, J. E. Coster, and G. D. Hertel, Eds.). USDA, Forest Service, Tech. Bull. 1631; 31-54.

Berryman, A. A. 1976. Theoretical explanation of mountain pine beetle dynamics in lodgepole pine forests. Environ. Entomol. 5: 1225-1233.

Blanche, C. A., J. D. Hodges, and T. E. Nebeker. 1985. Changes in bark beetle susceptibility indicators in a lightning-struck loblolly pine. Can. J. For. Res. 15: 397-399.

Blanche, C. A., J. D. Hodges, T. E. Nebeker, and D. M. Moehring. 1983. Southern pine beetle: the host dimension. Mississippi Agricultural Forest Experiment Station Publ. 917, 29 p.

Brown, A. A. and K. P. Davis. 1973. Forest fire: control and use. New York: McGraw-Hill.

Cates, R. G. and H. Alexander. 1982. Host resistance and susceptibility. In: Bark beetles in North American conifers (J. B. Mitton and K. B. Sturgeon, Eds.). Austin, TX: Univ. Texas; 212-263.

Coulson, R. N., R. O. Flamm, P. E. Pulley, T. L. Payne, E. J. Rykiel, and T. L. Wagner. 1986. Response of the southern pine bark beetle guild (Coleoptera: Scolytidae) to host disturbance. Environ. Entomol. 15: 850-858.

Coulson, R. N., F. P. Hain, J. L. Foltz, and A. M. Mayyasi. 1975. Techniques for sampling the dynamics of southern pine beetle populations. Texas Agricultural Experiment Station Misc. Publ. 1135, 19 p.

Coulson, R. N., P. B. Hennier, R. O. Flamm, E. J. Rykiel, L. C. Hu, and T. L. Payne. 1983. The role of lightning in the epidemiology of the southern pine beetle. Z. Angew. Entomol. 96: 182-193.

Coulson, R. N., A. M. Mayyasi, J. L. Foltz, F. P. Hain, and W. C. Martin. 1976. Resource utilization by the southern pine beetle, Dendroctonus frontalis (Coleoptera: Scolytidae). Can. Entomol. 108: 353-362.

Coulson, R. N., E. J. Rykiel, M. C. Saunders, T. L. Payne, R. O. Flamm, T. L. Wagner, and P. B. Hennier. 1985. A conceptual model of the role of lightning in the epidemiology of the southern pine beetle. In: The role of the host in the population dynamics of forest insects (L. Safranyik, Ed.); Proceedings, IUFRO Conference; 1983 September 4-7; Banff, Alberta. Victoria, BC: Canadian Forestry Service and USDA, Forest Service; 136-146.

Flamm, R. O., T. L. Wagner, S. P. Cook, P. E. Pulley, R. N. Coulson, and T. McArdle. (1987). Host colonization by cohabiting Dendroctonus frontalis, Ips avulsus, and I. calligraphus (Coleoptera: Scolytidae). Environ. Entomol. 16: 390-399.

Foltz, J. L., A. M. Mayyasi, F. P. Hain, R. N. Coulson, and W. C. Martin. 1976. Egg-gallery length relationship and within-tree analysis for the southern pine beetle, Dendroctonus frontalis (Coleoptera: Scolytidae). Can. Entomol. 108: 341-352.

Haack, R. A., J. L. Foltz, and R. C. Wilkinson. 1984a. Longevity and fecundity of Ips avulsus (Coleoptera: Scolytidae) in relation to slash pine phloem thickness. Ann. Entomol. Soc. Am. 77: 657-662.

Haack, R. A., R. C. Wilkinson, J. L. Foltz, and J. A. Corneil. 1984b. Gallery construction and oviposition by Ips calligraphus (Coleoptera: Scolytidae) in relation to slash pine phloem thickness and temperature. Can. Entomol. 116: 625-632.

Hetrick, L. A. 1949. Some overlooked relationships of southern pine beetle. J. Econ. Entomol. 42: 466-469.

Hodges, J. D. and L. S. Pickard. 1971. Lightning in the ecology of the southern pine beetle, Dendroctonus frontalis (Coleoptera: Scolytidae). Can. Entomol. 103: 44-51.

Komarek, E. V. 1964. The natural history of lightning. Proceedings, Third Annual Tall Timbers Fire Ecology Conference; Tallahassee, FL: Tall Timbers Research Station; 139-186.

Linit, M. J. and F. M. Stephen. 1983. Parasite and predator component of within-tree southern pine beetle (Coleoptera: Scolytidae) mortality. Can. Entomol. 115: 679-688.

Lorio, P. L. and W. H. Bennett. 1974. Recurring southern pine beetle infestations near Oakdale, La. USDA, Forest Service, Res. Pap. SO-95.

McClelland, W. T., F. P. Hain, C. J. DeMars, W. S. Fargo, R. N. Coulson, and T. E. Nebeker. 1978. Sampling bark beetle emergence: a review of methodologies, a proposal for standardization and a new trap design. Bull. Entomol. Soc. Am. 24: 137-140.

Miller, M. C. 1983. Lightning strike simulation for studying southern pine bark and engraver beetle attacks. USDA, Forest Service, Pap. SO-296.

Moore, G. E. 1971. Mortality factors caused by pathogenic bacteria and fungi of the southern pine beetle in North Carolina. J. Invert. Path. 17: 28-37.

Pulley, P. E., J. L. Foltz, A. M. Mayyasi, and R. N. Coulson. 1976. Topological mapping to estimate numbers of bark-inhabiting insects. Environ. Entomol. 5: 640-643.

Pulley, P. E., R. N. Coulson, J. L. Foltz, W. C. Martin, and C. L. Kelly. 1977. Sampling intensity, informational content of samples, and precision in estimating within-tree population of Dendroctonus frontalis. Environ. Entomol. 6: 607-615.

Rykiel, E. J. 1985. Towards a definition of ecological disturbance. Aus. J. Ecol. 10: 361-365.

Wagner, T. L., W. S. Fargo, R. O. Flamm., R. N. Coulson, and P. E. Pulley. 1987. Development and mortality of Ips calligraphus (Coleoptera: Scolytidae) at constant temperatures. Environ. Entomol. 16: 484-497.

Wagner, T. L., P. B. Hennier, R. O. Flamm, and R. N. Coulson. (In press 1987). Development and mortality of Ips avulsus (Coleoptera: Scolytidae) at constant temperatures. Environ. Entomol.

25

The Role of Spruce Monoterpene Derivatives as Oviposition Stimuli for *Rhizophagus grandis*, a Predator of the Bark Beetle, *Dendroctonus micans*

M. Baisier, J.-C. Grégoire, K. Delinte, and O. Bonnard

The literature provides abundant examples of secondary compounds produced by conifers, which have been turned against the trees by bark beetles. For example, toxic monoterpenes may be used by the insects as cues for host selection (see references in Moeck et al. 1981) and moreover are converted to less toxic oxygenated derivatives (e.g., Hughes 1973a, 1973b; Renwick et al. 1973), which serve as aggregation pheromones for the adult beetles or their larvae (Borden 1982, Francke and Vité 1983). One step further along the food web, these original defensive compounds of the host-plant take another twist: bark beetle pheromones are notably used by predators and parasitoids for locating their prey or host (Vité and Francke 1976, Borden 1982).

This kind of complex interaction between three trophic levels is well illustrated by the association Picea excelsa/Dendroctonus micans/Rhizophagus grandis. Rhizophagus grandis (Coleoptera: Rhizophagidae) is a specific predator of the scolytid, Dendroctonus micans, against which it has been used in several programs of biological control (King and Evans 1984, Grégoire et al. 1984). As far as the chemically-mediated relationships of these two species are concerned, we already know that verbenone, trans-verbenol, cis-verbenol and myrtenol (oxidation products of α-pinene) are all compounds of the aggregation pheromone of Dendroctonus micans larvae (Grégoire et al. 1982). Rhizophagus grandis larvae are attracted by these substances at close range and also by the larval frass of their prey in laboratory conditions (Merlin et al. 1984). Placed in odor gradients, R. grandis adults respond positively to Dendroctonus larval frass (Tondeur and Grégoire 1980), and in an air flow are strongly attracted by D. micans larval frass as well as to racemic α-pinene alone (Grégoire and Wainhouse unpublished).

We shall describe here another aspect of the complex functions of these compounds; they appear to play a significant role as oviposition stimuli for *R. grandis*. Egg-deposition stimulants have not, to our knowledge, been investigated in bark beetle associates and have been only briefly described for predators and parasitoids of other insects (Nettles and Burks 1975, Greany and Hagen 1981 and references therein, Jones 1981). Preliminary observations suggested that the presence of *D. micans* larvae *per se* is not essential to induce oviposition by *R. grandis*, but that their frass alone is sufficient. In the experiments presented here, we investigated, more precisely, the role of frass in egg-laying and present preliminary results suggesting the nature of the active compounds.

MATERIAL AND METHODS

Insects

Rhizophagus grandis adults were reared according to Grégoire *et al*. (1986). The young adults were sorted just before emergence and stored at 4 ^{o}C, so that they had not mated or laid eggs before being used for the experiments.

Bioassay Set-up

The oviposition arena used for all our experiments consisted of a 33 ml polysterene box filled with rehydrated spruce bark powder, a piece of fresh bark, a pair of *R. grandis* adults, and a food supply. In the control boxes, *D. micans* larvae served as the food supply and while boring in the piece of bark, produced frass which was the oviposition stimulant. Such boxes are usually used in mass-rearing (Grégoire *et al*. 1986). In the experimental boxes, the food supply was a muscid maggot, and the potential oviposition stimuli to be tested (frass, extracts, or synthetic compounds) were mixed with the bark powder. All boxes were kept at 20$\pm$2 ^{o}C.

Frass and Frass Extract as Oviposition Stimulant

Three series of egg-laying boxes were prepared: the bark powder was mixed (1) with bark powder mixed with larval *D. micans* frass, (2) with bark powder mixed with a methylene chloride frass extract, and (3) with bark powder alone, without frass or frass extract. The frass was collected in the field in fresh brood chambers full of *Dendroctonus micans* larvae and stored at -18 ^{o}C. The extract was made by immersing frass in methylene chloride for about 15 hours. After filtration, the extract was mixed with bark powder and the solvent eliminated by evaporation with a rotoevaporator.

Extraction With Different Solvents

One sample of frass was successively extracted with different solvents: first with hexane for 3 hours, after which it was filtered and the residual frass immersed in acetone for several hours. It was then re-filtered, immersed in methanol for 17 hours, and again filtered. The different extracts were mixed with bark powder, the solvents evaporated, and the resulting bark powders put in oviposition boxes. Another sample of frass was extracted only with methylene chloride, and a third was mixed directly with bark powder.

Column Chromatography Separation

To isolate the active compounds of the frass, a frass extract with hexane was made as above and then concentrated. The extract was placed on top of a silicagel chromatography column which was eluted successively by hexane, a 9 to 1 hexane-acetone mixture, a 7 to 3 hexane-acetone mixture, then acetone alone, and finally a 9 to 1 acetone-methanol mixture. For each solvent, we collected the fractions separately, mixed them with bark powder, and after drying put them in oviposition boxes.

We preferred the hexane frass extract over the methylene chloride one because the residual solvent vapors of the latter killed *Rhizophagus* adults, but hexane caused no such problems.

Synthetic Compounds

Previous experiments (Grégoire *et al*. 1982) showed that *trans*-verbenol, *cis*-verbenol and verbenone (oxidation products of α-pinene) are components of the aggregation pheromone of *Dendroctonus micans* larvae. We therefore tested the effectiveness of synthetic *trans*-verbenol, *cis*-verbenol, and verbenone (Borregaard) as oviposition stimuli by placing an aliquot of the synthetic compound in each oviposition box. For each substance, we tested two doses--for *trans*-verbenol and verbenone, either 2 or 20 μl per box and for *cis*-verbenol, which is a solid, either 1.7 or 17 mg. In a fourth series of boxes, the aliquots of the three compounds were put together.

Chemical Analyses

Gas chromatography analyses were done on a Hewlett Packard model 429 fitted with a DB5 (SE-54) capillary column (1.:30 m) (60-220 °C; 2 °C/min.). Additional analyses were done with a Hewlet Packard model 402 fitted with a conventional column packed with Carbowax 20 M 10 percent (ℓ.:1.80 m, i.d.:0.27 cm). GC/MS analyses were performed with a Ribermag R 1010C.

The chemical compounds were identified by comparison of their mass spectra with those of references (Swigar and Silverstein 1981, Heller and Mille 1980), and some of them by comparison of their retention times with those of commercial standards.

RESULTS AND DISCUSSION

Effectiveness of Frass and Frass Extracts as Oviposition Stimulants

D. micans larval frass was sufficient alone to elicit Rhizophagus grandis oviposition (see Table 1). Likewise, methylene chloride frass extracts stimulated oviposition. However, we cannot completely exclude the possibility that the odor of the artificial food-supply (fly larvae) enhanced the frass's stimulating effect. Nevertheless, it is clear that in the absence of frass, no oviposition occurs (see Table 1, (control)).

Table 1. Ovipositional response of Rhizophagus grandis in the presence of larval frass of Dendroctonus micans or a methylene chloridic frass extract.

Treatment	No. of ♀ that laid eggs n = 8	No. of R. grandis larvae/ egg-laying ♀ ($\overline{X} \pm$ se)
Frass	7	49.9 ± 8.7
Extract	6	11.8 ± 2.8
Bark powder (control)	0	0
Boxes with D. micans	299 (100%)	73.7

Figure 1 shows the ovipositional response of R. grandis females in the presence of frass extracts with different solvents. The mean number of larvae produced by egg-laying females was highest in the control with D. micans larvae, then in the presence of the hexanoic extract, then with acetone, and finally with methylene chloride. The number of females that laid eggs decreased correspondingly. A t-test showed no significant difference between the mean number of larvae produced in boxes with frass and with a hexane frass extract ($t=0.42$, and $\alpha=0.05$). No eggs were laid in boxes with the methanol extract nor in the control boxes without any extracts. The low values obtained with the methylene chloride extract were probably due to toxic effects of the solvent. Indeed, we had to change the pair of R. grandis adults in these boxes twice because residual vapors had killed them after 24 hours.

Out of all the treatments, Rhizophagus adults continued to oviposit only in the boxes with Dendroctonus larvae. Females in the other series rapidly reduced their oviposition rate. This can probably be explained by the continuous production of stimulating frass in the boxes containing D. micans larvae, whereas in the other boxes the frass was not renewed. If volatile compounds of the frass are the cue for oviposition, it is to be expected that the number of eggs laid will decrease when volatiles progressively disappear from the egg-laying boxes.

Composition of the Frass

Gas chromatography and mass spectrometry were used to make preliminary analyses of the composition of the frass and to compare it with the composition of the bark. These analyses suggest that the bark contains mainly monoterpenes, while a frass extract contains, moreover, many oxygenated monoterpenes which were nearly absent in the bark. The main monoterpenes of the frass sample that were identified are the same as in the bark, i.e., α-pinene, β-pinene, limonene, delta-3-carene, myrcene, camphene and terpinolene. The oxidation derivatives are namely fenchol, fenchone, camphor, borneol, isoborneol, isopinocamphone, 4-terpineol, α-terpineol, myrtenol, and verbenone. Another peak was identified as cis-verbenol or trans-pinocarveol. Unfortunately, in spite of numerous trials with different chromatography columns, we have not yet been able to distinguish between the two compounds.

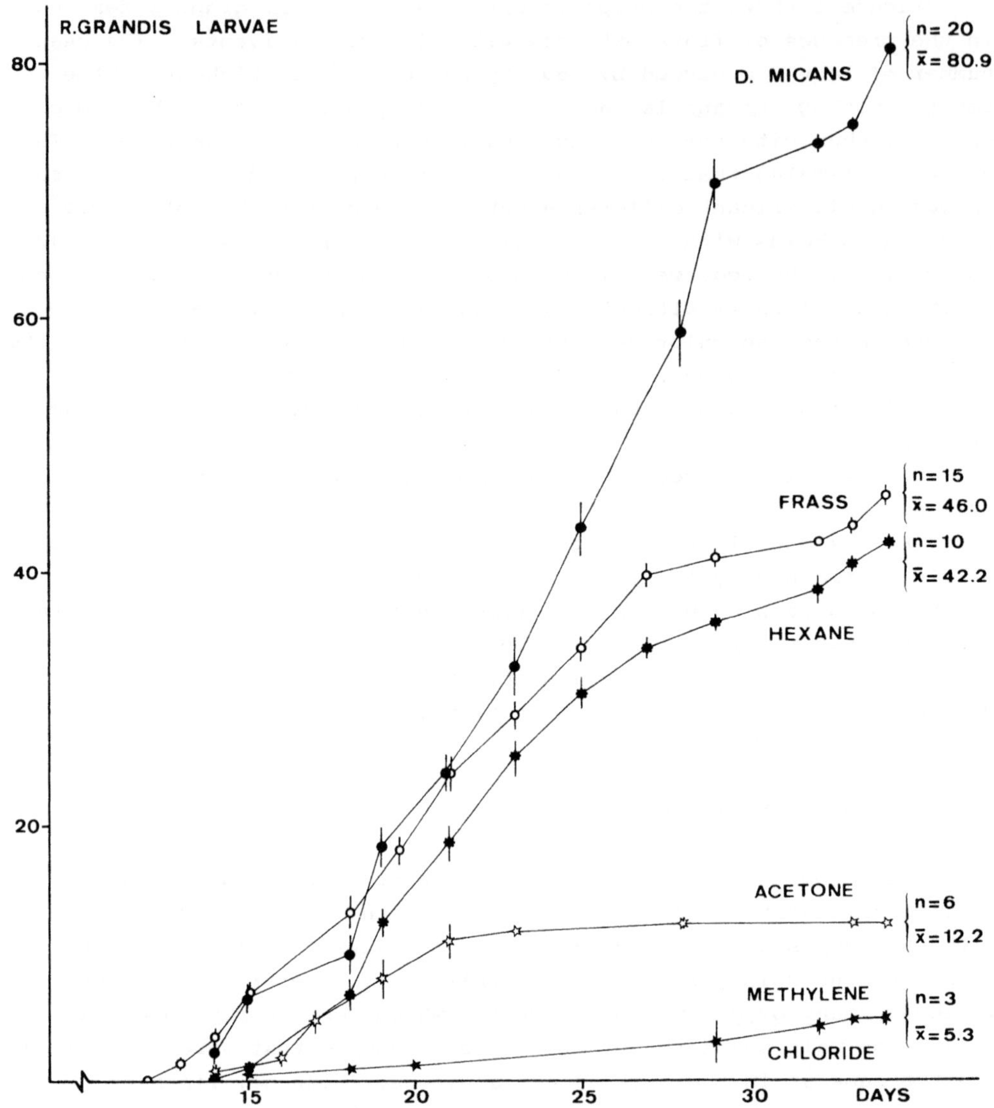

Figure 1. Oviposition by <u>Rhizophagus grandis</u> in the presence of different extracts of <u>Dendroctonus micans</u> larval frass. n = Number of females that laid eggs. $\overline{x}$ = total mean number of larvae produced after 34 days by females that laid eggs.

Column Chromatography Separation

Of the different fractions of a hexane extract, one appeared to induce the highest female response; this was the fraction collected after acetone alone had percolated on a hexanoic frass extract through the silicagel chromatography column (Table 2). Gas chromatographic analysis of this fraction revealed that it contained mainly two peaks. One has been identified as α-terpineol. The nature of the second one remains uncertain, since, as we noted before, we have not been able so far to determine if this peak corresponds to *cis*-verbenol or to *trans*-pinocarveol.

Table 2. Ovipositional response of *Rhizophagus grandis* in the presence of different fractions of a hexanoic extract of *Dendroctonus micans* larval frass.

Solvent used	No. of ♀ that laid eggs n = 20	No. of larvae/ egg-laying ♀ ($\overline{X}$ ± se)
Hexane, then:		
Hexane	4	30.8 ± 11.9
Hexane-Acetone 9:1	5	12.4 ± 5.6
Hexane-Acetone 7:3	0	-
Acetone	12	26.3 ± 4.8
Acetone-Methanol 9:1	0	-
Control (frass)	18	42.2 ± 4.5

α-terpineol, derived from sabinene or limonene, is known as a component of the adult frass of *Ips typographus* , and as an effective attractant for the adults of another scolytid, *Phloeosinus armatus* (see references in Francke and Vité 1983). *Trans*-pinocarveol has been reported as a compound of the hindgut of *Dendroctonus frontalis* after exposure to β-pinene (Renwick *et al*. 1973). *Cis*-verbenol is a wide-spread attractant among *Ips* and *Dendroctonus* species (Francke and Vité 1983).

In this fraction, monoterpenes are present in very small quantities compared with the frass, and oxygenated monoterpenes are the main compounds. Moreover, we have seen before that *Rhizophagus* females are not stimulated to oviposit in the presence of the bark alone, and the chromatographic analysis of the bark showed the relative absence of oxygenated monoterpenes. These results suggest that oxygenated monoterpenes may play a role in oviposition stimulation by R. grandis.

Oviposition Stimulation by Synthetic Compounds

The results suggest that each synthetic substance alone is effective in stimulating at least a small amount of egg-laying (Table 3). At the lower concentrations, a mixture of the three compounds did not seem more effective than each single one. On the other hand, at the higher concentration, a mixture of the three compounds elicited much higher oviposition. It is possible that the three substances acted synergistically above a certain concentration.

Table 3. Ovipositional response of *Rhizophagus grandis* in the presence of synthetic compounds of the aggregative pheromone of *Dendroctonus micans* larvae.

Synthetic compound	No. of ♀ that laid eggs n = 20	No. of larvae/ egg-laying ♀ ($\overline{X} \pm$ se)
Trans-verbenol 2 μl[a]	3	3.3 ± 0.6
20 μl	5	6.4 ± 2.4
Cis-verbenol 1.7 mg	4	6.0 ± 1.9
17 mg	4	3.0 ± 1.0
Verbenone 2 μl	4	2.3 ± 0.7
20 μl	6	2.7 ± 1.0
Mix 2 + 2 + 1.7	4	3.0 ± 0.8
20 + 20 + 17	15	11.6 ± 2.9

[a]dose per box.

It is interesting that even though the results are not as high as with *D. micans* larvae or frass, several synthetic compounds are able to induce some degree of oviposition. Some other oxygenated monoterpenes such as α-terpineol and perhaps *trans*-pinocarveol, which are the main compounds of the effective fraction collected after acetone had percolated through a hexanoic frass extract, are probably also efficient and should be tested in the same way.

CONCLUSION

The results suggest that oxygenated monoterpenes play an important role as inducers of egg-deposition in R. grandis. The frass of Dendroctonus micans larvae, shown by chromatographic analysis to contain many oxygenated monoterpenes, is sufficient by itself to elicit strong oviposition. Moreover, some synthetic components of the aggregative pheromone of their prey's larval frass, and a fraction containing mainly α-terpineol and trans-pinocarveol or cis-verbenol stimulate Rhizophagus grandis females to lay eggs.

The experimental procedure used in this study adequately reproduce R. grandis's natural subcortical life conditions. Our study represents a first effort at the problem of global olfactory stimulation, without detailing the components of the oviposition behavior. No efforts have yet been made to locate the receptors (on antennae and/or ovipositor), nor to determine a possible tactile component in the oviposition stimulation.

Rhizophagus grandis has adapted to use, as oviposition stimuli, volatiles that are produced by its prey's larvae from host plant precursors, which may be a secondary, delayed defensive mechanism of Picea excelsa against Dendroctonus micans. These compounds are shared by many other scolytids, among which Ips typographus (Birgersson et al. 1984) is sympatric with Dendroctonus micans. However Rhizophagus grandis is never found in other species' galleries, only those of D. micans (Merlin, personal communication). This enlarges the number of hypotheses about the level at which the specific link between predator and prey occurs.

ACKNOWLEDGEMENTS

We gratefully acknowledge C. Everaerts for chemical analyses, C. Tilman for technical assistance, and J. M. Pasteels, D. Wainhouse, J. Merlin, and S. Goss for critical reading of the manuscript. S. Goss also corrected the English. This work was partly supported by IRSIA grant no. 840342.

REFERENCES

Birgersson, G., F. Schlyter, J. Lofqvist, and G. Bergstrom. 1984. Quantitative variation of pheromone components in the spruce bark beetle Ips typographus from different attack phases. J. Chem. Ecol. 7: 49-83.

Borden, J. H. 1982. Aggregation pheromones. In: Bark beetles in North American conifers (J. B. Mitton and K. B. Sturgeon, Eds.). Austin, TX: Univ. of Texas Press; 140-182.

Francke, W. and J. P. Vité. 1983. Oxygenated terpenes in pheromone systems of bark beetles. Z. Angew. Entomol. 96: 146-156.

Greany, P. D. and K. S. Hagen. 1981. Prey selection. In: Semiochemicals, their role in pest control (D. A. Nordlund, R. L. Jones, and W. J. Lewis, Eds.). New York: J. Wiley and Sons; 121-135.

Grégoire, J.-C., J.-C. Braekman, and A. Tondeur. 1982. Chemical communication between larvae of Dendroctonus micans Kug. (Coleoptera: Scolytidae) Les colloques de l'INRA, 7 Les médiateurs chimiques: 253-257.

Grégoire, J.-C., J. Merlin, R. Jaffuel, Ph. Denis, P. Lafont, and D. Schvester. 1986. Elevage à petite et moyenne échelle du prédateur Rhizophagus grandis Gyll. en vue de la lutte biologique contre Dendroctonus micans Kug. Rev. For. Fr. 47(5): 457-464.

Grégoire, J.-C., J. Merlin, J. M. Pasteels, R. Jaffuel, G. Vouland, and D. Schvester. 1984. Mass-rearings and releases of Rhizophagus grandis in Lozère. In: Proceedings, EEC Seminar on the biological control of bark beetles (Dendroctonus micans); 1984 October 3-4; Brussels; 122-128.

Heller, S. R. and G. W. A. Mille. 1980. EPA/NIH Mass spectral data base. National standard reference data system NBS 63, suppl. 1 (U.S. Department of Commerce, Ed.).

Hughes, P. R. 1973a. Effect of alpha-pinene exposure on trans-verbenol synthesis in Dendroctonus ponderosae Hopk. Naturwissenschaften 60: 261-262.

Hughes, P. R. 1973b. Dendroctonus: production of pheromones and related compounds in response to host monoterpenes. Z. Angew. Entomol. 73: 294-312.

Jones, R. L. 1981. Chemistry of semiochemicals involved in parasitoid-host and predator-prey relationships. In: Semiochemicals, their role in pest control (D. A. Nordlund, R. L. Jones, and W. J. Lewis, Eds.). New York: J. Wiley and Sons; 239-250.

King, C. J. and H. F. Evans. 1984. The rearing and release of Rhizophagus grandis against Dendroctonus micans in the United Kingdom. In: Proceedings, EEC Seminar on the biological control of bark beetles (Dendroctonus micans); 1984 October 3-4; Brussels; 87-97.

Merlin, J., J.-C. Grégoire, M. Baisier, and J. M. Pasteels. 1984. Some new data on the biology of Rhizophagus grandis. In: Proceedings, EEC Seminar on the biological control of bark beetles (Dendroctonus micans); 1984 October 3-4; Brussels; 107-121.

Moeck, H. A., D. L. Wood, and K. Q. Lindahl, Jr. 1981. Host selection behavior of bark beetles (Coleoptera: Scolytidae) attacking Pinus ponderosa, with special emphasis on the western pine beetle, Dendroctonus brevicomis. J. Chem. Ecol. 7: 49-83.

Nettles, W. C., Jr. and M. L. Burks. 1975. A substance from Heliothis virescens larvae stimulating larviposition by females of the tachinid, Archytas marmoratus. J. Insect Physiol. 21: 965-978.

Renwick, J. A. A., P. R. Hughes, and T. De J. TY. 1973. Oxydation products of pinene in the bark beetle Dendroctonus frontalis. J. Insect Physiol. 19: 1735-1740.

Swigar, S. R., and R. M. Silverstein. 1981. Monoterpenes. Infrared, Mass, ^{1}H NMR, and ^{13}C NMR Spectra, and Kovats Indices (Aldrich Chemical Company, Ed.).

Tondeur A. and J.-C. Grégoire. 1980. Chemical orientation of Rhizophagus grandis (Coleoptera: Rhizophagidae) towards mates and towards preys: Dendroctonus micans (Coleoptera: Scolytidae). In: Animals and environmental fitness (R. Gilles, Ed.). Oxford: Pergamon Press; 93-94.

Vité, J. P. and W. Francke. 1976. The aggregation pheromones of bark beetles: progress and problems. Naturwissenschaften 63: 550-555.

26

Host Orientation Behavior of *Dendroctonus ponderosae*: Integration of Token Stimuli Host and Defenses

Kenneth F. Raffa

All phytophagous insects must somehow identify suitable substrates for reproduction and development. For most insect species, the identifying process involves "decisions" about suitable plant species and suitable plant parts. Among polyphagous insects, many plant species can serve as hosts, but some host species provide a better substrate than others. In some cases, the insect may exhibit a preference for the more suitable species (e.g., Barbosa et al. 1983). Even within a single species of plants, individuals may vary in their suitability. For example, Cates et al. (1983) demonstrated that western spruce budworm larvae, Choristoneura occidentalis, from different Douglas fir trees, Pseudotsuga menziesii, yield adults of varying size and fecundity. The same was true for western spruce budworm from different Abies and Picea sites (Schmitt et al. 1983) and for gypsy moth, Lymantria dispar, from trees with different histories of defoliation (Schultz and Baldwin 1982, Valentine et al. 1983). In each of these cases, the effects of intraspecific variation on host suitability are quantitative. In other words, almost any member of the host population is suitable, but some individuals confer higher fitness to the insect than others.

Bark beetles (Coleoptera: Scolytidae), however, are faced with a much different and more stringent host selection task because only some members of the host population are exploitable. Most trees are usually capable of confining the attack and killing the attacking beetles or their broods (Vité and Wood 1961, Rudinsky 1962, Berryman 1972, Safranyik et al. 1975, Hodges et al. 1979, Raffa and Berryman 1983a, Stephen et al. 1983). Thus a bark beetle's choice of a member of the host tree population is absolutely critical to its reproductive success.

In this chapter, I consider the factors regulating host selection by the primary stem-invading bark beetles that colonize and kill living conifers. I will approach this problem by describing in sequence what is known about (1) the nature of their "target," i.e., factors that affect host susceptibility and suitability; (2) mechanisms by which "pioneer" beetles orient to host trees; (3) selective pressures governing host orientation behavior; and (4) the implications of host orientation behaviors to forest management. I will focus my discussion on mountain pine beetle, Dendroctonus ponderosae, colonization of lodgepole pine, Pinus contorta var. latifolia.

HOST AVAILABILITY

Detailed analyses of bark beetle population dynamics have invariably concluded that host availability is the most critical factor regulating their abundance (Rudinsky 1962, Berryman 1976, Coulson 1979, Cole 1981, Amman 1984, Waters et al. 1985). But what is "host availability" from the perspective of an individual beetle? This is, after all, the level of selection at which orientation behavior evolves (Alcock 1981; Raffa and Berryman 1983a, 1987).

Host Susceptibility

For host tissue to be available, the tree must be susceptible. That is, the tree will not respond to beetle invasion by killing either the beetle or its brood. The defense systems of conifers have been described in detail elsewhere (e.g., Vité and Wood 1961; Smith 1963, 1965; Reid et al. 1967; Lorio and Hodges 1968; Shrimpton and Whitney 1968; Berryman 1972; Shrimpton 1973a, 1973b, 1978; Cates and Alexander 1982; Raffa and Berryman 1982a, 1982b; Horntvedt et al. 1983; Paine 1984; Miller and Berryman 1985; Christiansen and Ericsson 1986; Lorio 1986; Raffa et al. 1985) and so will only be highlighted here. In short, conifers respond to invasion of their cortical tissues by secreting and accumulating high quantities of defensive compounds that soon reach concentrations sufficient to kill these insects. The attack is confined within a necrotic lesion and wound healing can commence. All living trees possess this ability to some extent, but their degree and rate of reaction vary.

Host Suitability

Assuming a tree is susceptible, host suitability depends on phloem quality, primarily thickness (Amman 1972). The number of brood produced per female is much higher on thick-phloemed trees since phloem is the larvae's major source of nutrition. Trees with thick bark are also more suitable because they provide better protection from environmental extremes and predation (Amman and Cole 1983). These variables more closely correspond to the quantitative host properties discussed earlier that affect defoliator fitness.

Conflicting Processes in Host Selection

To some extent, host susceptibility and host suitability are inversely related (Raffa and Berryman 1987). Vigorous, dominant trees with large crowns and good soil conditions have more available photosynthate, as well as both higher resistance capacity and higher growth rate (i.e., thick phloem) than suppressed trees. Although such processes as growth, reproduction, and defense do compete for the energy stores within a tree (Lorio 1986), this does not mean that between-tree comparisons will reveal an inverse relationship between growth or reproduction and defense, simply because the total photosynthate available to each tree varies (Waring and Pitman 1980, 1983; Larsson et al. 1983; Raffa and Berryman 1987). This relationship complicates the selective factors surrounding host choice. High densities of attacking beetles are required to kill vigorous trees, yet the available substrate per insect decreases with attack density (Cole 1962, 1981; Raffa and Berryman 1983a). So in addition to the problems of proper host selection, the beetles must also locate and colonize trees that require fewer beetles to kill them than can be supported in development. How do the beetles do this?

MECHANICS OF HOST SELECTION BY THE MOUNTAIN PINE BEETLE

The most direct approach to answering the above question, and certainly the most enlightening, would be to measure trees for their level of resistance and nutritive value and then apply some behavioral assay in which the beetle's positive excitation was inversely correlated with the former and directly correlated with the latter. Unfortunately, a pile of research notebooks with negative data prevents me from doing this. Instead I will present the results of bioassays from various levels of biological organization, each of which yields a certain amount of information. By integrating the information gained from these various physiological levels (of the plant), we can partially reconstruct host selection behavior by mountain pine beetles.

Whole Tree

The simplest approach, and a quite informative one, is to simply cage beetles on unattacked trees and observe them. Some beetles remain in their cage until they die, others enter the tree for awhile and then return to the cage, and others will enter the tree and remain. There is some consistency regarding which trees are entered. In one experiment, I caged beetles on lodgepole pines in an endemic area in the St. Joe National Forest in northern Idaho and observed them for three days. After entries on each tree were recorded, I waited 5 weeks and repeated the test. In general, those trees that were entered on the first occasion were more likely to be entered on the second occasion. However, there was also a very large between-test variation. This between-test variation is difficult to reduce: climatic differences are beyond the experimenter's control, shortening the interval between tests risks the attraction by beetles to olfactory cues caused by an earlier entry, and using the same beetles is not possible. However, the general point still holds that certain trees are more likely to elicit positive orientation by landed beetles than others.

This test also reveals that flight exercise is not a prerequisite for attack. But unfortunately, beetle entry under these conditions is not correlated with any of the parameters known to be related to resistance: oleoresin flow rate, periodic growth ratio, and monoterpene accumulation following fungal inoculation. Nor is it related to any host monoterpene or even whether or not the assayed tree is subsequently killed when the test is done in an outbreak area.

Detached Bark/Phloem Sections

A second assay of host acceptance is to remove bark/phloem sections, freeze them immediately in the field, and return them to the laboratory. Upon thawing, the perimeter is discarded, and the bark is inserted (phloem-down) into paraffin wax in a petri dish. One female beetle was released in each dish for three days. The rate of entry under these conditions was 2.8-fold higher than the entry rate by beetles caged on trees, even though these two assays were performed on the same trees (Raffa and Berryman 1982c). This was verified by a later experiment, when the whole-tree and detached bark/phloem sample assays were performed on different trees and a higher acceptance ratio (2.7X) was again obtained for bark/phloem sections (Raffa, unpublished data).

It is possible that the greater entry rate into bark/phloem sections relative to trees occurs because the laboratory offers a more hospitable environment for these beetles, but this could not explain what happens inside the bark: Beetles that enter a living tree are 5-fold more likely to abandon the attack during the test period than beetles that entered bark/phloem sections (Raffa and Berryman 1982c). This ratio reaches 12X if the test period is extended. Therefore, it appears that any repellency affecting these beetles is associated with the living, physiologically healthy plant. Static components of detached lodgepole pine bark/phloem cannot deter mountain pine beetles.

The bark/phloem assays revealed another interesting piece of information: Once the beetles had reached the phloem/paraffin interface, many of them continued to excavate galleries in the wax. Eventually the wax became embedded in the beetles' guts and they died. On the other hand, beetles walking on a paraffin wax surface will not bore into it. This suggests that once the preliminary stages of the orientation sequence have been satisfied, beetles abandon an attack only in the presence of repellents and not in the absence of chemical stimulants.

Bark Components Applied to Inert Substrates

The third series of bioassays are even further removed from the intact tree. Outer bark samples were collected and frozen in the field and then ground in solvents in the laboratory. The apolar and polar extracts were applied separately to Kimwipe paper towels. Female beetles were placed in vials containing one bark-treated and one solvent-treated towels. After three days, the number of holes eaten by the beetles and the size of each hole were recorded.

Both the apolar and polar extracts elicited more holes and greater hole size from chewing than did the solvent controls. However, there were striking differences in the pattern of feeding exhibited by beetles exposed to apolar and polar bark fractions. The response to apolar extracts was one of continuous biting. There were 3-fold more holes on the towels treated with apolar extracts than on the towels treated with polar extracts. Even the control towels in these apolar units had 7.3-fold more holes than the control towels in the polar-extract units (Raffa and Berryman 1982c). The polar extracts, on the other hand, elicited sustained feeding. The average induced hole size was 3.2-fold greater than that observed with apolar extracts.

Between-tree preference is reflected better by reactions to the polar than the apolar fraction, since there is a very strong relationship between the average hole size and number of holes for each tree to polar extracts. There is no such relationship among apolar extracts. This assay, however, does not predict what will happen in the field, because all trees contain the necessary stimulants. There were no differences in any of the feeding parameters between bark samples from trees that subsequently were killed or survived a natural outbreak (Raffa and Berryman 1982c).

Sequence of Host Orientation Behavior

Based on the above experiments, it is possible to partially reconstruct the orientation sequence of the mountain pine beetle to host plants. Obviously, these events are more likely overlapping components of a continuum (Table 1). First of all, flying mountain pine beetles land in response to visual cues (Shepherd 1966). While flying, they have no information about host susceptibility or suitability, or for that matter even host species that affect their

Table 1. Proposed sequence of beetle activities and relevance of host cues during host finding/accepting behavior of the pioneer mountain pine beetle. Absence of appropriate cues results in resumed walking or flight (from Raffa and Berryman 1982c).

Behavior	Host cues	Significance
1. Landing	Visual profile	Host finding
2. Walking and biting	Gustatory incitants (primarily nonpolar compounds)	Host recognition
3. Continued feeding	Gustatory stimulants (primarily polar compounds)	Host recognition
4. Gallery elongation	Absence of gustatory or olfactory repellents	Host diagnosis

movement (Moeck 1975, Hynum 1978, Raffa and Berryman 1980, Hynum and Berryman 1980, Moeck et al. 1981).

Once the beetle has landed on the tree, nonpolar compounds incite a biting response. This appears to correspond to the nondirected orientation by the southern pine beetle, Dendroctonus frontalis, in response to nonspecific host kairomones (Payne and Coulson 1985). If biting is elicited, then polar compounds stimulate continued feeding and arrest locomotion. These incitants and stimulants are probably needed for host species recognition. A similar process governs host recognition by Ips paraconfusus (Elkinton and Wood 1980, Elkinton et al. 1981), Scolytus quadrispinosus (Goeden and Norris 1964, 1965a, 1965b) and Scolytus multistriatus (Gilbert et al. 1967; Norris and Baker 1967; Doskotch et al. 1970, 1973; Norris 1970), and so is probably widespread among scolytids. If these cues are unsuitable, flight is resumed. Other chemical or physical cues that might be used by beetles to "measure" host suitability (but not susceptibility) are likely to be incorporated during this phase.

Once boring behavior has commenced, further chemical incitants and stimulants may no longer be required, and the absence of repellents results in continued attack. The identities of effective host repellents are unknown, but they appear to be associated with the active physiology of the tree. Beetles that are engaged in unsuccessful attacks in the field will continue to "shovel" large quantities of resin for several days. Eventually they either abandon the attack or become entombed. It is probably during this phase that host susceptibility is somehow "diagnosed" by the attacking beetle.

RELATIONSHIP OF HOST SELECTION BEHAVIOR TO REPRODUCTIVE SUCCESS

Relationship Between Host Susceptibility and Beetle Numbers

The preceding has described beetle behavior in relation to host trees in purely mechanistic terms, with the outcome being positive orientation to a susceptible host. However, this approach ignores the fact that tree susceptibility depends only partly on its innate level of resistance. Colonization success also depends on how many beetles simultaneously engage in the attack (Rudinsky 1962, Wood 1972, Waring and Pitman 1980, Larsson et al. 1983, Raffa and Berryman 1983a). When a beetle lands on a tree, the "correct" decision of whether or not to enter depends largely on how many other beetles will soon subsequently arrive (Fig. 1).

It has long been recognized that bark beetle populations are normally maintained in highly stressed trees during lengthy endemic periods. However, during outbreaks they usually attack all trees, including healthy ones. Remarks such as Keen's (1938, pg. 102, 99) are common in the older literature and are worth a careful reading: "During endemic infestations there is a tendency for the beetles [D.

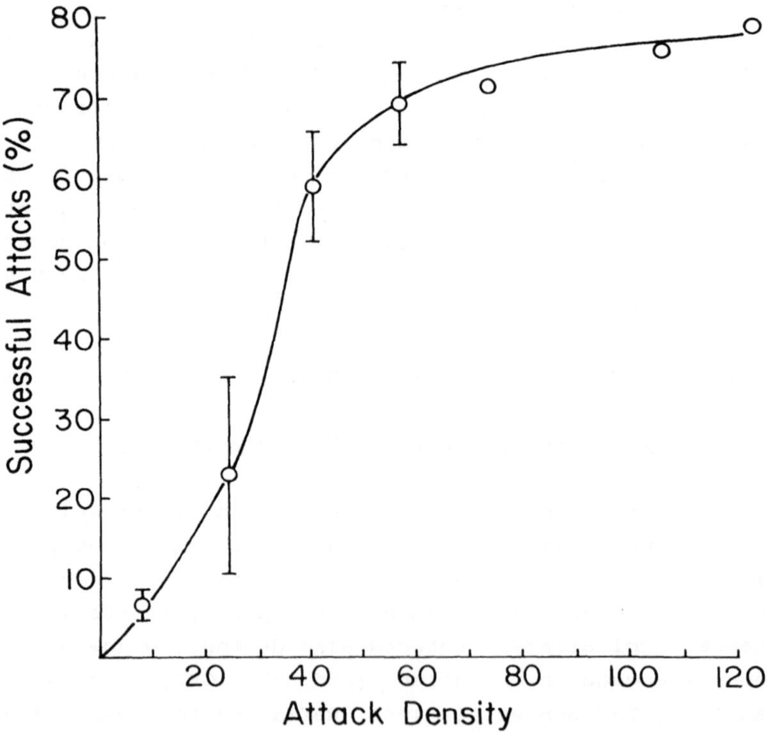

Figure 1. Effect of beetle attack density on the likelihood of successful reproduction. An attack is considered successful if it yields a replacement rate of one or greater (from Raffa and Berryman 1983a).

ponderosae] to select the weaker, less vigorous trees for attack, but no such selection is apparent during epidemic conditions." "Normally it [D. brevicomis] breeds in a few overmature trees, in windfalls, unhealthy trees, or in trees weakened by drought, stand stagnation, or fires. Under epidemic conditions it becomes aggressive and kills apparently vigorous trees of all age classes having bark sufficiently thick to protect it in its development." (The underscores are mine.) Similar observations were made by Beal (1939), Evenden et al. (1943), Schwerdtfeger (1955), Thalenhorst (1958), Zwolfer (1957), Rudinsky (1962), and others.

The question of how these attacks on healthy trees succeed is now relatively easy to answer. Several studies have illustrated that multiple entries reduce a tree's subsequent ability to resist (Christiansen and Horntvedt 1983; Raffa and Berryman 1983a, 1983b; Miller and Berryman 1985; Christiansen and Ericsson 1986). But these studies do not explain how and why beetles enter trees during epidemics that they apparently avoided during endemics, given the strict behavioral sequence described in the previous section.

Selective Pressures on Bark Beetles during Endemic and Epidemic Periods

Female beetles can fail to reproduce either by entering trees that subsequently intoxicate them or their brood, or by never ovipositing in any of the trees encountered during their lifespan. During endemic periods, females that enter and remain in relatively resistant trees are unlikely to reproduce because there are insufficient "recruits" within the range of their pheromone communication. Because a single beetle or a few beetles cannot erode a tree's defensive capacity, the pioneering beetle attacks will fail. During epidemic periods, however, females that enter healthy trees are likely to succeed because of the increased probability of rapid colonization by a high number of subsequent arrivals. Moreover, they are also each likely to produce very large broods because of the thick phloem present in these trees. Also, interspecific competition is generally quite low in these healthy trees compared to severely weakened trees, because the latter are also attacked by a large number of xylophagous species that can greatly reduce scolytid reproduction (Stark and Borden 1975). Beetles that orient solely to weakened trees incur an additional disadvantage during outbreaks because the usually scarce supply of truly decadent trees is rapidly exhausted.

This potential shift in host-mediated selective pressures during the transition from endemic to epidemic population conditions suggests that changes in the frequency or expression of genes affecting beetle responses to host stimuli may accompany changes in population density. This hypothesis is illustrated conceptually in Fig. 2. From the perspective of tree vigor, "aggressiveness" refers to the quality of tree that a beetle will enter, with aggressive beetles entering trees above a particular resistance capacity. From the perspective of beetle behavior, however, the terms "discriminating" and "nondiscriminating" are probably more accurate. Discrimination refers to a threshold of acceptance, i.e., a concentration of host deterrents, above which entry will not be elicited.

The emergent properties of Fig. 2 are that (1) If there are no density-related changes in beetle aggressiveness/discrimination, beetle reproduction due to nonentry will decline during outbreaks; (2) If there are changes in beetle aggressiveness/discrimination, beetle mortality due to entry of extremely resistant host will rise somewhat during outbreaks; (3) During the later stages of an outbreak, host discrimination by beetles will decline to such an extent that less favorable species will be attacked. The third prediction is commonly observed during Dendroctonus outbreaks (Wood 1982), although

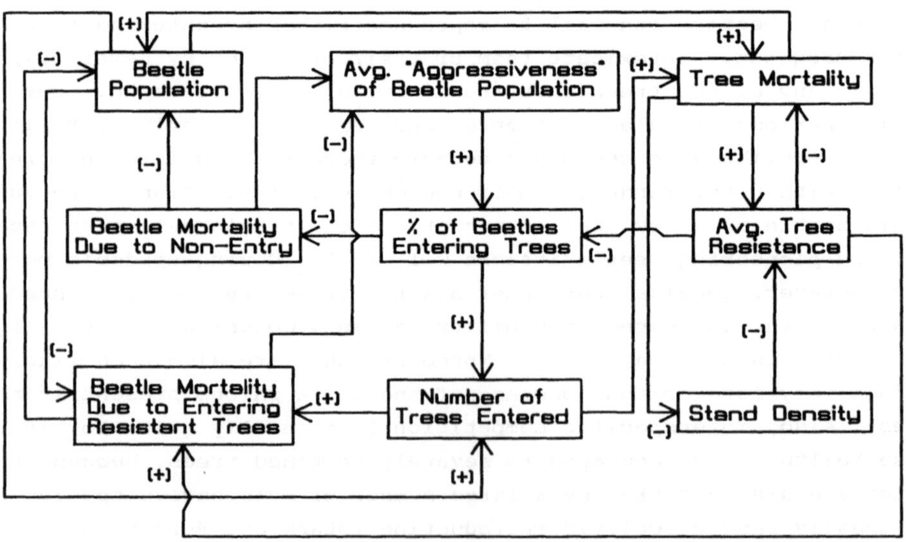

Figure 2. Proposed relationship between beetle population density and the relative "aggressiveness" (= indiscriminant orientation behavior) of tree-killing bark beetles. A plus (+) indicates a direct positive relationship and a minus (-) indicates an inverse relationship.

there is some host-related differentiation among local populations (Stock and Amman 1980, 1983; Sturgeon and Mitton 1986). There are less data with which to evaluate predictions 1 and 2. Life table studies on D. ponderosae during endemic and epidemic conditions (Cole 1981, Amman 1984) do not reveal any evidence of increased dispersal losses during epidemics, thereby supporting the hypothesis of density-related changes. Wright et al. (1984), however, did find a rise in attack abandonment by the fir engraver, Scolytus ventralis, a rather nonaggressive species (Wood 1982, Raffa and Berryman 1987). This suggests that one key difference between the so-called "aggressive" and "nonaggressive" species may be their ability to undergo such behavioral changes. The only data available for considering prediction 2 are provided by Amman (1984), who found that beetle mortality due to resinosis was higher during outbreaks.

The pathways indicated in Fig. 2 assume that beetle orientation to host cues is at least partially under genetic control and that levels of responsiveness vary among individuals. These ideas seem reasonable given current knowledge of insect behavior. For example, genetic strains of the American cockroach, Periplaneta americana, that are distinguished only by different behavioral thresholds to repellents show differences in their respective chemoreceptor reactivities (Rozental and Norris 1975, Norris 1976). However, these assumptions have not been tested for bark beetles, and so other hypotheses need to be considered.

Alternative Hypotheses

There are at least three alternative hypotheses (and interactions thereof) to the above-stated theory of density- (and frequency-) dependent selective pressures: (1) When populations are high, individual beetles may become less discriminating with time. That is, as a beetle's resources are depleted, it may enter and remain in a host that it previously would have rejected (see Miller and Strickler 1984); (2) Olfactory cues may override the strict gustatory cue sequence depicted in Table 1. For example, beetles may normally accept/reject trees on the basis of gustatory cues, but in the presence of aggregation pheromones they instead overwhelmingly accept and enter trees; (3) Perhaps the apparent "tendency for the beetles to select the weaker, less vigorous trees" as described by Keen (1938) and the early workers is not real, but rather the result of a mosaic of a few successful and many fatally incorrect attacks (on resistant trees) throughout the forest. In other words, only the successful attacks are noticed. In hypotheses (1) and (2), "discriminating" genotypes are conserved during outbreaks, offsetting their increased mortality due to nonentry (in the absence of genetic changes) shown in Fig. 2. In hypothesis (3), "nondiscriminating" genotypes are conserved during endemic periods because all beetles have an equal change of ending up in lightning-struck, diseased, and decadent trees.

Habituation to feeding deterrents and nonpreferred hosts has been demonstrated for a number of insect species (e.g., Yazima et al. 1969; Schoonhoven 1969, 1982; Fitt 1986). There are also cases where deterrence is "absolute," and insects will starve to death in the presence of host tissue treated with an exogenous inhibitor or nonpreferred species (e.g., Hosozawa et al. 1974a, 1974b; Munakata 1977; Schoonhoven 1982; Fitt 1986). My whole-tree bioassays (see "Whole Tree" section) revealed cases where beetles would starve before entering the test tree as occurs in some other species when confronted with nonpreferred hosts. But my results are not definitive. For example, I have shown that flight exercise is not essential for host entry, but I have not quantitatively compared flown and unflown females, nor females that had been exposed to different numbers of "unsatisfactory" hosts.

The issue of whether pheromones affect beetle entry in addition to landing behavior is also unclear. Hynum (1978) monitored beetle arrival rates before, during, and after attack, and also marked individual galleries as they were started. He found that the proportion of landing females that initiated attacks remained constant during the acceleration phase. This ratio actually declined within 1 day, while aggregation was still underway. These results suggest that gustatory-mediated behavior is not pheromone-influenced. However, some other observations suggest that mandibular movements are elicited by olfactory cues of beetle and/or host origin. For example, in the screening tests described earlier, beetles frequently chewed the fiberglass mesh, duct tape, and the processed lumber of my cages. The beetles were no closer than 17 cm to the stem, and the screening materials are not in themselves attractive. Returning to the orientation model in Table 1, however, we see that my observations are not necessarily in disagreement with Hynum's. The biting behavior I observed may have been at the levels prior to sustained attack, whereas gallery formation represents the completion of this sequence.

There is currently insufficient data with which to evaluate hypothesis (3), i.e., that a large proportion of beetles do indeed enter healthy trees during endemics and that these beetles die in the process. Amman's (1984) data shows that mortality due to resinosis is lower during endemic periods than during epidemics, and therefore seems to argue against this view. However, because his sampling was limited to killed trees, his results are not necessarily inconsistent with this hypothesis. Likewise, the common experience of most entomologists is that beetle mortality due to resinosis is simply not all that common. Still, no definitive experiments have been performed.

In discussing the available data surrounding these hypotheses, I have considered the alternative hypotheses before the genetic change hypothesis, because the former can be directly tested. There are well-established procedures for testing habituation and multiple-sensory inputs (Schoonhoven 1982). However, we currently have no means of testing the genetic change hypothesis. The most straightforward way would be to collect beetles from endemic and epidemic areas within a reasonably close geographic region and assay them. In fact, I have already tried such experiments with inconclusive results. Beetles were collected from infested trees near Ukiah, Oregon (epidemic), and Clark Fork, Idaho (endemic), and then caged on whole trees near Bovill, Idaho, which is located roughly midway between the two (all beetles were recovered from trees and cages after this experiment). The results reveal that between-test variation is disconcertingly high in the whole-tree bioassay (Table 2). The between-population difference is not statistically significant, which refutes the hypothesis of changes in the frequencies of genes affecting behavior. But the nagging question is whether my sample size (151 Ukiah females, 162 Clark Fork females, and 56 trees) was large enough to be certain that there were no differences. Until more is known about the genetic and environmental contributions to behavioral variation, one cannot estimate the required sample size for endemic versus epidemic behavioral comparisons. Electrophoretic studies (e.g., Stock and Guenther 1979) enable us to estimate a reasonably close geographic region within which to compare endemic and epidemic populations, but they do not necessarily identify phenotypes. The mechanistic approach to orientation behavior described earlier (see "MECHANICS OF HOST SELECTION BY THE MOUNTAIN PINE BEETLE") can provide some guidance to future experiments. Because I have found consistent tree-to-tree differences with respect to repellency but not with respect to incitants or stimulants, I propose that the bioassays for studying behavioral heritability should be directed at the "diagnosis" level behavior in Table 1. This necessitates developing a reliable repellency bioassay in the lab.

Table 2. Comparing the percentage of beetles from epidemic (Ukiah) and endemic (Clark Fork) populations that enter healthy host trees, along with analysis of variance of data.

Population	Percent Entry				
	Test 1	Test 2	Test 3	Test 4	Mean
Epidemic	39	33	18	38	32
Endemic	22	30	19	36	27

Source	Analysis of Variance		
	F	df	Significance
Population	1.60	1	0.30
Test	3.92	3	0.15

MANAGEMENT IMPLICATIONS

Currently Aggressive Species

The question of whether host selection behavior is linked to the colonization capacity and whether this relationship is altered by genetic changes needs to be addressed. Most programs aimed at controlling insects by genetic means strive to incorporate some debilitating defect into the population. These seem unlikely to succeed because natural selection will normally reduce the frequency of genes conferring defect. Instead, when dealing with the "aggressive" species such as *D. frontalis*, *D. brevicomis*, and *D. ponderosae*, we may have to develop strategies along the same lines being employed to hinder the development of resistance against insecticides and immune plant cultivars, e.g., refugia from the toxin or pest-resistant variety (Brattsten *et al*. 1986). If there are large differences in defensive capability between most host plants and the fewer highly weakened ones, then intraspecific competition may favor less aggressive beetles. This may partially explain why most scolytid species never exhibit aggressive behavior (Raffa and Berryman 1987). The available tactics for employing the refugia strategy could include silvicultural treatments such as creation of mosaics, early harvesting, or perhaps even felling trees in advance of an outbreak to buy time for salvage-removal (as opposed to cutting and leaving infested, previously living trees).

We are obviously a long way from realizing some of the possibilities described above. I offer them only as enticement for studies aimed at the genetics of host selection behavior. To actually implement such ideas, we would also have to be able to more accurately quantify host resistance and determine the level of beetle pressure that a particular stand could sustain before it erupted into outbreak behavior (Berryman 1976, 1982, 1985).

Effects of Changing Forestry Practices on Moderately Aggressive Bark Beetles

The question of how host-selective pressures relate to beetle behavior is even more critical with regard to the moderately aggressive species. There may be historical precedent for this. For example, Shavliashvili and Zharkov (1985) have reconstructed the sequence of events that led to the emergence of *Ips typographus* as a major pest in the Georgian SSR: *Ips typographus* was accidentally introduced in 1881, but remained exclusively as a colonizer of fallen timber. Next, *Dendroctonus micans* was accidentally introduced in 1956. After drought conditions in 1957 favored the increased reproduction of *D. micans*, *I. typographus* populations began colonizing living trees previously attacked by *D. micans*. In recent years, *I. typographus* has begun colonizing apparently healthy trees uninfested by *D. micans*. Shavliashvili and Zharkov (1985) surmised that the combined factors of *D. micans* and increased host susceptibility had changed the ecological role of *I. typographus* from a secondary invader during its first 85 years in the USSR to a primary invader. I would submit that behavioral changes along the pathways depicted in Fig. 2 and manifested at the level of responses to token stimuli as in Table 1, likely accompanied this ecological shift.

If so, then reforestation practices that favor reproduction by certain insects could be the ecological equivalent of the *D. micans* introduction. Plantation-style growth is particularly conducive to root-and lower stem-infesting insects, such as root weevils, turpentine beetles, etc. (Kearby 1965, Millers 1965, Goyer 1971, Godbee and Franklin 1976, Wilson and Millers 1983). The features of plantation growth that favor these insects are not well understood but probably include increased immigration rates and host finding (Kearby 1965, Millers 1965, Goyer 1971, Schowalter 1985, Witcosky *et al*. 1986). The stresses imposed by these insects include interference with normal water and carbohydrate transport, and inoculation with virulent fungal species (Barras and Perry 1971, Goheen and Cobb 1978, Goheen and Hansen 1978, Wingfield 1983, Owen 1985, Witcosky 1985, Witcosky and Hansen 1985). Each of these factors can predispose trees to bark beetle attack, including the moderately aggressive species. The critical question, then, is whether a series of events could be triggered by certain aspects of modern growing practices. A proposed sequence would be (1) increased populations of root and lower stem-infesting species due to favorable silvicultural conditions (analogous to the introduction of D. micans); (2) predisposition by these species to subsequent scolytid attack (as suggested by various studies on host resistance to bark beetles) (e.g., Kennedy 1969, Cobb et al. 1974, Hertert et al. 1975), which would increase the local population of the moderately aggressive bark beetle and be analogous to the population rise of I. typographus; and (3) sufficiently high populations of moderately aggressive scolytids to favor a shift in host selection behavior (as proposed in Fig. 2 and suggested in retrospect as "increased vitality and aggression" (Shavliashvili and Zharkov 1985) of I. typographus.

ACKNOWLEDGEMENTS

I greatly appreciate the critical reviews of J. S. Elkinton, Department of Entomology, University of Massachusetts; D. M. Norris, Department of Entomology, University of Wisconsin; and T. L. Payne, Department of Entomology, Texas A & M University.

REFERENCES

Alcock, J. 1981. Natural selection and communication among bark beetles. Flor. Entomol. 65: 17-32.

Amman, G. D. 1972. Mountain pine beetle brood production in relation to thickness of lodgepole pine phloem. J. Econ. Entomol. 65: 138-140.

Amman, G. D. 1984. Mountain pine beetle (Coleoptera: Scolytidae) mortality in three types of infestations. Environ. Entomol. 13: 184-191.

Amman, G. D. and W. F. Cole. 1983. Mountain pine beetle dynamics in lodgepole pine forests. Part II: Population dynamics. USDA, Forest Service, Gen. Tech. Rep. INT-145, 59 p.

Barbosa, P., M. Waldvogel, P. Martinat, and L. W. Douglass. 1983. Developmental and reproductive performance of the gypsy moth Lymantria dispar (L.) (Lepidoptera: Lymantriidae) on selected hosts common to Mid-Atlantic and southern forests. Environ. Entomol. 12: 1858-1862.

Barras, S. J. and T. Perry. 1971. Leptographium terebrantis sp. nov. associated with Dendroctonus terebrans in loblolly pine. Mycopathol. Mycol. Appl. 43: 1-10.

Beal, J. A. 1939. The Black Hills beetle, a serious pest of Rocky Mountain pines. USDA Farmer's Bull. 1824; 1-22.
Berryman, A. A. 1972. Resistance of conifers to invasion by bark beetle-fungal associations. BioScience 22: 598-602.
Berryman, A. A. 1976. Theoretical explanations of mountain pine beetle dynamics in lodgepole pine forests. Environ. Entomol. 5: 1225-1233.
Berryman, A. A. 1982. Biological control, thresholds, and pest outbreaks. Environ. Entomol. 11: 544-549.
Berryman, A. A. 1985. Threshold theory and its application to pest population management. In: Pest and pathogen control: strategy, tactics and policy models (G. R. Conway, Ed.). Chinchester, England: Wiley-Interscience; 40-57.
Brattsten, L. B., C. W. Holyoke, Jr., J. R. Leeper, and K. F. Raffa. 1986. Insecticide resistance: challenge to pest management and basic research. Science 231: 1255-1260.
Cates, R. G. and H. Alexander. 1982. Host resistance and susceptibility. In: Bark beetles in North American conifers (J. B. Mitton and K. B. Sturgeon, Eds.). Austin: Univ. of Texas Press; 212-263.
Cates, R. G., R. A. Redak, and C. B. Henderson. 1983. Patterns in defensive natural product chemistry; Douglas fir and western spruce budworm interactions. In: Plant Resistance to Insects (P. A. Hedin, Ed.). Washington: Amer. Chem. Soc., ACS Symposium, Ser. No. 208; 3-20.
Christiansen, E. and A. Ericsson. 1986. Starch reserves in Picea abies in relation to defense reaction against a bark beetle transmitted blue-stain fungus, Ceratocystis polonica. Can. J. For. Res. 16: 78-83.
Christiansen, E. and R. Horntvedt. 1983. Combined Ips Ceratocystis attack on Norway spruce, and defensive mechanisms of the trees. Z. Angew. Entomol. 96: 110-118.
Cobb, F. W., Jr., J. R. Parmeter, Jr., D. L. Wood, and R. W. Stark. 1974. Root pathogens as agents predisposing ponderosa pine and white fir to bark beetles. In: Proceedings, 4th Int. Conference on Fomes annosus; 1973 September 17-22; Athens, GA; 8-15.
Cole, W. E. 1962. The effects of intraspecific competition within mountain pine beetle broods under lab conditions. USDA, Forest Service, Res. Note 97, 4 p.
Cole, W. E. 1981. Some risks and causes of mortality in mountain pine beetle populations: a long-term analysis. Res. Popul. Ecol. 23: 116-144.
Coulson, R. N. 1979. Population dynamics of bark beetles. Annu. Rev. Entomol. 24: 417-447.
Doskotch, R. W., S. K. Chatterji, and J. W. Peacock. 1970. Elm bark derived feeding stimulants for the smaller European bark beetle. Science 167: 380-382.
Doskotch, R. W., A. A. Mikhair, and S. K. Chatterji. 1973. Structure of the water soluble feeding stimulant for Scolytus multistriatus: A revision. Phytochemistry 12: 1153-1155.
Elkinton, J. S. and D. L. Wood. 1980. Feeding and boring behavior of the bark beetle, Ips paraconfusus, on the bark of a host and non-host tree species. Can. Entomol. 112: 797-809.
Elkinton, J. S., D. L. Wood, and L. E. Brown. 1981. Feeding and boring behavior of the bark beetle, Ips paraconfusus, in extracts of ponderosa pine phloem. J. Chem. Ecol. 7: 209-220.
Evenden, J. C., W. E. Bedard, and G. R. Struble. 1943. The mountain pine beetle, an important enemy of western pines. USDA Circular 664; 1-25.
Fitt, G. P. 1986. The influence of a shortage of hosts on the specificity of oviposition behavior in species of Dacus (Diptera: Tephritidae). Physiol. Entomol. 11: 133-143.

Gilbert, B. L., J. E. Baker, and D. M. Norris. 1967. Juglone (5-hydroxy-1, 4-naphthoquinone from Carya ovata, a deterrent to feeding by Scolytus multistriatus. J. Insect Physiol. 13: 1453-1459.
Godbee, J. F., Jr., and R. T. Franklin. 1976. Attraction, attack patterns and seasonal activity of the black turpentine beetle. Ann. Entomol. Soc. Am. 69: 653-655.
Goeden, R. D. and D. M. Norris, Jr. 1964. Attraction of Scolytus quadrispinosus (Coleoptera: Scolytidae) to Carya spp. for oviposition. Ann. Entomol. Soc. Am. 57: 141-146.
Goeden, R. D. and D. M. Norris, Jr. 1965a. The behavior of Scolytus quadrispinosus (Coleoptera: Scolytidae) during the dispersal flight as related to its host specificities. Ann. Entomol. Soc. Am. 58: 250-252.
Goeden, R. D. and D. M. Norris, Jr. 1965b. Some biological and ecological aspects of ovipositional attack in Carya spp. by Scolytus quadrispinosus (Coleoptera: Scolytidae). Ann. Entomol. Soc. Am. 58: 771-777.
Goheen, D. J. and F. W. Cobb, Jr. 1978. Occurrence of Verticicladiella wagnerii and its perfect state, Certocystis wagenerii sp. nov., in insect galleries. Phytopathology 68: 1192-1195.
Goheen, D. J. and E. M. Hansen. 1978. Black-stain root disease in Oregon and Washington. Plant Dis. Rep. 62; 1098-1102.
Goyer, R. A. 1971. Effects of soil fertility and other stand factors on infestation by the pine root weevil, Hylobius rhizophagus Millers, in Wisconsin jack pine plantations. Madison, WI: Univ. of Wisconsin; Ph.D. Dissertation.
Hertert, H. D., D. L. Miller, and A. D. Partridge. 1975. Interactions of bark beetles (Coleoptera: Scolytidae) and root rot pathogens in grand fir in northern Idaho. Can. Entomol. 107: 899-904.
Hodges, J. D., W. W. Elam, W. F. Watson, and T. E. Nebeker. 1979. Oleoresin characteristics and susceptibility of four southern pines to southern pine beetle (Coleoptera: Scolytidae) attacks. Can. Entomol. 111: 889-896.
Horntvedt, R., E. Christiansen, H. Solheim, and S. Wang. 1983. Artificial inoculation with Ips typographus-associated blue-stain fungi can kill healthy Norway spruce trees. Medd. Nor. Inst. Skogforskning. 38: 1-20.
Hosozawa, S., N. Kato, and K. Munakata. 1974a. Antifeeding active substances for insects in Caryopteris divaricata Maxim. Agric. Biol. Chem. 38: 823-826.
Hosozawa, S., N. Kato, K. Munakata, and Yuk-Lin-Chen. 1974b. Antifeeding active substances for insects in plants. Agric. Biol. Chem. 38: 1045-1048.
Hynum, B. G. 1978. Migration phase interactions between the mountain pine beetle and lodgepole pine. Pullman, WA: Washington State Univ.; Ph.D. Dissertation.
Hynum, B. G. and A. A. Berryman. 1980. Dendroctonus ponderosae (Coleoptera: Scolytidae): pre-aggregation landing and gallery-initiation on lodgepole pine. Can. Entomol. 112: 185-191.
Kearby, W. H. 1965. The bionomics of the pine root weevil, Hylobius rhizophagus Millers and the weevil complex associated with plantation deterioration. Madison, WI: Univ. of Wisconsin; Ph.D. Dissertation.
Keen, F. P. 1938. Insect enemies of western forests. USDA Misc. Pub. No. 273.
Kennedy, P. C. 1969. Causes of the 1966 Ips pini outbreaks. Mich. Acad. 2: 87-92.
Larsson, S., R. Oren, R. H. Waring, and J. W. Barrett. 1983. Attacks of mountain pine beetle as related to tree vigor of ponderosa pine. Forest Sci. 29: 395-402.

Lorio, P. L. 1986. Growth-differentiation balance: a basis for understanding southern pine beetle-tree interactions. For. Ecol. Manage. 14: 259-274.
Lorio, P. L., Jr., and J. D. Hodges. 1968. Microsite effects on oleoresin exudation pressure of large loblolly pines. Ecology 49: 1207-1210.
Miller, R. H. and A. A. Berryman. 1985. Energetics of conifer defense against bark beetles and associated fungi. In: The role of the host in the population dynamics of forest insects (L. Safranyik, Ed.); Proceedings, IUFRO Conference; 1983 September 4-7; Banff, Alberta. Victoria, BC: Canadian Forestry Service and USDA, Forest Service; 13-23.
Miller, J. R. and K. L. Strickler. 1984. Finding and accepting host plants. In: Chemical ecology of insects (W. J. Bell and R. T. Carde, Eds.). New York: Chapman and Hall; 127-157.
Millers, I. 1965. The biology and ecology of the pine root collar weevil, Hylobius radicis Buchanan, in Wisconsin. Madison, WI: Univ. of Wisconsin; Ph.D. Dissertation, 151 p.
Moeck, H. A. 1975. Host selection behavior of bark beetles (Coleoptera: Scolytidae) attacking Pinus ponderosa with special emphasis on the western pine beetle, Dendroctonus brevicomis LeC. Berkeley, CA: Univ. of California; Ph.D. Dissertation.
Moeck, H. A., D. L. Wood, and K. Q. Lindahl, Jr. 1981. Host selection behavior of bark beetles (Coleoptera: Scolytidae) attacking Pinus ponderosae, with special emphasis on the western pine beetle, Dendroctonus brevicomis. J. Chem. Ecol. 7: 49-83.
Munakata, K. 1977. Insect feeding deterrents in plants. In: Chemical control of insect behavior (H. H. Shorey and J. J. McKelvey, Eds.). New YorK: Wiley; 93-102.
Norris, D. M. 1970. Quinol stimulation and quinone deterrency of gustation by Scolytus multistriatus. Ann. Entomol. Soc. Am. 63: 476-478.
Norris, D. M. 1976. A molecular and submolecular mechanism of insect perception of certain chemical information in their environment. Colloq. Int. C. N. R. S. 265: 81-102.
Norris, D. M. and J. E. Baker. 1967. Feeding response of the beetle Scolytus to chemical stimuli in the bark of Ulmus. J. Ins. Physiol. 13: 955-962.
Owen, D. R. 1985. The role of Dendroctonus valens and its vectored fungi in the mortality of ponderosa pine. Berkeley, CA: Univ. of California; Ph.D. Dissertation, 64 p.
Paine, T. D. 1984. Seasonal response of ponderosa pine to inoculation of the mycangial fungi from the western pine beetle. Can. J. Bot. 62: 551-555.
Payne, T. L. and R. N. Coulson. 1985. Role of visual and olfactory stimuli in host selection and aggregation by Dendroctonus frontalis. In: The role of the host in the population dynamics of forest insects (L. Safranyik, Ed.); Proceedings, IUFRO Conference; 1983 September 4-7; Banff, Alberta. Victoria, BC: Canadian Forestry Service and USDA, Forest Service; 73-82.
Raffa, K. F. and A. A. Berryman. 1980. Flight responses and host selection by bark beetles. In: Proceedings, second IUFRO Conference on dispersal of forest insects: evaluation, theory, and management implications (A. A. Berryman and L. Safranyik, Eds.); Pullman, WA: Cooperative Extension Service, Washington State Univ.; 213-233.
Raffa K. F. and A. A. Berryman. 1982a. Physiological differences between lodgepole pines resistant and susceptible to the mountain pine beetle and associated microorganisms. Environ. Entomol. 11: 486-492.

Raffa, K. F. and A. A. Berryman. 1982b. Accumulation of monoterpenes and associated volatiles following inoculation of grand fir with a fungus transmitted by the fir engraver Scolytus ventralis (Coleoptera: Scolytidae). Can. Entomol. 114: 797-810.
Raffa, K. F. and A. A. Berryman. 1982c. Gustatory cues in the orientation of Dendroctonus ponderosae (Coleoptera: Scolytidae) to host trees. Can. Entomol. 114: 97-104.
Raffa, K. F. and A. A. Berryman. 1983a. The role of host plant resistance in the colonization behavior and ecology of bark beetles (Coleoptera: Scolytidae). Ecol. Monogr. 53: 27-49.
Raffa, K. F. and A. A. Berryman. 1983b. Physiological aspects of lodgepole pine wound responses to a fungal symbiont of the mountain pine beetle, Dendroctonus ponderosae (Coleoptera: Scolytidae). Can. Entomol. 115: 723-734.
Raffa, K. F. and A. A. Berryman. 1987. Interacting selective pressures in conifer-bark beetle systems: A basis for reciprocal adaptations? Am. Nat. 129: 234-262.
Raffa, K. F., A. A. Berryman, J. Simasko, W. Teal, and B. L. Wong. 1985. Effects of grand fir monoterpenes on the fir engraver beetle (Coleoptera: Scolytidae) and its symbiotic fungi. Environ. Entomol. 14: 552-556.
Reid, R. W., H. S. Whitney, and J. A. Watson. 1967. Reactions of lodgepole pine to attack by Dendroctonus ponderosae Hopkins and blue stain fungi. Can. J. Bot. 45: 1115-1126.
Rozental, J. M. and D. M. Norris. 1975. Genetically variable olfactory receptor sensitivity in Periplaneta americana. Life Sci. 17: 105-110.
Rudinsky, J. A. 1962. Ecology of Scolytidae. Annu. Rev. Entomol. 7: 327-348.
Safranyik, L., D. M. Shrimpton, and H. S. Whitney. 1975. An interpretation of the interaction between lodgepole pine, the mountain pine beetle and its associated blue stain fungi in western Canada. In: Management of lodgepole pine ecosystems (D. M. Baumgartner, Ed.). Pullman, WA: Cooperative Extension Service, Washington State Univ.; 406-428.
Schmitt, M. D. C., M. M. Cyaporowskyi, D. M. Allen, E. H. White, and M. E. Montgomery. 1983. Spruce budworm fecundity and foliar chemistry: Influence of site. In: Forest defoliator--host interactions: A comparison between gypsy moth and spruce budworm (R. L. Talerico and M. Montgomery, Eds.). USDA, Gen. Tech. Rep. NE-85; 97-104.
Schoonhoven, L. M. 1969. Sensitivity changes in some insect chemoreceptors and their effects on food selection behavior. Proc. K. Ned. Akad. Wet., C. 72: 491-498.
Schoonhoven, L. M. 1982. Biological aspects of antifeedants. Entomol. Exp. and Appl. 31: 57-69.
Schowalter, T. D. 1985. Insect adaptations to disturbance. In: The ecology of natural disturbance and patch dynamics (S. T. A. Pickett and P. S. White, Eds.). New York: Academic Press; 135-152.
Schultz, J. C. and I. T. Baldwin. 1982. Oak leaf quality declines in response to defoliation by gypsy moth larvae. Science 219: 149-151.
Schwerdtfeger, F. 1955. Pathogenese der Borkenkafer-Epidemie. In: Nordwestdeutschland. Schriftenreihe Forstl. Fak. Univ. Gottingen, Band 13/14, 135 p.

Shavliashvili, I. A. and D. G. Zharkov. 1985. Effects of ecological factors on the interaction between populations of Dendroctonus micans and Ips typographus (Coleoptera: Scolytidae). In: The role of the host in the population dynamics of forest insects (L. Safranyik, Ed.); Proceedings, IUFRO Conference; 1983 September 4-7; Banff, Alberta. Victoria, BC: Canandian Forestry Service and USDA, Forest Service; 227-232.
Shepherd, R. F. 1966. Factors influencing the orientation and rates of activity of Dendroctonus ponderosae Hopkins (Coleoptera: Scolytidae). Can. Entomol. 98: 507-518.
Shrimpton, D. M. 1973a. Extractives associated with the wound response of lodgepole pine attacked by the mountain pine beetle and associated microorganisms. Can. J. Bot. 51: 527-534.
Shrimpton, D. M. 1973b. Age- and size-related response of lodgepole pine to inoculation with Europhium clavigerum. Can. J. Botany 51: 1155-1160.
Shrimpton, D. M. 1978. Resistance of lodgepole pine to mountain pine beetle infestation. In: Theory and practice of mountain pine beetle management in lodgepole pine forests (A. A. Berryman, G. D. Amman, R. W. Stark, and D. L. Kibbee, Eds.). Moscow, ID: College of Forest Resources, Univ. of Idaho.
Shrimpton, D. M. and H. S. Whitney. 1968. Inhibition of growth of blue stain fungi by wood extractives. Can. J. Bot. 46: 757-761.
Smith, R. H. 1963. Toxicity of pine resin vapors to three species of Dendroctonus bark beetles. J. Econ. Entomol. 56: 827-831.
Smith, R. H. 1965. Effect of monoterpene vapors on the western pine beetle. J. Econ. Entomol. 58: 509-510.
Stark, R. W. and J. H. Borden. 1975. Observations on mortality factors of the fir engraver beetle, Scolytus ventralis (Coleoptera: Scolytidae). J. Econ. Entomol. 58: 1162-1163.
Stephen, F. M., T. D. Paine, and M. P. Lih. 1983. Understanding bark beetle/host interactions: a means for improving decision strategies. Z. Angew. Entomol. 96: 257-265.
Stock, M. W. and G. D. Amman. 1980. Genetic differentiation among mountain pine beetle populations from lodgepole pine and ponderosa pine in northeast Utah. Ann. Entomol. Soc. Am. 73: 472-478.
Stock, M. W. and G. D. Amman. 1983. Host effects on the genetic structure of mountain pine beetle, Dendroctonus ponderosae, populations. In: The role of the host in the population dynamics of forest insects (L. Safranyik, Ed.); Proceedings, IUFRO Conference; 1983 September 4-7; Banff, Alberta. Victoria, BC: Canandian Forestry Service and USDA, Forest Service; 83-95.
Stock, M. W. and J. D. Guenther. 1979. Isozyme variation among mountain pine beetle (Dendroctonus ponderosae) populations in the Pacific Northwest. Environ. Entomol. 8: 889-893.
Sturgeon, K. B. and J. B. Mitton. 1986. Allozyme and morphological differentiation of mountain pine beetles Dendroctonus ponderosae Hopkins (Coleoptera: Scolytidae) associated with host tree. Evolution 40: 290-302.
Thalenhorst, W. 1958. Grundzuge der Populationsynamik des grossen Fichtenborkenkafers. Ips typographus L. Schriftenreihe Forstl. Fak. Univ. Gottingen, Band 21, 126 p.
Valentine, H. T., W. E. Wallner, and P. W. Wargo. 1983. Nutritional changes in host foliage during and after defoliation, and their relation to the weight of gypsy moth pupae. Oecologia 57: 298-302.
Vité, J. P. and D. L. Wood. 1961. A study on the applicability of the measurement of oleoresin exudation pressure in determining susceptibility of second-growth ponderosa pine to bark beetle infestation. Contrib. Boyce Thompson Inst. 21: 67-78.

Waring, R. H. and G. B. Pitman. 1980. A simple model of host resistance to bark beetles. Corvallis, OR: School of Forestry, Oregon State Univ., Res. Note 65, 2 p.
Waring, R. H. and G. B. Pitman. 1983. Physiological stress in lodgepole pine as a precursor to mountain pine beetle attack. Z. Angew. Entomol. 96: 265-270.
Waters, W. E., R. W. Stark, and D. L. Wood. 1985. Integrated pest management in pine-bark beetle ecosystems. New York: John Wiley and Sons.
Wilson, L. F. and I. Millers. 1983. Pine root collar weevil--its ecology and management. Washington, DC: USDA, Forest Service, Tech. Bull. No. 1675, 34 p.
Wingfield, M. J. 1983. Association of Verticicladiella procera and Leptographium terebrantis with insects in the Lake States. Can. J. For. Res. 13: 1238-1245.
Witcosky, J. J. 1985. The root insect-black-stain root disease association in Douglas-fir: Vector relationships and implications for forest management. Corvallis, OR: Oregon State Univ.; Ph.D. Dissertation, 134 p.
Witcosky, J. J. and E. M. Hansen. 1985. Root-colonizing insects associated with Douglas-fir in various stages of decline due to black-stain root disease. Phytopathology 75: 399-402.
Witcosky, J. J., T. D. Schowalter, and E. M. Hansen. 1986. The influence of time of precommercial thinning on the colonization of Douglas-fir by three species of root-colonizing insects. Can. J. For. Res. 16: 745-749.
Wood, D. L. 1972. Selection and colonization of ponderosa pine by bark beetles. In: R. E. S. Symposium No. 6: Insect/Plant relationships (H. F. van Emden, Ed.). Oxford: Blackwell Sci. Publ.; 101-107.
Wood, S. L. 1982. The bark and ambrosia beetles of North and Central America (Coleoptera: Scolytidae) a taxonomic monograph. The Great Basin Nat. Memoirs 6. Provo, Utah: Brigham Young Univ.
Wright, L. C., A. A. Berryman, and B. E. Wickman. 1984. Abundance of the fir engraver, Scolytus ventralis, and the Douglas-fir beetle, Dendroctonus pseudotsugae, following tree defoliation by the Douglas-fir tussock moth, Orgyia pseudotsugata. Can. Entomol. 116: 293-305.
Yazima, N., K. Tsuzuki, N. Kato, and K. Munakata. 1969. Insect antifeeding substance in Orixa japonica. Abstract Ann. Meeting Agr. Chem. Soc. Japan; 145.
Zwolfer, W. 1957. Ein Jahrzehnt forstentomologischer. Forschung. 1946-1956. Z. Angew. Entomol. 40: 422-432.

27

Investigating the Hypothesis of Primary Attraction in Conifer-Specific Scolytidae Using a Chemometrical Approach

D. N. Rutledge, C. Chararas, C. J. Ducauze

Our intention here is to show the different ways in which chemometrics can aid in the comprehension of the biological phenomenon of primary attraction. First of all, what is chemometrics? Chemometrics represents a group of mathematical, statistical, and computing methods which are used to optimize the collection of chemical information and to structure that data to answer whatever question has been posed.

The particular biological phenomenon which we propose to address with chemometrics could be entitled "Primary attraction in different conifer-specific Scolytidae." The particular aspect of this problem which interests us here is the way in which the adult insect selects its host plant while in flight. It is generally accepted that terpenoid compounds, although having no nutritional role, play an important part in the host selection of Scolytidae (Chararas 1958, 1970, 1980a, 1980b) and that some scolytids breed only in one particular tree species, while others may use several species within a genus or even species of different genera, despite large differences in their odor spectra.

The object of our work is first to determine the degree and strictness of host specificity as a function of scolytid and conifer species. This raises the first question we are going to treat--that of the reliability of the tests used, both on the experimental level and in terms of the interpretation of the data.

At the same time, we also know that terpene compositions differ from one conifer to another. For example, some are rich in α-terpene (Pinus halepensis, P. pinaster), others in limonene (P. picea), others in phellandrene (P. contorta) and still others in delta-3-carene (P. muricata). This gives rise to the second question: how can we represent the terpene composition of a conifer (its odor spectrum) and then bring out the similarities or differences among several species? Why is it, in fact, that two conifers, with what appear a priori to be quite different odor spectra, nevertheless sometimes have equally attractive effects on an insect? Inversely, why do similar conifers sometimes have very different effects on the behavior of an insect? The second part of this paper will treat the various methods which are appropriate to answer this question.

However, before one tries to understand the mechanism, one must verify the existence of the phenomenon, that is: demonstrate the more or less strict specificity of a conifer-specific scolytid. This may be done by means of olfaction tests.

OLFACTION TESTS

Choice of the Experimental Conditions. For the tests to have meaning from a biological point of view, a certain number of conditions must be fulfilled. The hypothesis of primary attraction assumes that the insect is in flight when it makes its host choice. Therefore trials should be carried out in large flight cages rather than in small Y or T olfactometers in order to approach near natural conditions. Classical olfactometers produce questionable results because the experimental enclosure is quickly saturated by a mixture of odors and the insect is tested only while walking.

The flight cages must be large enough so that the insects are effectively tested in flight. There must also be sufficient aeration to avoid saturating the atmosphere with terpene vapors. And finally, the cages must be cleaned between trials to avoid "memory" effects due to the adsorption of volatile terpenes. For example, the tests may be performed in large 50-m^3 breeding cages (Chararas 1980b) made from wire netting, which are sufficient to provide continuous aeration and avoid saturation. If smaller wire mesh cages are used, for example, 100 m (l) x 0.70 m (h) x 0.45 m (d) (Chararas et al. 1986), then small pumps must be added in order to have an adequate aeration and no saturation. Moreover, the wire meshing must be carefully cleaned to eliminate any adsorbed substances.

Each test consists of measuring the attraction specificity of, for example, 20 physiologically mature male (or female, if a monogamous species) adults confronted with two or more different conifer species as represented by logs of a certain size (e.g., 20 cm or 50 cm long for a diameter of from 7 to 10 cm). Care must be taken in both the choice of the individual insects (sex, degree of maturity, previous nutritional conditions) and of the logs (thickness of the bark, length, width, original position along the tree). After the test, the number of insects attracted by each species is counted. Statistically, these counts represent conditional frequencies for attraction. Three replications should be carried out for each test. For each test, the insects are observed over a period of 24 hours, which allows time for effective penetration of the insect into the log prior to counting.

Because one uses cut logs, their oleoresin pressure is low and therefore insects are not rejected. However, some individuals may not become established by the end of the 24 hours, especially if the conifer choices are unfavorable. The question of whether or not to take unestablished insects into account in the statistical computations must be carefully considered in the light of the experimental conditions and of the statistical methods used. If one wished to test in triplicate 10 different tree species in pairs, then 135 (3 x 45) trials must be performed for just one insect species, each requiring 20 insects.

Statistical Interpretation of the Tests

The first question to be asked is whether these olfaction tests are to be interpreted, as is often the case, by simply examining the tables of results. We will show how the use of statistical methods can help in the interpretation of these tables and can eventually uncover certain errors.

Our first example is based on five insects--*Ips sexdentatus* (Is), *Ips acuminatus* (Ia), *Carphoborus minimus* (Cm), *Pityogenes chalcographus* (Pc) and *Orthotomicus erosus* (Oe)--each tested in the presence of three, then two, conifer species.

The first olfaction tests were Triangle Preference Tests, using in one case *Pinus radiata* (PR), *Picea orientalis* (PO) and *Abies cephalonica* (AC), and in the other case *Picea abies* (PA) instead of *Pinus radiata* (Table 1). For these analyses, the olfaction test data were treated as matrices where the variables (columns) corresponded to the different insect species and the objects (rows) were the types of conifer logs preferred to all other possibilities, plus an extra object corresponding to the non-establishment of the insects.

The first analysis, a classical sensory discrimination test (Roessler *et al*. 1978), defines the specificity of the attraction of each insect group in relation to each conifer group. For the trio [PR,PO,AC], the estimated significance levels of the Triangle Preference Test are at the 0.1 percent level for Is/PO (PR,AC) and Ia/PO (PR,AC) as well as for Cm PR (PO,AC), Pc/PR (PO,AC) and Oe/PR (PO,AC).

Table 1. Triangle Preference Tests. Total number of insects (out of 60) established on the logs PA, PO, AC, and PR.[a] N (PR,PO, AC) and N (PA,PO,AC) represent the nonestablished insects.[b]

Preference	Insect Species				
	Is	Ia	Cm	Pc	Oe
PR (PO,AC)	18	21	35***	38***	37***
PO (PR,AC)	37***	34***	18	17	17
AC (PR,PO)	5	4	7	4	4
N (PR,PO,AC)	0	1	0	1	2
PA (PO,AC)	18	26	15	22	27*
PO (PA,AC)	32**	28*	34***	28*	28*
AC (PA,PO)	10	6	10	10	5
N (PA,PO,AC)	0	0	1	0	0

[a]PR (PO,AC) signifies PR preferred in the presence of PO and AC.
[b]Significance levels: *** $\leq$ 0.1 percent; ** $\leq$ 1.0 percent; * $\leq$ 5.0 percent.

Similarly, for the trio [PA,PO,AC], the significance level attains 0.5 percent for Is/PO (PA,AC) and 0.1 percent for Cm/PO (PA,AC). However, values of 3.0 percent are obtained for Ia/PO (PA,AC) Pc/PO (PA,AC) and Oe/PO (PA,AC) while at the same time, Ia/PA (PO,AC) and Oe/PA (PO,AC) approach 5.0 percent.

It is apparent when one considers the original data (Table 1) that these significance levels exaggerated the preferences of the insects for PA, PR, or PO due to their rejection of, or indifference to, AC. This is especially true for the trio [PA,PO,AC] where the data reveal that the insects Ia and Oe have no real preference between PA and PO but where the significance levels are from 3 percent to less than 10 percent simply because the presence of AC necessitates a Triangle Preference Test treatment. In fact, when one examines the results obtained in a previous study, where Is and Oe were tested in the presence of pairs of conifers (Chararas et al. 1982), one sees that Oe demonstrated no real preference between PA, PO, and AC while Is showed no strong preference between PA and PO but preferred PA to AC and PO to AC at the 1.0 percent significance level. This is clearly shown in Fig. 1 where the results of Duo-Preference Tests, interpreted as before by means of the probability tables (Roessler et al. 1978), are visualized in a different way.

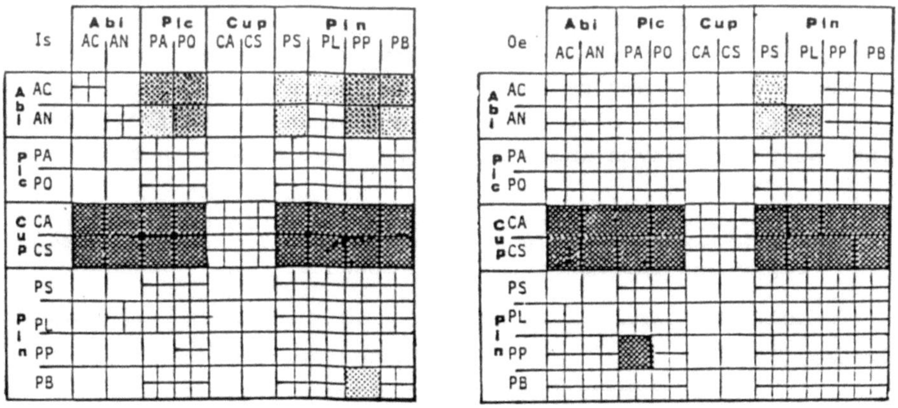

Figure 1. Preference Test results for Ips sexdentatus (Is) and Orthotomicus erosus (Oe) in the presence of the following pairs of tree species: AC = Abies cephalonica, AN = Abies nordmanniana, PA = Picea abies, PO = Picea orientalis, CA = Cupressus atlantica, CS = Cupressus sempervirens, PS = Pinus sylvestris, PL = Pinus laricio, PP = Pinus pinaster, PB = Pinus brutia. This figure should be read starting from the top going down each individual column. If the square corresponding to the intersection is more or less darkly shaded (as in the case of the square AC/CA for top row AC and left column CA), then the species in the top identifying row was more or less statistically preferred to that in the left identifying column during the pairing test. On the other hand, the square corresponding to the opposite combination (in the above case, the CA/AC square on top row CA and left column AC) remains white. When no preference was observed, the square is filled by a light cross (+). Levels of confidence are directly proportional to intensity of dots, with the following three levels: 0.1 percent, 1 percent, and 5 percent.

It therefore appears that the presence of AC in the Triangle Preference Test has biased the results in two ways. Firstly, because AC is not at all attractive to the insects, its presence does not bring any extra information to the test while rendering a Triangle Preference Test necessary. This test, in fact, is based on the supposition that the alternatives proposed are a priori equiprobable. Secondly, the nonattractive or repulsive effect of AC influences the behavior of the insects, altering their reactions to the other two conifers being tested.

For these reasons, complementary tests were carried out using the five insects and the Duo [PR,PO] and only for Is and Ia, the Duo [PA,PO] (Table 2). The statistical bias introduced by the need to take AC into account now being absent, Pc and Oe still show a preference for PR (PO) but only at the 0.5 percent and 4 percent levels, while Is shows a much weaker preference for PO (PR) (not far from 5 percent). Ia and Cm no longer demonstrate any significant preference. The values observed for Is PA (PO) and Ia PA (PO) confirm the interpretation given above in the Triangle Test results.

Table 2. Duo-Preference Tests. Total number of insects (out of 60) established on PR, PO, or PA.[a] N (PR,PO) and N (PO,PA) represent the nonestablished insects.[b]

Preference	Insect Species				
	Is	Ia	Cm	Pc	Oe
PR (PO)	21	23	33	43**	39*
PO (PR)	38	33	27	16	20
N (PR,PO)	1	4	0	1	1
PA (PO)	33	34			
PO (PA)	26	25			
N (PO,PA)	1	1			

[a]PR (PO) signifies PR preferred in the presence of PO.
[b]Significance levels as in Table 1.

The presence of a nonattractive tree species, AC, not only leads to the use of a statistical test which exaggerates the levels of significance, but also perturbs the insects. After this perturbation has been eliminated, the two conifers PA and PO are not significantly different in their attraction. These Duo-Preference Test results also confirm those obtained in the previous study (see Fig. 1) where Is demonstrated no significant preference for either PA or PO.

In conclusion, a rigorous interpretation of the tests permits a validation of the data. It is thus possible to extract information which is clearer and, above all, more certain. We have, in particular, shown that a Duo-Preference Test is simpler to apply and easier to exploit than a Trio-Preference Test. In fact, for the latter we have revealed errors which can occur due to the choice of inappropriate experimental hosts.

Until now, we have studied the results insect-by-insect, using extremely simple tables. In order to go further, one can also globally evaluate the results of a group of tests, e.g., several species of insects placed in the presence of the same pairs of conifers. The aim here is to bring out certain regularities in differences between conifers, which could be of help in later interpretations. In this case, we make use of multidimensional statistical methods such as Factorial Analysis of Correspondence which is well suited to large frequency tables of this sort.

This method involves a transformation of data which usually leads to a more stable analysis than that obtained by direct application of principal component analysis. Being based on a distance measure, Factorial Correspondence may provide a clustering of insects and conifers according to their respective distances. One should, however, be aware that no conclusion may be drawn from the proximity of an insect (object) to a conifer (variable), and it is therefore not possible, in this way, to define the specificity of the attraction of each insect group in relation to each conifer group. To do this, one should apply, as above, a sensory discrimination test such as the Duo-Preference Test.

Let us go back to the example in Fig. 1. Ten conifers were tested by pairs in the presence of *Ips sexdentatus* and then *Orthotomicus erosus*. The same tests were also performed using seven other insects. The Factorial Analysis of Correspondence applied to olfaction tests can permit a simple graphical interpretation of these results. Projecting the conditional preferences of all the insects for each conifer onto the first two factorial axes gives an excellent clustering of the plant species (Fig. 2). We see that the conifers form four groups corresponding to the four genera considered in this study: *Cupressus*, *Abies*, *Picea*, and *Pinus*. To simplify the diagram, only the zones of clustering have been traced; the clustering of nonestablished insects has not been shown as it was of little importance.

Abies and *Picea* overlap slightly, which indicates a poor discrimination of these two genera by the insects studied. Conversely, the clear separation of *Cupressus* indicates a much greater selectivity. We projected onto the same graph the points representing the insects coded from X1 to X9. As a first approximation, they form five groups (Fig. 2). In order to evaluate the specificity of behavior of these insect groups, we calculated their preference probabilities with respect to the ten conifer species. That finer analysis of the olfaction tests completes Fig. 2 by joining the insect groups to the conifer groups by means of arrows representing the specificity of the attraction: a single arrow indicates preference at a level of confidence of 0.5 percent, a double arrow 0.1 percent, and a triple arrow 0.01 percent.

We would like to present yet another means of interpreting the results of olfaction tests. Take the case of Blastophagus minor (Bm) presented with eight different Pinus taken in pairs. The results may be grouped together (as in Table 3) in the form of an 8 x 8 matrix where each row i corresponds to a conifer$_i$ taken as an object (O); while each column j represents the conifer$_j$ considered as a variable (V). The value vij therefore represents the number of insects installed on conifer (i) in presence of (j). Each element on the diagonal is taken as equal to the mean of the values in the corresponding row, and this gives an estimation of the attractive power of the conifer$_i$ vis-a-vis the other seven. In fact, an element on the diagonal would correspond to the case of an insect being given the choice between two logs of the same Pinus species. Because the diagonal is take into consideration only in the Principal Component Analysis (PCA), that approximation has no effect on the levels of signifance nor, as we shall see later, on the Bradley-Terry Proximity Coefficients--it does, however, take into account the information collected and avoids biasing the PCA.

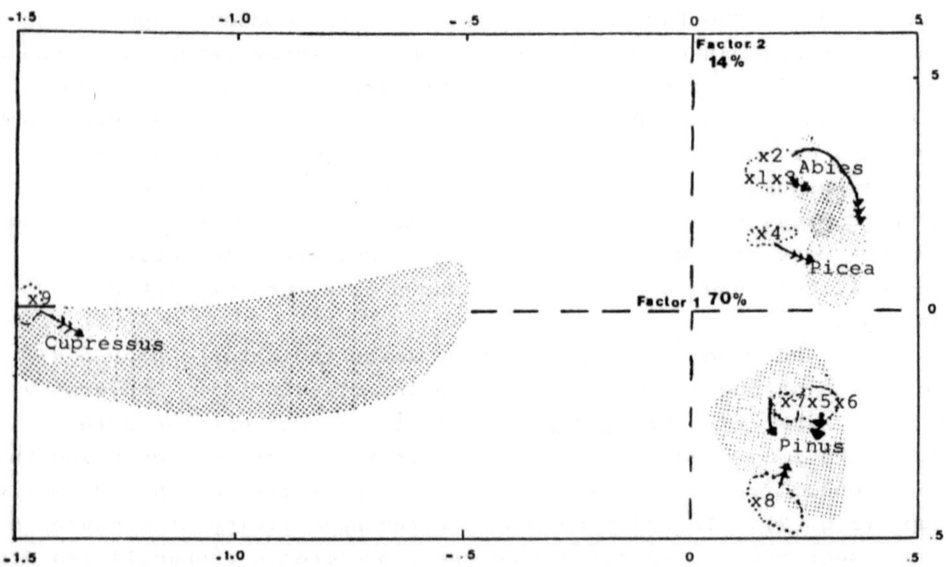

Figure 2. Two factorial projection of insect/tree preferences following a Factorial Analysis of Correspondence. Insect codes are as follows: Cryphalus picaea = X 1, Cryphalus abietis = X 2, Pityokteines curvidens = X 3, Dendroctonus micans = X 4, Ips sexdentatus = X 5, Ips typographus = X 6, Orthotomicus erosus = X 7, Tomicus piniperda = X 8, Phloeosinus bicolor = X 9.

Table 3. Data matrix for the olfaction pair tests on <u>Blastophagus minor</u> (Bm), in the presence of: <u>Pinus</u> <u>laricio</u> (A), <u>P</u>. <u>leiria</u> (E), <u>P</u>. <u>sylvestris</u> (S), <u>P</u>. <u>pinaster</u> (I), <u>P</u>. <u>ponderosa</u> (P), <u>P</u>. <u>canariensis</u> (C), <u>P</u>. <u>caribea</u> (R), <u>P</u>. <u>longifolia</u> (O). The levels of significance for the tests are symbolized by: *(<0.5 percent for 60 insects); **(<0.05 percent for 60 insects; $(<0.5 percent for the installed insects); $$(<0.05 percent for the installed insects).

T	I	A	S	E	R	C	P	O	SUM
I	(32)	37	32	41*	33	32	41*	39*	255
A	22	(31)	30	30	35	43*	42*	45**	247
S	27	28	(31)	30	41*	35	41*	42*	244
E	19	28	29	(30)	39*	36$	38	47*	236
R	25	23	18	18	(22)	23	30	36$$	173
C	25	17	24	20	21	(20)	25	30$	162
P	19	16	19	22	16	19	(17)	21	132
O	20	15	16	13	11	15	11	(13)	101
NON	8	9	8	10	51	55	60	59	

A ninth column, SUM, has been added, containing the sum of the number of insects installed on each conifer-object (i) in the presence of the different conifer-variables (j) (i.e., SUM (i) = $\sum_{j \neq i} (V_{ij})$). A tenth line contains, for each conifer-variable (j), the sum NON, over all the conifer-objects (i), of the number of insects which did not settle on either of the two logs (i.e., NON (j) = $\sum_{i \neq j} (60 - (V_{ij} + V_{ji}))$). This is a means of appreciating the perturbing effect of a conifer (j).

It should be noted that the rows and columns have been ordered so as to have decreasing values of SUM from the top to bottom of the table. So as to more clearly visualize these data, one can now apply a PCA (Dagnelie 1975, Frontier 1983, de Lagarde 1983). The mathematical principle behind this technique is relatively simple. Starting with the matrix in Table 3, a correlation matrix for the variables is calculated. The eigenvalues and associated eigenvectors are then found for this correlation matrix. In this way, factors (or axes) which explain a certain percentage of the observed variations can be isolated. Objects and variables are then represented in the hyperspace of these eigenvectors--a correlation between objects being translated by their proximity in this hyperspace. Graphical representations may be had by projections onto the different planes formed by the axes.

Thus, in Fig. 3, the first two axes have been used to project the conifer-objects (O) (represented by asterisks)--the distance between them indicates their dissimilarity. The conifer-variables (V) are represented as vectors--the cosine of the angle between vectors being equal to their correlation coefficient. In the same way, the cosine of the angle formed between a vector (variable) and an axis (principal component) is proportional to the correlation between them.

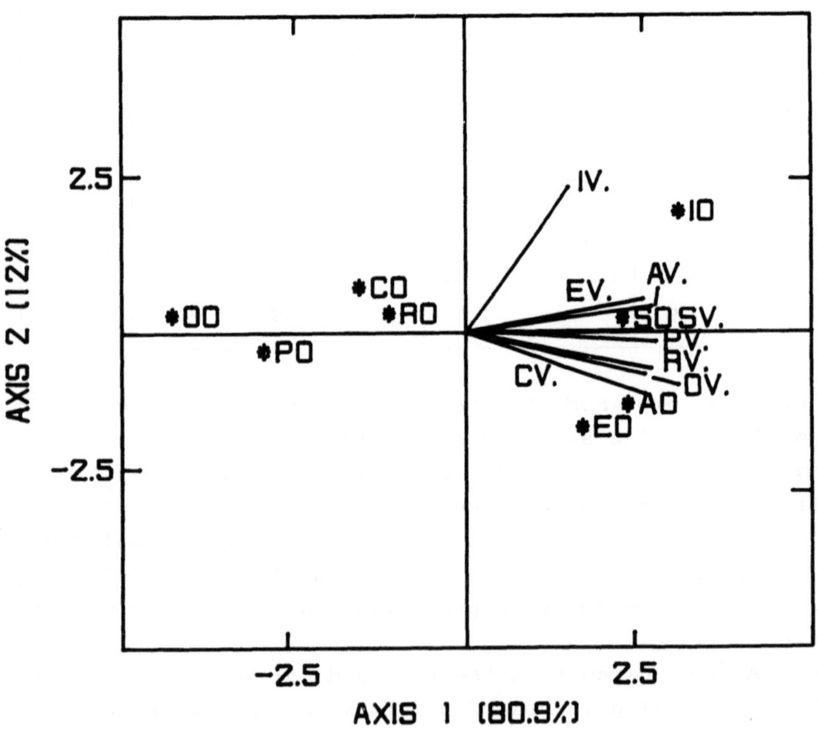

Figure 3. Principal Component Analysis (projection on the first two axes) applied to the results of the olfaction tests of <u>Blastophagus minor</u> (Bm). See Table 3 for symbols.

It is immediately apparent that the first axis explains more than 80 percent of the total variance and corresponds almost exactly to the order of preference, the greatest distance in the positive direction indicating the strongest attraction. That axis is strongly correlated with all the conifer-variables, except IV which contributes mostly to the second axis. The latter axis explains only 12 percent of the total variance and mainly opposes the object IO to the objects E and A, the others being close to the origin. We will come back to this later.

At this level of the interpretation, when considering the values of SUM, the diagonal elements or the results of the PCA, it seems that the conifers can be classed into two groups: I,S,A,E and R,C,P,O. However, that difference is not very clear, and we can try to confirm it by applying another method, a hierarchical classification of preferences based on the Bradley-Terry Proximity Coefficients (Fig. 4).

The mathematical model used here initially postulates the existence of parameters π_{ij}, which are functionally independent and which represent the relative probability of choosing the element T_i

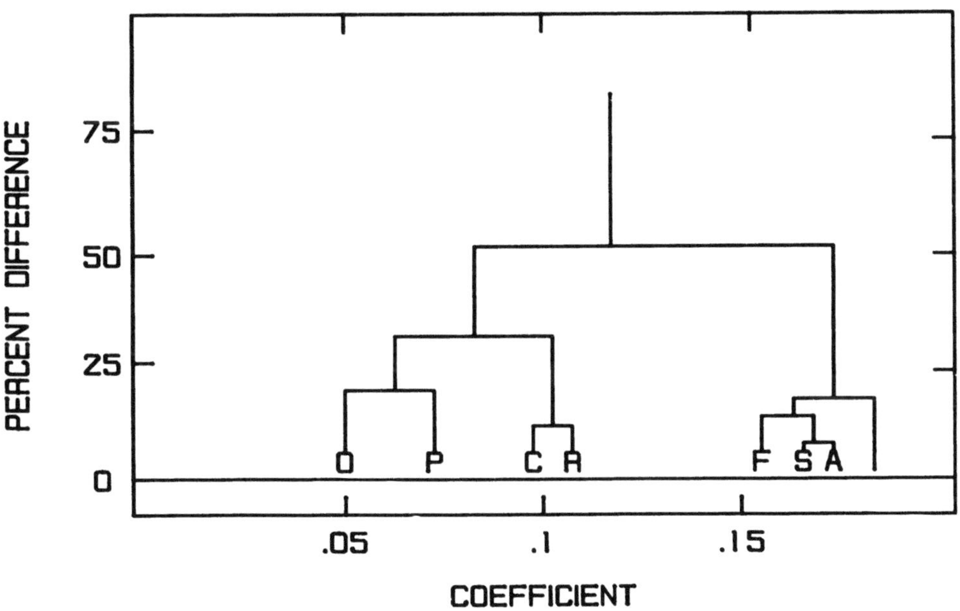

Figure 4. Hierarchy based on Proximity Coefficients (Bradley-Terry) calculated from the olfaction test results of Blastophagus minor in the presence of eight conifers.

rather than T_j in the alternative T_i/T_j. Then values π_i can be estimated by maximizing the likelihood function. The equations may be simply resolved by an iterative method (Bradley 1976).

Figure 4 presents, in the form of a dendrogram, the Bradley-Terry Proximity Coefficients (PC) for Blastophagus minor (Bm). A chi-square test permitted us to verify the validity of the underlying model--a level of significance of 0.1 percent was found for 20 degrees of freedom. This dendrogram confirms clearly that for Bm the conifers are divided into two groups: (I,A,S,E), on the one hand, and (R,C,P,O), on the other.

At the same time, the PCA (Fig. 3) showed an opposition along the axis 2 between I, on one side, and E and A, on the other side. This could come from the fact that I competes more effectively than expected against the other members of the same attractive group while competing less effectively against members of the unattractive group. In fact, if one goes back to the original table of data (Table 3), one sees that the Duo-Preference Tests A/I and E/I gave fairly weak values when compared to the average and even lower than those for the Duo-Preference Tests R/I and C/I.

So far, we have considered the case of Blastophagus minor but the same Pinus species were also tested by pairs in presence of three other insects--Pityogenes bistridentatus (Ps), Orthotomicus erosus (Oe) and Pityogenes bidentatus (Pd). We could therefore try, as in the previous case, to give a global interpretation of the tests. A Factorial Analysis of Correspondance when applied to the whole set of results was not at all informative. The most probable explanation for this would be the very great similarity of all the conifers tested as they all belong to the Pinus genus.

One can, however, represent together on the same figure the values of SUM (Fig. 5a) or of NON (Fig. 5b for the four insects). The same two groups - (I,A,S,E) and (R,C,P,O) - once again appear clearly; within these groups a finer analysis can then be made. For I,A,S, and E, the attraction is strong (SUM>200), and the number of nonestablished (NON) insects is low (N<20), for R,C,P, and O on the other hand, a large number of insects do not settle (N>30), and those that do, in fact, preferred the other conifer.

An examination of the Bradley-Terry Proximity Coefficients--represented in Fig. 6 for the four insects--leads to the same conclusion. This is not really astonishing as the strong resemblance between Fig. 5a and 6 is due to the Proximity Coefficients being calculated using the SUM. A difference between the two figures would appear only if there were important variations in the size of the populations n_{ij} for each preference test.

In conclusion, this last example, which also reveals the wealth of statistical methods available, shows that one should not be content to simply apply a single method. A number of methods used in conjunction can lead to a much better interpretation. Up to now, we have considered a set of statistical methods applied to the interpretation of biological data, and in that case, it would be more correct to speak of biometrics than of chemometrics. However, the methods used to interpret chemical data are very analogous. Moreover, as we have already said, it is first necessary to be sure that the information is

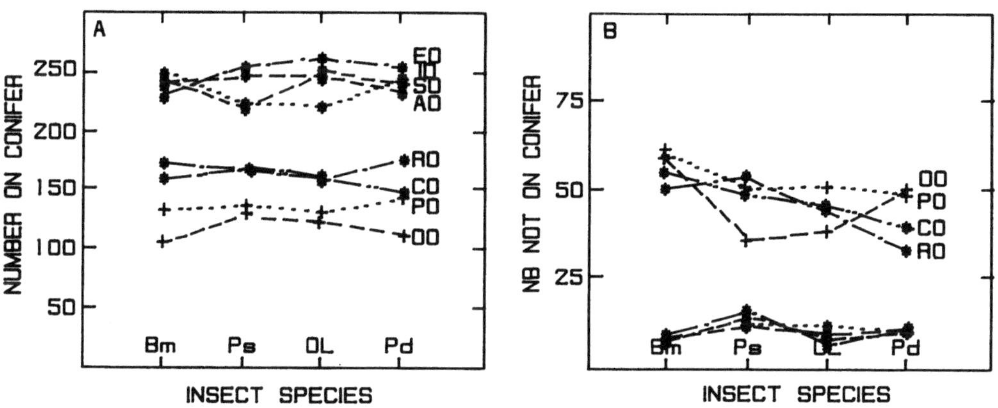

Figure 5. Total number of insects established (5a) nonestablished (5b) on the conifer-objects (O) in the presence of the different conifer-variables (V):

IO: Pinus pinaster
SO: Pinus sylvestris
RO: Pinus caribea
PO: Pinus ponderosa
Bm: Blastophagus minor
Ol: Orthotomicus laricio
AO: Pinus laricio
EO: Pinus leiria
CO: Pinus canariensis
OO: Pinus longifolia
Ps: Pityogenes bistridentatus
Pd: Pityogenes bidentatus

solid--that the biological data has been validated--before undertaking an interpretation of the results of the chemical analyses.

These data should allow us to answer the second question which was posed: can the odor spectra of conifers explain the results of the olfaction tests?

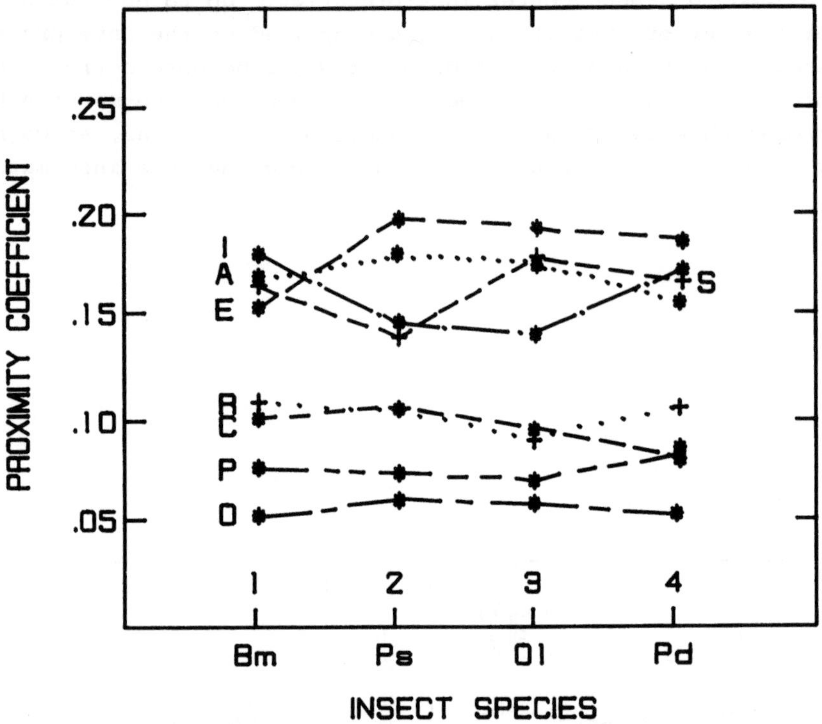

Figure 6. Bradley-Terry Proximity Coefficients for eight conifers and four insects. See Figure 5 for meaning of symbols.

ODOR SPECTRA OF THE CONIFERS

Definition and Representation of an Odor Spectrum

Experimental Conditions. The odor spectrum of a conifer is its composition of volatile constituents. It is that composition which must then be determined. If one assumes that all the problems concerning the sampling (time of the year, position of the sampling points) have been resolved, difficulties then arise as to both the preparation of the sample and the measurement. How does one, in fact, operate? As a general rule, one first of all performs a cold extraction on a few grams of ground phloem using an organic solvent. Then after having concentrated the extract to a few milliliters, the analysis is performed using capillary gas chromatography--mass spectrometry. The chromatogram obtained, called the "odor spectrum," reveals dozens or even hundreds of peaks--most of them corresponding to terpenoid compounds.

Two questions immediately arise. The first is how critical is the solvent used? It is quite easy to demonstrate that chromatograms vary according to the polarity of the solvent. But we do not know _a priori_ which compounds are to be taken into account to explain attraction. If it is mainly the volatile compounds, would it not be better to use a headspace technique? One would then have another chromatogram, different from the others because here it is the vola-tility and not the polarity of the constituents which is brought into play. Which chromatogram should be chosen? The answer cannot in fact be given before having interpreted the chemical data. Therefore we suggest that an odor spectrum should be represented by a whole set of chromatograms. This is possible if one stores the data in computer files.

The second question to be considered is the repeatability of the measurements when one realizes that each chromatogram contains a great number of peaks and that the statistical interpretation necessitates multiple odor spectra. Each compound will be characterized by its retention time and, for each chromatogram, a set of data pairs (retention time/peak area) will be stored in the computer file. It is these data that will be the basis of the interpretations, and so it is necessary for all the data to be comparable from the beginning to the end of the study.

In order to do this, we have developed a computerized Data Acquisition System (Rutledge _et al_. 1984)--the main characteristics of which can be described in a few words. The system was developed around a Commodore CBM-8032 central unit and Eristel 12-bit analog-digital converter (Fig. 7). A multichannel data-acquisition program can acquire up to 90,000 points per channel with a sampling period of between 60 msec and 15.3 sec. The chromatograms are stored on floppy disks. The raw data files are subsequently processed, first by a peak-detection program and then by a peak-quantification program. A new reduced file is then created containing, along with peak retention-times and areas, information concerning the integration method, peak saturation, etc. A final program then corrects this reduced data by eliminating spurious peaks and, above all, by correcting for retention-time drift and displacement against a reference chromatogram.

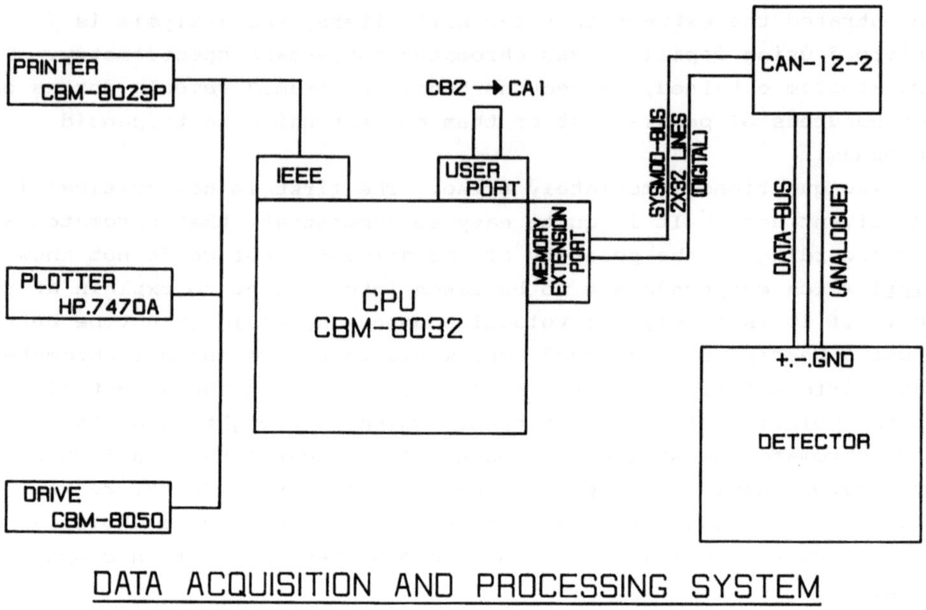

Figure 7. Microcomputer-based data acquisition and processing system.

It is quite apparent that computerization of the acquisition, treatment, and storage of data can give an answer to the main questions raised by the representation of odor spectra. We now have at our disposition validated data in a form that also enables them to be more easily interpreted statistically.

Comparison of Odor Spectra

At this level, only multidimensional statistical methods, such as those presented above, can be applicable. We can present here the example of a treatment carried out on the 10 conifers in Fig. 1 which had been tested in presence of 9 insects. A data base was formed using the odor spectra in order to check whether the terpene composition would give the same clustering pattern as that obtained with the olfaction tests. The terpene concentrations for each species are statistical variables of a different nature than the attraction frequencies previously studied. We used the hierarchical classification method.

As we have shown, the olfaction tests lead to a grouping by genus of the different conifer species. Examination of the odor spectra should normally lead to the same result. Actually, a rapid examination of the data does not reveal, in any simple way, what the two Cupressus, for example, have in common, or what distinguishes them from the other species. We are therefore forced to admit that although it may be possible to recognize a pattern particular to the odor spectra of the Cupressus, that pattern does not immediately appear.

Olfaction is a complex phenomenon resulting from the synergism of the different terpenoid compounds present in the odor spectrum at particular concentrations. It is not possible in this study, where we only considered two Cupressus species, to recognize their spectral similarities. The sample size is insufficient to be able to legitimately apply a method of statistical analysis. However, if all ten odor spectra are treated globally, then hierarchical classification, using Euclidian distance, allows us to bring out a clustering of the Pinus, for which we already have four odor spectra (Fig. 8).

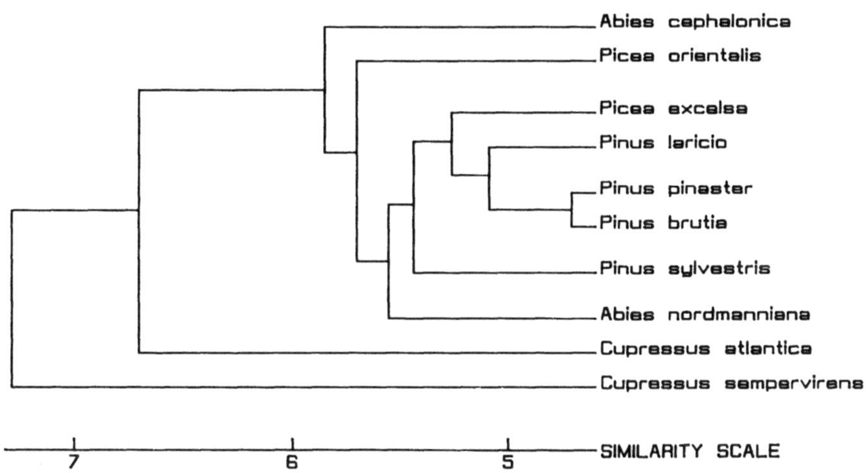

Figure 8. Hierarchical classification of 10 conifers based on their odor spectra.

The value of having a great number of chromatograms can be easily seen from this example and this alone justifies the computerization of the measurements. At the same time, although we have not yet applied it in this domain, we intend to apply a Discriminant Analysis method which would necessitate a smaller set of odor spectra.

Factorial Discriminant Analysis is related both to Canonical Analysis and Principal Component Analysis (Dagnelie 1975, Bertier and

Bouroche 1975): one tries to describe the links between (1) a qualitative characteristic to be explained and which can take k modes--for example, membership in a group (k = 2 for the example of the 8 Pinus) and (2) p quantitative explicative characteristics--for example, the pairs (retention time/peak area) or total concentrations in alcohols, monoterpenes, oxyterpenes, and sesquiterpenes. That analysis, in fact, comes down to a PCA on the cloud of k centers of gravity, each with its ponderation in the R^p hyperspace with the metric V^{-1} (V being the matrix of total variance).

That method can be used to test many classifications, and the one which is the same as the classification obtained using the olfaction tests is retained. It is then possible to calculate, as a function of the variables, the equations of the factorial axes which best explain the separation of the k groups. These equations may then be considered as functions capable of classifying any new conifer. Each group will thus become bigger and the classification functions will be recalculated iteratively.

One can see, with the presentation of the method, its usefulness as a means of predicting from the odor spectrum of a conifer whether it will attract a given insect or not.

GENERAL CONCLUSIONS

The problem that was posed was to explain the phenomenon of primary attraction by means of the odor spectrum of a conifer. The economic interest of such a procedure is evident--it would permit the prediction of the attractive power of a conifer species vis-a-vis an insect it may have never encountered, by using chemical data and without performing any olfaction tests. Some of the dire consequences of using an exotic species in afforestation might then be avoided.

In order to attain this goal, we have seen that it is necessary that the interpretation be based on consistent, valid information--that is, information that has been validated, whether it be the results of olfaction tests or the determination of the odor spectra of conifers. To do this, a large number of statistical or chemometrical methods are available. We have illustrated, using examples, the interest of Duo- and Trio-Preference Tests, PCA, FAC, Hierarchical Classification, and FDA.

We have attempted to show what these methods are capable of. We have also shown that a computerized system of data acquisition and treatment can become indispensable. If it is true that the problem we have posed has not yet been solved, it is because the volume of information collected to this date is insufficient. The necessary data is now being accumulated and there should be real progress in the future.

For the moment we have demonstrated, more than anything else, the potential of a methodology whose practical application is extremely easy. We hasten to add that nearly all the calculations and operations described in the present article can be performed on the average personal computer (contact authors for software).

REFERENCES

Bertier, P. and J. M. Bouroche. 1975. Analyse des données multidimensionnelles. 3rd Edition. Paris: Presses Universitaires de France, 270 p.

Bradley, R. A. 1976. Science, statistics and paired comparisons. Biometrics 32(2): 213-232.

Chararas, C. 1958. Rôle attractif de certains composants des oléorésines à l'égard des Scolytidae des résineux. Comptes Rendus de l'Académie des Sciences de Paris 247: 1653-1654.

Chararas, C. 1970. Biologie des Scolytidae. Bull. Soc. Ecologie 3: 169-188.

Chararas, C. 1980a. Attractions primaire et secondaire chez trois espèces de Scolytidae (Ips): mécanisme de la colonisation. Comptes Rendus de l'Académie des Sciences de Paris 290: 375-378.

Chararas, C. 1980b. Ecophysiologie des insectes parasites des forêts. 38bis, Avenue René Coty, 75014 Paris, 297 p.

Chararas, C., C. J. Ducauze, D. N. Rutledge, C. Revolon, and P. Arpino. 1986. Adaptation de cinq coléoptères Scolytidae à des essences autres que leurs essences d'origine. Comptes Rendus de l'Académie des Sciences de Paris 303(8): 335-340.

Chararas, C., C. Revolon, M. Feinberg, and C. J. Ducauze. 1982. Preference of certain Scolytidae for different conifers: a statistical approach. J. Chem. Ecology 8(8): 1093-1109.

Dagnelie, P. 1975. Analyse statistique à plusieurs variables. Belgium: Les Presses Agronomiques de Gembloux, 362 p.

Frontier, S. 1983. Stratégies d'échantillonnage en écologie. Paris: Masson--Les Presses de l'Université Laval-Québec, 512 p.

De Lagarde, J. 1983. Initiation à l'analyse des données. Paris: Dunod, 157 p.

Roessler, E. B., R. M. Pangborn, J. L. Sidel, and H. Stone. 1978. Expanded statistical tables for estimating significance in paired-preference, paired-difference, duo-trio and triangle tests. J. Food Sci. 43: 940-943.

Rutledge, D. N., J. L. Excoffier, and C. J. Ducauze. 1984. Package for on-line data acquisition and processing with microcomputers. Trends in Analytical Chemistry 3(8): 191-193.

Index

MIX
Papier aus verantwortungsvollen Quellen
Paper from responsible sources
FSC® C105338

If you have any concerns about our products,
you can contact us on
ProductSafety@springernature.com

In case Publisher is established outside the EU,
the EU authorized representative is:
Springer Nature Customer Service Center GmbH
Europaplatz 3, 69115 Heidelberg, Germany

Printed by Libri Plureos GmbH
in Hamburg, Germany